Prentice-Hall Biological Science Series

William D. McElroy and Carl P. Swanson, *Editors*

Actions of Chemicals on Dividing Cells, BENGT A. KIHLMAN
*Biochemical Systematics,** RALPH E. ALSTON AND B. L. TURNER
The Cellular Functions of Membrane Transport, JOSEPH F. HOFFMAN, ED.
Classic Papers in Genetics, JAMES A. PETERS
Experimental Biology, RICHARD W. VAN NORMAN
Foundations of Experimental Embryology, BENJAMIN H. WILLIER AND
 JANE M. OPPENHEIMER
General and Comparative Physiology, WILLIAM S. HOAR
An Introduction to Animal Behavior: Ethology's First Century, PETER H. KLOPFER
 AND JACK P. HAILMAN
Mechanisms of Body Functions, DEXTER M. EASTON
Milestones in Microbiology, THOMAS D. BROCK
Molecular Architecture in Cell Physiology, TERU HAYASHI AND
 ANDREW SZENT-GYORGYI, EDS.
Papers on Human Genetics, SAMUEL H. BOYER, IV
Poisonous Plants of the United States and Canada, JOHN M. KINGSBURY
Principles of Biology, NEAL D. BUFFALOE
Principles of Microbial Ecology, THOMAS D. BROCK
*Radiotracer Methodology in Biological Science,** C. H. WANG AND DAVID L. WILLIS
Readings in Ecology, EDWARD J. KORMONDY, ED.
Selected Botanical Papers, IRVING W. KNOBLOCH
Selected Papers on Virology, NICHOLAS HAHON
The Specificity of Cell Surfaces, BERNARD DAVIS AND LEONARD WARREN, EDS.
A Synthesis of Evolutionary Theory, HERBERT H. ROSS

BIOLOGICAL TECHNIQUES SERIES

Alexander Hollaender, *Editor*
Techniques in Ultraviolet Photobiology, JOHN JAGGER

CONCEPTS OF MODERN BIOLOGY SERIES

*Behavioral Aspects of Ecology,** PETER H. KLOPFER
Molecular Biology: Genes and the Chemical Control of Living Cells, J. M. BARRY
Processes of Organic Evolution, G. LEDYARD STEBBINS

FOUNDATIONS OF MODERN BIOLOGY SERIES

Adaptation, 2nd ed., BRUCE WALLACE AND A. M. SRB
Animal Behavior, 2nd ed., VINCENT DETHIER AND ELIOT STELLAR
Animal Diversity, 2nd ed., EARL D. HANSON
Animal Physiology, 2nd ed., KNUT SCHMIDT-NIELSEN
The Cell, 2nd ed., CARL P. SWANSON
Cell Physiology and Biochemistry, 2nd ed., WILLIAM D. MCELROY
Chemical Background for the Biological Sciences, EMIL H. WHITE
Growth and Development, 2nd ed., MAURICE SUSSMAN
Heredity, 2nd ed., DAVID M. BONNER AND STANLEY E. MILLS
The Life of the Green Plant, 2nd ed., ARTHUR W. GALSTON
Man in Nature, 2nd ed., MARSTON BATES
The Plant Kingdom, 2nd ed., HAROLD C. BOLD

* These titles are also in the PRENTICE-HALL INTERNATIONAL SERIES IN BIOLOGICAL SCIENCE.
Prentice-Hall, Inc.; Prentice-Hall International, United Kingdom and Eire; Prentice-Hall of
Canada, Ltd., Canada.

PRENTICE-HALL INTERNATIONAL, INC., *London*
PRENTICE-HALL OF AUSTRALIA, PTY. LTD., *Sydney*
PRENTICE-HALL OF CANADA, LTD., *Toronto*
PRENTICE-HALL OF INDIA (PRIVATE) LTD., *New Delhi*
PRENTICE-HALL OF JAPAN, INC., *Tokyo*

PRINCIPLES OF

Microbial
Ecology

THOMAS D. BROCK

E. B. Fred Professor of Natural Sciences
The University of Wisconsin

Prentice-Hall, Inc. / Englewood Cliffs, New Jersey

11/1972
Repl.

Current printing (last digit):
10   9   8   7   6   5

Library of Congress Catalog Card Number 66-19898

Printed in the United States of America

C-70951

For Korby
AND HIS FRIENDS

Preface

The field of microbiology has undergone revolutionary changes in recent years due to the impact of new developments in cell and molecular biology. Microbes make excellent research tools for the study of many fundamental biological problems, and work along these lines is now being vigorously pursued. Yet, recent concern for problems of air and water pollution, pesticide accumulation, hunger and disease in the emerging nations, and the population explosion make us aware that microorganisms are more than research tools and that they have impact on our human problems in many ways.

The task of microbial ecology is to provide an understanding of the place of microorganisms in nature and in human society. In the past, microbial ecology has been fragmented into a number of subfields, such as soil microbiology, food microbiology, marine microbiology, medical microbiology, etc. I believe it is now possible, and desirable, to integrate these fields, which is what I have tried to do in this book. I know of no book, in English or any other language, which has made this attempt, and I hope therefore that this book fills a definite need.

My purpose has been to write a book of principles, but I have tried to provide a sufficient number of facts and illustrations so that the principles will not exist in the abstract. I have assumed some previous experience with microbiology and have avoided providing details which are better covered in other microbiological texts. I hope, however, that the macro-ecologist without previous microbiological experience will be able to read this book intelligently.

I have tried to make the coverage truly microbial. Thus, this is not a book on bacterial ecology with a few stabs toward the fungi and algae, but an attempt to give all microorganisms their due. I am aware, however, that I have probably slighted the protozoa somewhat, and for this I must plead my relative ignorance of this group, and the lack of any strong research effort in protozoan ecology.

I believe that this book could be used directly as a text in a microbial ecology course, or it could be used in conjunction with some other book in courses in soil, aquatic, or applied microbiology. I have tried to provide an extensive bibliography, but where possible I have referred to the most recent paper on a subject, or to review papers. Because the literature in this field is so widely scattered, it is quite likely that I have missed important papers, and I would appreciate having these called to my attention.

This book has benefited greatly from the existence of the Biology Library at Indiana University; its completeness in microbiology is due to the foresight and persistence of L. S. McClung. The direction of this book was determined at an early stage through a very fruitful conversation with E. P. Odum. Jacob Schramm has provided many insights on terrestrial matters, especially on the mycorrhiza, and David Frey and Robert Wetzel have given me many ideas involving freshwater environments. Jean S. Poindexter and Warren S. Silver read the manuscript and provided many useful ideas. And my wife, Louise, has helped me greatly in matters of style, usage and clarity of expression and did all the typing. But any errors or omissions are, of course, my own responsibility.

THOMAS D. BROCK

Contents

CHAPTER 3

The Ecology of the Cell   23

Pure cultures, 25; Techniques for obtaining pure cultures, 26; Enrichment of desired organisms, 27; Are pure cultures abnormal? 28.

CHAPTER 1

Introduction

Ecology has been defined in many ways, but probably the most general definition is that ecology is the study of the relationships of organisms to their environments. There are two groups of people who study ecological problems: those who are habitat-oriented, and those who are organism-oriented. The first type is characterized by the limnologist, oceanographer, and soil scientist, who are interested in all aspects of a habitat and may be at various times chemist, biologist, geographer, and physicist. The second type is characterized by the plant and animal ecologists, who are interested primarily in organisms and reckon with the habitat only in so far as necessary to explain the distribution or behavior of specific organisms in nature. Microbial ecology embraces both approaches to ecology. Because microbes are so closely coupled to their environments, the habitat must always be taken into account. And because of the peculiar experimental difficulties of microbiology, requiring the use of pure cultures for almost any study, the organism must always be reckoned with. In addition to their inherent interest, microorganisms greatly ·influence the activities and habitats of higher organisms, and consequently microbes must be taken into consideration in any approach to macroecology. Thus I visualize microbial ecology not as a peripheral but as a central aspect of ecology and have written this book with the idea that it would be of interest to all kinds of ecologists as well as to laboratory microbiologists.

Microbes play far more important roles in nature than their small sizes would suggest. Briefly, we can summarize these roles:

1. As biogeochemical agents
   (a) weathering and soil formation
   (b) decomposition of organic remains
   (c) transformations of elements such as nitrogen, sulfur, and iron
   (d) primary production of organic matter
   (e) deposition of economically important substances (e.g., oil, coal, sulfur)
2. As specific pathogens
3. As producers of specific antagonistic or stimulatory factors (e.g., antibiotics, vitamins)
4. As specific symbionts
   (a) essential agents in the digestive processes of ruminants and many other herbivores
   (b) producers of specific growth factors for higher organisms
   (c) biological nitrogen fixation.

In no environment where higher organisms are present are microorganisms absent. In many environments devoid of and inimical to higher organisms, microorganisms exist and even flourish. Because microorganisms are usually invisible, their existence in an area may be unsuspected. Yet without them, higher organisms would quickly disappear from the earth.

Microbial ecology has developed more slowly than other branches of ecology, partly because of experimental difficulties, and partly because it is a subject which has been out of fashion with microbiologists. Yet, microbial ecology has the potential of becoming the most sophisticated branch of ecology for two reasons: (1) The tremendous store of fundamental knowledge on the genetics, physiology, and biochemistry of microorganisms provided by microbiologists is now ripe for ecological exploitation. (2) Microbial ecology can become a meaningful experimental science, since in many cases a simple test tube or flask can be converted into a precise, reproducible, and meaningful ecosystem. Just as it is possible to do meaningful microecological experiments in the laboratory, so is it also possible to make meaningful ecological observations in the field. Thus field and laboratory can complement each other. The microbial ecologist can have his roots in the soil, but his feet in the laboratory.

CHAPTER 2

The Microbial Environment

The Macroenvironment

Environmental factors are measured with the tools of the chemist and physicist. For the macroenvironment these measurements present no special difficulties and can be made as precisely as we wish. A general summary of environmental factors is given in Table 2-1.

The abundance and distribution of the chemical elements is well tabulated in geochemical texts (Mason, 1958; Goldschmidt, 1954; Clarke, 1924) and a brief collection of certain relevant data of biological interest is given in Table 2-2. The values given are geographical averages and it should be assumed that wide local variations occur, especially where pollution or unusual geological conditions exist. From these data it can be noted

TABLE 2-1. Environmental Factors of Ecological Significance

I. *Physical environment*	II. *Chemical environment*
Temperature	Water activity
Hydrostatic pressure	Water structure (crystalline, liquid,
Osmotic pressure	vapor, adsorbed water)
Surface tension	pH
Visible radiation	Inorganic nutrients, quality and quantity
Ultraviolet radiation	Gases, quality and quantity
Ionizing radiation	Organic nutrients, quality and quantity
Gravity	Hormones, growth regulators, metabolic
Adsorption phenomena	control substances
Viscosity	Poisons, inhibitors, nutrient analogues
	Oxidation-reduction potential

The quality and quantity of these factors should be considered in any analysis of the microbial environment.

that most natural waters are low in carbon, nitrogen, and phosphorus, and the development of living organisms is most likely to be limited by accessibility of these materials; also both carbon and nitrogen exist in gas phases (CO_2 and N_2) which can be assimilated by appropriate living organisms under appropriate conditions. Phosphorus, which lacks a stable gas phase (although phosphine may occur in local situations), is most likely to be the element limiting growth in many environments. While spatial discontinuities exist for all elements, the greatest discontinuities exist for organic carbon. Large amounts of organic carbon exist in deposits of such fossil fuels as coal, oil, and peat, but the greatest concentration is within the bodies of living and dead plants and animals, and it is to the environments where these organisms live that we must look for the heterotrophic microorganisms.

WATER

Water is an unusual liquid in many ways, and its admirable utility as a menstruum for the evolution of living creatures has been often emphasized (Hutchinson, 1957). Water is the only inorganic liquid found in any significant quantities on earth, and even organic liquids such as petroleum are relatively rare.

Water vapor consists of single molecules of the formula H_2O. Air at 20°C will contain about 17 grams/m³ (or 17 mg/liter) when it is completely saturated. If any more water vapor is added, condensation to a liquid will take place with the formation of a cloud or rain. Water vapor can also be adsorbed on surfaces, such as glass or clay, and can be absorbed directly by plants like Spanish moss and many filamentous fungi. When leather goods, for instance, get moldy in humid summer weather, the

TABLE 2-2. GEOCHEMICAL DATA OF ECOLOGICAL INTEREST

I. *Mass distribution*[a] (%)

Lithosphere	93
Hydrosphere	7
Atmosphere	0.03

II. *Atmosphere composition* (% weight[a])

Nitrogen	76
Oxygen	23
Argon	1.3
Carbon dioxide	0.046
Water vapor (variable)	0.02–4

III. *Composition of aqueous environments* (mg/liter)

Substance	Rain water (provisional estimate)[b]	Wisconsin lakes (minimum conc.)[b]	North American river and lake waters (average composition)[a]	Sea water
CO_3			33	73
SO_4	2.0	0.75	15	2,700
Cl	0.5	0.1	7.4	20,000
Na	≥ 0.4	0.13	7.5	11,000
K	≥ 0.03	0.25	1.8	380
Ca	0.1-10	0.13	19	420
Mg	≥ 0.1	< 0.5	4.9	1,300
NO_3	0.2	< 0.01	1.2	0
NH_3	0.5	< 0.004		0
SiO_2			8.6	0
$(Fe, Al)_2O_3$			0.64	0
P			0.07	0.03
Organic matter			10	3–6

IV. *Average composition of known terrestrial matter*[a] (%)

Element	Lithosphere	Hydrosphere
Oxygen	46	86
Silicon	28	
Aluminum	8.1	
Iron	5.1	
Magnesium	2.1	0.14
Calcium	3.6	0.05
Sodium	2.8	1.1
Potassium	2.6	0.04
Hydrogen	0.14	10.7
Carbon	0.09	0.002
Chlorine	0.05	2.1
Phosphorus	0.12	
Sulfur	0.06	0.09
Manganese	0.09	
Nitrogen	0.0046	
Plus others		
	100	100

[a] Data of Clarke (1924).
[b] Data of Hutchinson (1957).

moisture for the growth of the fungus came from the air in the form of water vapor.

Ice is crystalline water. The small hydrogen atoms can essentially be ignored in the structure of the crystal, and the distance between oxygen atoms is 2.76 Å. If water containing dissolved solutes is cooled it does not freeze at 0°C but at some lower temperature which is a function of the concentration of solute molecules. When crystals form, the solute molecules are excluded so that the unfrozen solution in the presence of ice is more concentrated in solute and less concentrated in water than was the initial solution. The size of the ice crystals is a function of the rate of cooling, the presence or absence of convection, and many other factors. Probably some solute molecules become occluded within the crystal structure, but the bulk will be excluded, and when the solution is completely frozen the solute molecules will be mainly between the crystals. Ice can form directly from water vapor without the intermediate formation of liquid (frost), and water vapor can form directly from ice without melting (sublimation).

Liquid water retains some residual lattice structure at low temperatures which is gradually destroyed as the temperature is raised, being completely absent above 85°C. Drost-Hansen (1956) has postulated the existence of abrupt changes in the structure of water at 15, 30, 45, and 60°C presumably related to altered lattice configurations or stabilities, and Oppenheimer and Drost-Hansen (1960) have attempted to relate these to temperature optima for growth of bacteria, but later work (Ingraham, 1962) has not confirmed this.

The high dielectric constant of water and its tendency to hydrate ions is responsible for its unusual solvation properties. Water also has a relatively high viscosity, a factor of significance in controlling the rate of settling of particles and organisms. Optically, water absorbs red light better than blue, a factor of importance in deep bodies of water.

Water adsorbs strongly to colloidal and particulate surfaces by hydrogen bond formation and by dipole-dipole interactions. This bound water is probably present in an ordered structure analogous to the ice crystal lattice and has properties different from liquid or gaseous water. The difficulties of measuring the amount of bound water and of assaying its biological significance have been discussed by Lamanna and Mallette (1959). The adsorption of water to glass surfaces is responsible for the phenomena of capillarity and electroosmosis (Gortner, 1949).

The density of water is influenced by temperature, being greatest at 4°C. This fact is of considerable hydrobiological interest, explaining the stratification of waters in lakes. Ice, with a density of around 0.9, floats on water. Sea water is noticeably denser (1.025) than fresh water because dissolved salts increase the density of water, and where fresh water enters the ocean from a river it will form a surface layer which mixes only slowly.

The specific gravity of a substance is its density related to that of pure water. The specific gravity of microorganisms is variable and is influenced by the specific gravity of the various cell substances: proteins, 1.5; carbohydrates, 1.4-1.6; nucleic acids, 2.0; mineral salts, about 2.5; silica, 2.66; lipids, around 0.9. The density, and therefore specific gravity, of a substance will be influenced by its degree of hydration. If organisms are able to retain gases, such as blue-green algae which have gas vacuoles (Fogg, 1965), these will decrease their density.

A substance or cell will settle if it is more dense than water and float if it is less dense. The rate of fall is a function not only of its density but also of the frictional force resisting its fall and the viscosity of the liquid. Some organisms can control their position in a water mass by retaining or releasing gases. Objects more dense than water may still float if they are supported by energy derived from surface tension. The familiar game room trick of floating a needle on water is an example of this.

Viscosity is the internal friction of a liquid, its resistance to shear or flow. It is at least partly due to the tendency of the molecules of the liquid to associate and become structured. The viscosity of water is increased by the addition of salts, and is decreased by a rise in temperature. For instance, at 37°C the viscosity of water is less than one half what it is at 0°C. Brownian movement and motility are strongly decreased in viscous solutions. At the microscopic level there may be marked variations in viscosity of water due to the presence of high local concentrations of solutes or to the production by organisms of slimes and oozes. The viscosity of concentrated sucrose solutions may play a role in the problem of microbial spoilage of syrups.

Diffusion is a process by which a molecule moves from one place to another under the influence of its own kinetic energy. It should be clearly distinguished from convection, which is due to the mass movement of many molecules. Diffusion is a slow process. The rate of diffusion of sucrose in water is 5.35×10^{-6} square centimeter per second. If molecules of sucrose were localized at a point in the center of a petri dish 65 sq cm in area, it would take over 10^7 seconds (or over 3 years) for complete equilibration to occur by diffusion alone! The diffusion rate of a protein molecule is about 10 times less than that of sucrose. In addition to molecular size, diffusion is affected by temperature, shape of particle, and viscosity. Diffusion in agar is not much slower than diffusion in water, although convection is almost completely absent in agar.

Gaseous molecules diffuse much more rapidly than do molecules in liquids due to their higher kinetic energy and the low viscosity of the medium through which they are passing.

The movement of molecules through membranes is probably mainly due to diffusional processes. The factors controlling movement through membranes are complex and involve pore size, electric charge of membrane and diffusing substance, the ability of a molecule to react with or dissolve in the membrane, and thickness of the membrane. Inorganic substances can also be formed into membranes, and Hutchinson (1957) has described how the formation of a thin layer of ferrous phosphate at the surface of a mud layer will retard the diffusion of substances from the mud layer into the water. Similar phenomena probably occur in other environments.

Once nutrients have passed through a cell membrane, they must be distributed throughout the interior. This also may be accomplished by diffusion in small organisms, but for organisms much larger than bacteria diffusion would be too slow a process by itself, and there are many mechanisms for creating internal convection currents, such as protoplasmic streaming, pinocytosis, and membrane flickering. Even small organisms that have flexible cells, such as spirochetes and myxobacteria, probably create internal convection currents.

BROWNIAN MOVEMENT. Particles can be caused to move when they collide with molecules of the liquid in which they are suspended. Small particles move with a greater velocity than large particles, and particles much greater than 4 μ do not move at all (Gortner, 1949). Thus Brownian movement is a significant factor only for colloidal particles and small bacteria. Brownian movement can be a counterforce to gravitation so that these particles may not settle out, even after long periods of time, unless the gravitational field is markedly increased.

OXYGEN

Oxygen gas (O_2) is poorly soluble in water, and its solubility is greatly affected by temperature. Representative values are given in Table 2-3.

At higher temperatures the availability of oxygen may be seriously limiting in many biological situations. The entrance of oxygen into the liquid

TABLE 2-3. SOLUBILITY OF BIOLOGICALLY IMPORTANT GASES IN PURE WATER AS A FUNCTION OF TEMPERATURE

Temperature (°C)	Oxygen	Carbon dioxide	Nitrogen	Hydrogen sulfide
0	69.4	3346	29.4	7066
10	53.7	2318	23.1	5112
20	43.4	1688	19.0	3846
30	35.9	1257	16.2	2983
40	30.8	973	13.9	2361
50	26.6	761	12.2	1883

Data from Lange (1956). Figures are mg/liter at 760 mm atmospheric pressure.

The data emphasize the low solubility of oxygen gas as compared to the other biologically important gases CO_2 and H_2S.

phase occurs by diffusion with a rate proportional to the surface area of liquid exposed to the gas. Aeration is much more efficient when the liquid is agitated to produce bubbles and is best when the bubbles are very small. Molecular diffusion across an undisturbed water surface plays a quite insignificant role in oxygen solubility on a large scale. In the presence of large numbers of respiring living organisms the dissolved oxygen may be rapidly consumed. Under these conditions the rate of oxygen uptake by the system as a whole is controlled by the rate of solution of oxygen. The solubility of oxygen is greater in pure water than in water containing dissolved salts but is not greatly influenced by pH. For a discussion of some of these factors, see Umbreit et al. (1957).

CARBON DIOXIDE AND pH

CO_2 is many times more soluble in water than is oxygen (Table 2-3). On solution, CO_2 reacts with water:

$$CO_2 \text{ (gas)} \rightleftharpoons CO_2 \text{ (dissolved)}$$

$$CO_2 \text{ (dissolved)} + H_2O \rightleftharpoons H_2CO_3 \rightleftharpoons H^+ + HCO_3^- \rightleftharpoons H^+ + CO_3^{2-}$$

Carbonic acid is formed first, but this dissociates almost completely and is usually present only at about 0.1% of the total. The proportions of the various substances are strongly influenced by pH (Table 2-4). Below pH

TABLE 2-4. PROPORTIONS OF CARBON DIOXIDE SPECIES IN WATER AT VARIOUS pH VALUES

pH	CO_2	HCO_3^-	CO_3^{2-}
4	0.996	0.004	1.25×10^{-9}
5	0.962	0.038	1.20×10^{-7}
6	0.725	0.275	9.1×10^{-5}
7	0.208	0.792	2.6×10^{-4}
8	0.025	0.972	3.2×10^{-3}
9	0.003	0.966	0.031
10	0.000	0.757	0.243

Data of Hutchinson (1957).

5 only free CO_2 is of any significance. Between pH 7 and 9 bicarbonate (HCO_3^-) is the major species, and above pH 10 CO_3^{2-} becomes significant. In the pH range in which most organisms live only CO_2 and bicarbonate are important. The solubility of CO_2 is only slightly influenced by pH or salt concentration, but since it can produce bicarbonate, and since bicarbonate is nonvolatile and very water soluble, the amount of material potentially convertible to CO_2 is greatly influenced by pH and salt concentration. Thus if a solution of sodium bicarbonate at pH 8 is acidified to

pH 5, most of the bicarbonate will be converted to CO_2. In the presence of normal atmospheric conditions most of this CO_2 will be driven off until equilibrium with the atmosphere has occurred. Alternatively, the pH of a solution can be poised by varying the bicarbonate concentration and the CO_2 content of the atmosphere. These factors are considered in detail for the Warburg vessel by Umbreit et al. (1957) but they have wider applications. Most natural waters are in the pH range of 6-10 and are buffered with the CO_2-HCO_3^--CO_3^{2-} system, as are most animal tissue fluids.

Free CO_2 in a liquid cannot be determined from the pH or bicarbonate ion content but can be determined only by allowing the liquid to equilibrate with CO_2 free air and measuring the amount of CO_2 then present in the gas phase (Hutchinson, 1957).

In hard waters more CO_2 is present as bicarbonate ion than as CO_2 or CO_3^{2-}, and some may also be present as colloidal $CaCO_3$. The solubility of CO_2 is greatly increased in water containing suspended $CaCO_3$, and conversely, CO_2 increases the solubility of $CaCO_3$. The dissolution of limestone rocks by CO_2 and its equilibrium products is well known.

In conclusion, the interrelations between CO_2 and pH are complex and should be carefully considered. The question of whether the active species in biological situations is the more hydrophobic free CO_2 or one of its derivatives does not concern us, although the evidence would favor free CO_2, especially in acid conditions.

pH

The effect of hydrogen ion concentration on the CO_2^--HCO_3^--CO_3^{2-} system has been discussed above.

The buffering system in the sea and most fresh waters is the bicarbonate system. Humus, a polymer containing carboxyl groups, is an organic acid buffer occasionally found in nature. In very acid waters the acidity is usually due to H_2SO_4 derived from the oxidation of sulfides.

The pH of the medium controls the precipitation of metal hydroxides from solution, as shown in Table 2-5. The importance of pH in controlling the ionic status of iron is discussed on page 13.

The ionization of acidic and basic groups is controlled by pH. The pK of a substance is the pH at which its ionizable group is half in the dissociated form and half undissociated. The pK of the carboxyl group in most compounds is similar to that of acetic acid, 4.76; at pH 7 essentially all of the molecules will be in the dissociated form (COO^-), whereas at pH 2 they will be mostly in the undissociated form ($COOH$). The two forms behave entirely differently chemically and biologically. Discussions of pK can be found in most biochemistry texts, and values of pK for a wide variety of acids and bases are given in Lange (1956).

TABLE 2-5. EFFECT OF pH ON PRECIPITATION OF HYDROXIDES

pH	Hydroxide precipitated	Example of natural medium
11		
	Magnesium	
10		Alkali soils
9		
	Bivalent manganese	
		Sea water
8		
7	Zinc	River water
6	Copper	Rain water
5	Bivalent iron (Fe^{2+})	
4	Aluminum	Peat water
3		Mine waters
	Trivalent iron (Fe^{3+})	
2		
		Acid thermal springs
1		

Taken from Mason (1958). As the pH is raised from 1, the metal hydroxides begin to precipitate at the values given. These data emphasize that at normal pH values iron and aluminum will be found mainly as the insoluble hydroxides, but that magnesium and manganese will exist generally as soluble forms. Iron especially forms many soluble organic chelates, and much iron may be kept in solution in this manner.

The solubility of a wide variety of biologically and geochemically important substances, such as $CaCO_3$, is affected by pH.

REDOX POTENTIAL

The oxidation-reduction potential is a measure of the ability of a system to donate or accept electrons. It is always referred to a normal hydrogen electrode which is assumed to have zero potential and is expressed by the equation:

$$E_h = E_o - \frac{RT}{F} \ln \frac{Ox}{Red}, \qquad E_h = \text{redox potential}$$

When the concentrations of oxidant and reductant are equal, $E_h = E_o$, and it is this value of E_o which is used in comparing different systems. The redox potential is an intensity factor like temperature and does not indicate the actual reducing or oxidizing capacity of the system. The potential is influenced by pH.

In most biological systems the redox potential is controlled by the oxygen concentration, and Hutchinson has given the equation for oxygen at 18°C:

$$E_h = 1.234 - 0.058 \text{ pH} + 0.0145 \log \text{pO}$$

where pO is the partial pressure of oxygen. The redox potential is relatively insensitive to oxygen concentration and is reduced only 0.03 volt when the pO is reduced from 100% to 1% of saturation. At pH 7 and 25°C when the system is in equilibrium with 1 atmosphere of air the potential is 0.80 volt. Thus O_2 will become analytically undetectable before the redox potential shows a significant drop.

Actual measurements of redox potentials with a platinum electrode are usually lower than the theoretical value, due to technical difficulties. At the surface of a lake measured potentials are around +0.5 volt, whereas in strongly reducing sediments the potential is around zero. Colorimetric methods may also be used to measure potentials. Details are given in biochemistry textbooks.

IRON

Iron is a quantitatively important metal in many environments and is also of interest because of its susceptibility to oxidation and reduction.

$$\underset{\text{oxidized}}{Fe^{3+}} \rightleftharpoons \underset{\text{reduced}}{Fe^{2+}}$$

As shown in Table 2-5, trivalent iron will begin to precipitate above pH 3, and divalent iron, above pH 5. The presence of Fe^{3+} or Fe^{2+} will be determined by the redox potential and by the pH. At pH 3 and below, the redox potential for the iron couple is high (around 0.8 volt) so that ferrous ions will be formed in moderately reducing environments. Above pH 5 the redox potential is near zero and ferric ions will predominate. Since ferric hydroxide begins to precipitate even at pH 3, at usual pH values and redox potentials NO ionic iron will be detectable. In deep fresh waters and in sediments ionic Fe^{2+} may occur frequently due to the reducing conditions, although it is not found in sea water because of the high pH. Most of the iron available to biological systems is probably in the form of iron chelates, and the importance of soil humus and organic acids as reservoirs of soluble iron is well established. Iron may be precipitated when the organic molecule to which it is chelated is metabolized by living organisms.

Because Fe^{2+} is readily autoxidized, especially at neutral pH, it is difficult to establish the existence of biological oxidation. In very acid environments, such as acid mine waters, autoxidation does not occur, and biological oxidation is well established (Kuznetsov et al., 1963).

In the sediments, conditions are frequently reducing and Fe^{2+} may be present in ionic form, but if the mud surface becomes oxygenated, Fe^{3+} will be formed, leading to a several millimeter thick layer of ferric hydroxide.

The precipitation of FeS will be discussed below.

The other metals will not be discussed, and the reader is referred to Hutchinson (1957) for pertinent material.

PHOSPHATE

Phosphorus is present naturally in only two forms, orthophosphate (PO_4^{3-}) and organic orthophosphate esters. Pyrophosphate hydrolyzes readily to orthophosphate, and reduced compounds such as phosphine, hypophosphite, and phosphite probably autoxidize, if they exist at all in nature.

Ferric phosphate is very insoluble, and some phosphate may be kept out of solution in this way. If H_2S is present, this may remove some of the iron as FeS, bringing phosphate back into solution. In the lithosphere, phosphate is most commonly present in the mineral apatite, which has the formula $Ca_5X(PO_4)_3$, the anion X representing F, Cl, or (OH). The most common mineral is fluorapatite, $Ca_5F(PO_4)_3$, and the bones of animals are mainly hydroxylapatite, $Ca_5(OH)(PO_4)_3$, although in high fluoride environments some of the (OH) may be replaced by F.

Phosphate can be liberated under acid conditions, but apatite is much less soluble than calcium carbonate. As mentioned earlier, phosphorus is an element often likely to be limiting biologically.

SULFUR

The biological sulfur cycle is discussed in Chapter 9 and the present discussion relates only to global aspects of sulfur distribution. Sulfur exists in the lithosphere mainly as sulfates and as FeS which is oxidizable either biologically or chemically to sulfate. All of the common sulfate salts, including $CaSO_4$, are fairly soluble, and the sulfate ion is readily available in most environments (see Table 2-2). Hydrogen sulfide, H_2S, formed biologically by the reduction of sulfate, is freely soluble in water (see Table 2-3) and ionizes only slightly, so that at normal pH values it is present as the undissociated form.

$$H_2S \rightleftharpoons H^+ + HS^-, \qquad k_1 = 9.1 \times 10^{-8} \text{ at } 18°C$$

$$HS^- \rightleftharpoons H^+ + S^{2-}, \qquad k_1 \simeq 10^{-15}$$

The small amount of HS^- present may be significant biologically as the active form used by sulfur oxidizing bacteria. The sulfides of the metals are extremely insoluble, and FeS, MnS, and CuS precipitate readily even when the reactants are present in small amounts. The dark color of aquatic sediments is often due to metallic sulfides, usually FeS.

Sulfur also exists in volatile form in the atmosphere as H_2S and SO_2, and consequently the cycling of sulfur between the atmosphere and the earth's surface is of considerable importance in the overall sulfur budget. Sulfur enters the atmosphere as SO_2 as a result of volcanic activity and industrial pollution. It also reaches the atmosphere as H_2S which has been released from marine environments and the soil through microbiological processes or from volcanoes. Since H_2S oxidizes spontaneously, it will be converted to SO_2 in the air. The sulfate in rain water comes primarily from atmospheric SO_2, although on or near the sea some of it may come from sulfate which is carried aloft from the ocean surface.

Sulfur has a large number of oxidation states and is one of the most interesting elements both geochemically and biologically.

Silicon

The silicates are discussed in more detail in the section on surface adsorption. Silicon is present in only small amounts in solution, mainly as the orthosilicate. Most silicon is in colloidal or particulate form. Insoluble aluminosilicates may be dissolved by CO_2, producing aluminum carbonate and silica (SiO_2). Because of the widespread use of glass in experimental work, there are almost always traces of silica in nutrient solutions. Diatoms have a specific silicon requirement and have developed a specific means of acquiring this otherwise insoluble material (Hutchinson, 1957, p. 790).

Nitrogen

The biological nitrogen cycle is discussed in detail in Chapter 9. The main forms of nitrogen are: N_2, NO_3^-, NO_2^-, and NH_3. As can be seen from Table 2-2, the nitrogen content of the lithosphere is quite low, and there are also only very small amounts of nitrogen compounds in sea water. The atmosphere, on the other hand, has a high proportion of nitrogen, and it is present there almost exclusively as the chemically unreactive form N_2. Because of the great activity of living organisms towards nitrogen compounds, the nonbiological transformations of this element are probably of less general importance. Some N_2 is converted into NH_3 and nitrogen oxides through photochemical action or lightning discharges and is then carried to earth as ammonium and nitrate ions in rain water (*see* Table 2-2, rain water).

Carbon

The geochemical carbon cycle is shown in Figure 2-1. This figure emphasizes the importance of living organisms in carbon transformations. It also shows that the bulk of the carbon of the earth is fixed in the lithosphere in the form of carbonate rocks and fossil fuels.

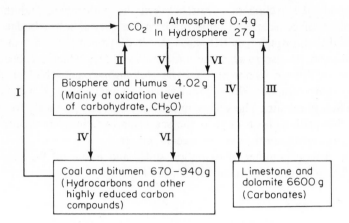

Values are in grams per square centimeter of earth's surface.

Annual turnover of CO_2 per square centimeter of earth's surface (in $\mu g/cm^2$)

Additions of CO_2 to atmosphere:

    I. Combustion of coal and oil   800
    II. Respiration and putrefaction ~40,000
    III. Additions from lithosphere   3−6

Subtractions of CO_2 from atmosphere:

    IV. New carbonaceous sediments 0.3−2
    V. Photosythesis   ~40,000
    VI. Weathering processes   3−4

Fig. 2-1. Quantities of carbon per unit area of earth surface and rate of movement of carbon from one location to another (after Goldschmidt, 1954). This figure emphasizes the fact that the bulk of carbon on earth is tied up in deposits of fossil fuels and rocks. The figure also shows that, although some of the carbon transformations are nonbiological, living organisms are quantitatively the most important both in reducing CO_2 and in oxidizing reduced carbon compounds. Note, however, the significant production of CO_2 by the burning of coal and oil.

The Micro-environment

"No cell lives by itself. It always depends on the environment which surrounds it, part of which is other cells. 'Isolating' a cell means merely transferring it from one environment to another. No cell can act independently. Whatever it manifests is an interaction between it and its environment" (Weiss, 1962).

The cell is small, and therefore its environment is also small. Some aspects of the environment, such as temperature and pressure, are the same at both the macro- and microenvironmental level, so that a measurement by traditional methods can be expected to have microbiological meaning. Yet for many other factors, a microenvironment may differ greatly from its surrounding macroenvironment. A single soil crumb, for instance, may contain numerous microenvironments differing in moisture content, nutrient concentration, pH, or other factors.

Chemical analysis of the microenvironment requires the use of a microscope. Micromanipulation techniques can be used in chemistry (el-Badry, 1963), and there seems to be no reason why they could not also be used in microbial ecology for this purpose. For instance, el-Badry describes methods by which colorimetric chemical analyses can be carried out under the microscope, and the measurement of pH with microelectrodes is described by Caldwell (1954). Many histochemical and histoenzymological methods (Glick, 1961, 1963) could probably also be used in ecology. Micromanipulation techniques could be applied to the analysis of biologically active substances such as antibiotics, for instance by carrying out inhibition studies with known test organisms inoculated into microcapillaries containing the unknown material. The rough biological assay of small amounts of oxygen in microdroplets, using microorganisms which require oxygen for motility, is a time-honored procedure which goes back to Engelmann (1894) and is illustrated in Figure 2-2.

Wherever surfaces occur, there is an opportunity for adsorption phenomena leading to the creation of two-phase or heterogeneous systems. Adsorption occurs even in the laboratory but is of much greater importance in nature because of the preponderance of insoluble matter in both aquatic and terrestrial environments.

LIQUID SURFACES

The molecules at the surface of a liquid are attracted from below only. A measure of the strength of this attraction is the surface tension. Water has a surface tension considerably higher than that of most liquids, an

Fig. 2-2. Collection of motile bacteria along the illuminated half of a diatom cell (after Jennings, 1906, based on Englemann, 1894). This figure demonstrates the use of bacteria which require oxygen gas for motility to indicate the generation of oxygen in a microenvironment. Only on the illuminated half of the diatom have they accumulated in large numbers. Other kinds of biological assays for assessing the chemical nature of microenvironments may be possible.

indication of the tendency of water molecules to form hydrogen bonds with each other. The surface tension of water can be decreased by the addition of solutes or other liquids.

Insoluble substances such as hydrocarbons and waxes will spread on the surface of water and form films. The state of the film depends on the nature of the forces acting between water and the substance and on how the molecules orient themselves. Thus molecules with polar and nonpolar groups (such as fatty acids) orient themselves so that the polar groups approach the water and the nonpolar groups are pushed away from the water. Surface films can also be formed by substances soluble in water due to the fact that the water molecules at the surface are pulled towards the inside of the liquid more strongly than are the solute molecules. If the solution of a substance in water has a lower surface tension than that of water, then the solute is concentrated at the surface. In addition to bringing about a large increase in the concentration of the solute at the surface, this also leads to a decrease in surface tension. Most organic substances decrease surface tension and will be concentrated at the surface. Salts, on the other hand, usually increase the surface tension and consequently are driven away from the surface and into the bulk of the solution. Another role of surface films is in the production of emulsions which are stable or partially stable aggregates of water with an immiscible liquid.

In the aquatic environment films form in undisturbed areas where there is sufficient organic matter. When the light strikes the surface from the proper angle, it is occasionally possible to see this surface film. According to ZoBell (1946), the surface film serves as a mechanical support to which organisms and miscellaneous particulate materials attach. Organisms associated with the surface film are called NEUSTON. ZoBell has found two to four times more bacteria in the surface films of calm water than immediately below the surface. Bacterial neuston may lower the surface tension sufficiently in a localized area of the ocean to keep the water less ruffled than in surrounding areas. Sieburth and Conover (1965) have described the formation in the Sargasso Sea of localized "slicks" which are associated with blooms of the blue-green alga *Trichodesmium* and which are presumably due to the release by the alga of organic substances with surface active properties.

SOLID SURFACES

As is shown in Table 2-2, the bulk of the earth's crust is made up of silicon and aluminum. These elements are almost absent from solution in natural waters because they form numerous insoluble substances which are found in aggregates of various sizes and chemical compositions in soil, water, sediments, and subterranean deposits.

The breakdown of a rock occurs by weathering (much of which is due to microbial action, *see* Chapter 9) and erosion. During breakdown the complex assortment of minerals and elements is fractionated in a manner analogous to a qualitative chemical analysis (Mason, 1958). Minerals like quartz (SiO_2) which are especially resistant to decay remain as granular material. Further complex chemical and physical processes lead to the separation of the clay minerals, aluminosilicates. At the same time, but in separate processes, ferrous iron is oxidized to the ferric state and precipitated as colloidal ferric hydroxide; calcium is precipitated as calcium carbonate, either through biological or nonbiological processes; and the remaining materials, which are water soluble, wash out of the rocks and soil and are carried by the rivers to the sea, where they collect. This explains the high concentrations of Na^+, Cl^-, Mg^{2+}, and SO_4^{2-} ions in the ocean. When salt water evaporates, these soluble substances crystallize as NaCl and $MgSO_4$.

Soil scientists classify particles into fractions such as sand and clay on the basis of size as shown in Table 2-6. Stone and gravel are usually ag-

TABLE 2-6. CLASSIFICATION OF PARTICLES BASED ON SIZE

Particle	Diameter (microns)	Surface area (sq cm/g)
Fine gravel	2000-1000	11.3
Coarse sand	1000- 500	22.7
Medium sand	500- 250	25.4
Fine sand	250- 100	90.7
Very fine sand	100- 50	227
Silt	50- 2	454
Clay	< 2	11,300

Based on criteria established by the U. S. Department of Agriculture. Analysis by sedimentation. This table emphasizes the enormously greater surface area per unit weight in small particles such as clay as compared to large particles. A small amount of clay in a soil or sediment can make a significant contribution to its adsorptive properties.

gregates of many minerals, but the smaller particles are usually composed of single minerals with more or less constant chemical composition, which is determined by interatomic bonding within the crystal structure of the mineral.

It is also useful to consider these substances in terms of their chemical composition. The substances of interest are usually crystalline and can exist in the colloidal state in the size range of 1 μ to 0.001 μ. Colloidal suspensions are always metastable and under appropriate conditions of pH or ionic strength the particles may aggregate. Because of this, most colloids flocculate rapidly in sea water. Colloidal particles are always charged (Mason, 1958):

Positive charge	*Negative charge*
Aluminum hydroxide	Silica
Ferric hydroxide	Manganese dioxide hydrate
	Clay minerals
	Humus colloids

Adsorption to colloids occurs in two ways: (1) by physical or van der Waals forces, which provide loose binding, and (2) by chemical adsorption, which provides more firm binding. At the molecular level almost all solid surfaces are extremely irregular, providing greater surface areas than their average size would suggest. Another feature of solids is the tremendous increase in surface-to-volume ratio with decreasing particle size: clay has about 1000 times more surface area than the same weight of coarse sand.

Because of their enormous surface area, CLAY MINERALS are the most significant in sorption. Two important groups of silicate clays in temperate soils are kaolin and montmorillonite. The flat crystals of kaolin are composed of alternating sheets of silica and alumina. The molecules are held tightly together with little internal structure so that the crystals are very stable. A limited amount of substitution is possible, as Fe^{3+} for Al^{3+} and Al^{3+} for Si^{4+}, and kaolin minerals show low base exchange.

In montmorillonite the unit structure consists of three layers, an alumina layer between two silica layers. Substitution is common, and Fe^{3+} or Mg^{2+} may replace Al^{3+}, or Al^{3+} may replace Si^{4+}, with the development of a negative charge in both cases. Because of the larger spacing in montmorillonite crystals, a large amount of internal surface is available into which water, cations, and molecules can penetrate between the unit layers of the crystal. For this reason montmorillonite is highly absorptive and can absorb large amounts of organic substances.

In addition to absorption by imbibition, clay minerals, being negatively charged, adsorb by ionic binding. Any natural clay mineral possesses bound cations which it has picked up from its environment. Ion exchange occurs as a function of concentration and of the relative affinities of the various ions for the clay, in the order $H^+ > Ca^{2+} >> Mg^{2+} > Na^+ > K^+$. NH_4^+ also exchanges, and its adsorption is an important factor in nitrification by *Nitrobacter,* the dilute ammonium ions and the bacteria both being concentrated upon the clay, so that the probability of contact between cell and ion is much higher than in free solution (Quastel, 1954).

Detailed discussions of various aspects of adsorption and ion exchange can be found in books on soil sciences and geochemistry. Because of their small size, individual clay minerals could not adsorb microbial cells, but as a result of cation-induced flocculation clay frequently occurs in aggregates which provide extensive surfaces for adsorption of microbial cells, organic matter, and water. The adsorption of proteins to clay is well known, and kaolin preparations are used extensively to combat diarrhea, probably functioning through the adsorption of microbial toxins. McLaren (1963) has discussed in some detail the adsorption of enzymes to clay minerals. Even though they cannot be eluted from the clay, the enzymes are able to function, but the kinetics and the pH optima of an adsorbed enzyme may differ from those of the same enzyme in solution.

SAND is usually composed of quartz, a form of silica. The average formula of quartz is SiO_2, but in reality it is a large macromolecule with a network structure in which each silicon atom is bonded to four oxygen atoms, and each oxygen atom is bonded to two silicon atoms. Since quartz has a weak negative charge, adsorption by ionic interaction will be significant only when the adsorbed substance is a strong base, but adsorption can occur by the action of van der Waals and other weak forces. Glass is mainly silica, with small amounts of phosphates, borates, and other substances, depending on the type of glass. The adsorption of organic matter to glass is well known and probably plays a significant role in many laboratory experiments.

ORGANIC MATTER also occurs in colloidal and particulate form. In the soil this organic matter is in the form of complex materials called humus, composed of a number of organic polymers containing sugars, amino acids, phosphates, etc. Humus is negatively charged, shows strong base exchange, and forms complex aggregates with clay minerals. Presumably most microorganisms are associated closely with these colloids.

Particles are present in bottom deposits of aquatic environments and the principles of soil science can be applied more or less directly. Within the water mass itself particulate matter still occurs frequently, especially in shallow waters where there is sufficient wave action to keep the material in suspension. Recently it has been found that much of the organic matter in the ocean exists in particles of various sizes, mostly greater than 50 μ. Organic particles can be formed experimentally by bubbling air through sea water which has been clarified of larger existing particles by membrane filtration. It is assumed that each bubble provides a surface at which soluble organic matter can accumulate, and in some manner the molecules aggregate (Riley, 1963). The organic particles undoubtedly provide a surface to which microorganisms can attach and they may also provide a surface to which soluble organic substances may adsorb, thus bringing microbe closer to food. Organic particles are produced in sewage which is aerated for the activated sludge process, and it is considered (Heukelekian and Heller, 1940) that these surfaces play a role in microbial action.

Because of adsorption, any system that has both liquid and solid phases is heterogeneous. Although it is easy to measure the chemical and physical properties of a liquid, it cannot be concluded that the same concentrations of materials are present on the surface as are in the liquid and thus it is not possible to know the chemical and physical state of the surface to which a microorganism may be attached. To assess the chemical status of a solid phase, one can determine the selectivity of adsorption by mixing the solid with the liquid, allowing for equilibration, and then separating the two phases and assaying one or the other (usually the liquid) for the concentration of substances of interest. However, it is not possible to measure the spatial relations of two substances, both of which are adsorbed to the same solid, and which might interact. It is also important to remember that the bulk pH is not necessarily the pH at the surface of a particle. Methods of analysis in two-phase systems are greatly needed.

CHAPTER 3

The Ecology

of

the Cell

". . . ecology is physiology carried into the actual habitat. . . ."
CLEMENTS AND SHELFORD, 1939

"Ecology is physiology under the worst possible conditions."
(GRADUATE STUDENT MOTTO)

Methodologically the microbiologist has some kinship to the nuclear physicist or quantum chemist: his main job is to convert microscopic phenomena into macroscopic events which he can then measure. The implications of this problem, discussed in detail by Elsasser (1958), are so important for microbial ecology that they will be elaborated here. Elsasser states: ". . . immediate experience is macroscopic, and only in the macroscopic domain can we make unambiguous statements devoid of the large amount of statistical variance that charac-

23

terizes relationships in the microscopic realm." It is impossible to measure a microscopic event without altering it in some way by the very act of measurement. However, once the event has been converted into a macroscopic one, it is possible to measure the macroscopic event without inducing any significant disturbance. In microbial ecology, one cannot observe a single bacterial cell without disturbing it (i.e., putting it on a slide and looking at it under the microscope), but once this bacterial cell has been allowed to form a colony, the latter can easily be observed (as a colony, ALTHOUGH NOT AS INDIVIDUAL CELLS) without disturbing it. As Elsasser says: ". . . any measurement of individual phenomena in the microscopic domain constitutes a process of AMPLIFICATION." Amplification may be achieved either by the use of microscopes, photomultipliers, particle counters, etc., which possess precise macroscopic geometries and thus insure the accuracy of measurement of microscopic events, or by devices "where the localization of microscopic events is effected by means of an instability that can be made to act on a small scale." In physics, a Geiger tube or a photographic plate is such a device; in microbiology, the agar plate on which colonies or plaques develop is quite analogous.

Note that in the above discussion we are talking about the measurement of individual elements. If we do not care about individual elements, but only about an assemblage of elements which has already reached macroscopic dimensions, then our problem is much simpler. But in all cases it should be clearly remembered that we can be aware of events only if in some way they become amplified so that they approach our human dimensions. The science of microbiology has arisen out of necessity to cope with the problems of converting microscopic biological events into macroscopic ones. In our study of microbial ecology we can: (1) treat microbes as microscopic creatures and attempt to descend to their level and study their interactions microscopically, or (2) treat a selected habitat as a macroscopic system which happens to contain microorganisms and study it as a whole without reference to the individual microbes themselves, or (3) we can do both 1 and 2 simultaneously, although necessarily to different portions of the ecosystem. If we do the first, we are concerned with the analytical approach to the ecosystem (autecology), whereas if we do the second, we are concerned with the synthetic or integrative approach (synecology). In the following chapters we will follow a progression from the microscopic to the macroscopic level, beginning first with the ecology of cells, moving then to the ecology of populations, then to microbial ecosystems, and ending finally with a study of the role of microorganisms in macroscopic systems. But in most cases it will be evident that we cannot discuss events at one level without considering events at other levels, so that the organization of our work will impose certain limitations on the discussion. Thus, in the final analysis it will be necessary at the same time to think both microscopically and macroscopically. Indeed, the success of a microecological investigation can perhaps best be judged on the basis of how well it has succeeded in operating at both levels simultaneously.

PURE CULTURES

The microscope can be used to see where in a microenvironment various organisms are situated and how organisms are disposed with relation to one another. One can see that an organism is adsorbed to a soil particle or is epiphytic on a plant part; one cannot, however, make an absolute or frequently even approximate identification of an organism, and more importantly, one cannot determine at all the characteristics of an organism which are of most ecological interest, i.e., nutritional requirements, response to environment, metabolic products, etc. Thus at the very beginning of our investigations we are forced to perform cultural studies in order to characterize ecologically the organisms in which we are interested.

AXENIC means free of foreign elements or of other living organisms. This is a concept rather than a condition, since it depends greatly on what is meant by foreign. When the adjective axenic is used, it implies that it is possible to recognize all foreign elements and that it has been proven that none exist. Thus our idea of what is or is not axenic will change as our knowledge and technical facility for recognizing foreigners increase. A foreigner which we could not detect yesterday might still have been there, although we have no way of knowing. Today we have discovered its existence; tomorrow we may be able to eliminate it.

Viruses are obligate parasites which can be recognized only when they alter the host organism. Foreigners which are not obligate parasites may still be unrecognizable if we do not know how to culture them or see them. In examining an organism or culture microscopically for foreigners, it is almost impossible to detect a stray creature, especially if the scale of the host is much greater than that of the foreigner. A bacterial cell may blend into the background on the surface of almost any larger organism. Indeed, some bacteria are so small that they cannot be seen properly even with the best light microscopes. Further, the sensitivity of a microscopic examination is low. With the average oil immersion lens the field size is such that if the bacterial count is 1,000,000 cells/ml, there will be on the average only 1 cell per field! This means that if the bacterial count were 10^4/ml, one would have to examine 100 fields in order to find one organism. These simple calculations show the futility of proving absolutely that no foreigners are present.

Whether or not a pure culture is necessary depends on two things: (1) the size of the organism and (2) how closely we wish to study it. A large multicellular organism, such as a corn plant or a mouse, possesses ways of excluding foreign organisms from its interior, and even to some extent from its exterior, so that considerably over 99% of the protoplasm of the organism is corn or mouse protoplasm with only small amounts of bacterial, fungal, or protozoal protoplasm. Because of this, we can perform many significant experiments on such an organism and be fairly sure that whatever we are measuring is a function of it and not of foreigners. We can weigh the organism, study its gas exchange, measure its temperature, analyze its fluids, etc. These are properties of the organism in bulk. Since such an organism is of a size similar to our own, we find no special difficulty in studying these bulk properties.

But there are other properties of a multicellular organism whose study would present problems. (1) We might be interested in a small region of the organism, such as a single tissue or group of cells. Now we have reduced the scale of our study and immediately we enter the size range where foreigners, IF PRESENT IN THIS PARTICULAR REGION, might interfere. (2) We might be interested in a property of the whole organism which is very sensitive to outside influences, so that even if our foreigners were present in proportionately small amounts, they might still influence this property profoundly. In either of these cases, we could then perform our studies only if we had pure cultures.

As we study smaller and smaller organisms, we reach a stage at which the organisms we are interested in can no longer be studied as individuals but only as populations. This transition is a gradual one, and where it occurs may depend partly on our interests and partly on the degree of sophistication of our studies. When we have reached the point where populations must be our experimental organisms, we have reached the point where pure cultures are indispensable. Although a population of bacterial or protozoal cells possesses some defense mechanisms, it lacks the sophisticated methods for excluding strangers which the mouse or corn plant possesses. If we are to study the genetics, biochemistry, physiology, and the life cycles of such organisms, they must be in pure culture. This is absolutely essential for all bacteria, for most fungi, and for many algae and protozoa. Indeed, one might define microbiology as the study of living organisms which are so constituted that they cannot be studied in many respects without isolating them from all other organisms.

TECHNIQUES FOR OBTAINING PURE CULTURES

The first step is to find conditions in the laboratory in which the organism will grow, even in mixed culture with contaminants. Usually this presents no problems, but certain pathogens, protozoa, some sulfur bacteria, and pelagic phytoplankton have proved especially refractory. In difficult cases the investigator may have failed to duplicate in the laboratory the natural environment. For a useful discussion of the problems in cultivating marine algae, see Provasoli et al. (1957) and Hutner and Provasoli (1964); the principles they enunciate have wider utility.

Fortunately, the organisms that necessarily must be studied axenically are the ones which are the easiest to obtain in axenic culture. This is again a matter of scale; the technical difficulties in maintaining a large organism germ free are enormous, whereas a small organism can be kept nicely in a cotton-stoppered test tube. But in all cases the procedure is similar: the organism is removed from its contaminated environment and placed in a sterile one, and then all additions of materials are made in such a way that no new strangers are added. This means that the organism must be placed in an isolator and all food, water, air, and other substances must be added aseptically. Further, any experimental manipulation of the organism must be with aseptic tools and equipment. The most difficulty encountered in pure culture isolation is with protozoa, many of which obtain their nutrients by ingestion. In all organisms with cell walls, the nutrients must be able to pass through the cell wall mesh, and this means that only small molecular weight materials can be used. The requirement for proteins in such organisms is most likely only for the detoxification of other materials in the medium. If the medium cannot be autoclaved because of heat-labile factors, it can usually be filter sterilized, although it should be recognized that there are many organisms which can pass through ordinary bacteriological filters, such as pleuropneumonia-like organisms (PPLO), *Bdellovibrio* (Stolp and Starr, 1963), rickettsia, and viruses. In all cases the goal should be a heat-sterilizable nutrient medium.

The ability to isolate pure cultures of desired microorganisms is part of the microbiologist's stock in trade. Details of techniques will not be given here but can be found in most microbiology textbooks (Stanier et al., 1963) and laboratory manuals.

ENRICHMENT OF DESIRED ORGANISMS

An enrichment culture is essentially a device used to enlarge a microenvironment to macroscopic dimensions, so that organisms adapted to this microenvironment will proliferate extensively and can then be easily selected for study in pure culture. An enrichment culture is most useful for selecting an organism capable of carrying out a specific physiological function, but it can be used in a more general sense. If some properties of the organism are known, it may be possible to alter the environment in such a way that the growth of this organism is favored, or it may be possible to concentrate this organism in a particular area of the culture chamber. Most motile organisms exhibit tactic movements. Photosynthetic organisms are frequently phototactic and will concentrate in a region of brighter light where they can then be collected in enriched proportions. Aerobic organisms may exhibit positive aerotaxis, whereas anaerobes may be negatively aerotactic. Heavy organisms will settle to the bottom of a vessel, or they may be centrifuged in a light centrifugal field to concentrate them. In strong salt solutions or sea water some organisms may float and be concentrated at the surface of the liquid and a common procedure in parasitology makes use of flotation on sucrose solutions. Density gradients might be constructed so that after centrifugation organisms of different density are layered at different places in the centrifuge tube (Lammers, 1962, 1963). Organisms with thick cell walls, such as yeasts and some bacteria, would be expected to be denser than organisms containing much lipid or organisms which were highly hydrated. Some organisms are phototropic and will grow towards the light, while others are chemotropic. With filamentous fungi it is frequently possible to isolate pure cultures by allowing the filaments to grow across a solid surface such as an agar plate. Many fungi grow extremely rapidly by hyphal extension and can thus be isolated from distant regions of the plate, leaving behind all bacteria. The soil tube technique of Chesters (Warcup, 1960) is a modification of this method in which the fungus is allowed to grow vertically up a glass tube immersed in soil. Filamentous organisms can be separated from spores and unicellular organisms by selective filtration, and this procedure is very useful in separating yeasts from other fungi. Many organisms have stalks or holdfasts which enable them to attach to solid surfaces such as glass, plant material, or debris. In a flowing liquid medium the organisms which do not attach will be washed away. Henrici made considerable use of attachment to glass slides in his discovery and study of the Caulobacter group (Henrici and Johnson, 1935). Sphaerotilus cultures can be isolated (Dondero, 1961) by allowing them to attach to a glass surface in a current of flowing water.

An environment may be designed in which the organism in question will proliferate well, but other organisms will grow poorly or not at all. This may involve the use of a specific temperature, light regimen, osmotic pressure, pH, degree of aeration, degree of agitation, or the selection of a specific substrate or set of medium ingredients, or a combination of these things.

ARE PURE CULTURES ABNORMAL?

A common criticism of the use of pure cultures is that the organisms so obtained are atypical or abnormal and that they differ greatly from organisms in nature. This objection was presented in an extreme form by Winogradsky (1949) who stated: "Pure cultures . . . cannot tell us much about microbial activity in nature." However, this view, although long held by some workers, is not very prevalent today because it is now clear that pure cultures are an essential adjunct to ecological work, although they must be used with caution.

First, microorganisms do exist in pure cultures in nature in certain environments, frequently on a large scale. Algal blooms in certain lakes may often be restricted to a single species. Snow, glacier, and ice algae may show such an extensive development of a single species that the surface is brilliantly colored. Many hot springs contain essentially single species of blue-green algae, while sulfur springs may contain single species of sulfur bacteria. *Lactobacillus bifidus* is essentially pure in the intestines of infants fed only colostrum (Luckey, 1963). In many disease situations in animals and plants, microorganisms also exist as single species. In general, we can say that the more selective the natural environment, the more restricted we will find the microbial flora; the pure culture is thus merely a limiting case.

Second, even in unselective environments microorganisms occur in pure cultures, since usually they are present in the habitat in microcolonies. Jones and Griffiths (1964), using thin sections of soil crumbs, showed that bacteria always occurred as discrete microcolonies, well separated from other colonies, and a map of the microbial distribution in a single soil crumb is shown in Figure 3-1. Similar observations have been made from time to time for other microorganisms (e.g., *see* Figure 8-1). When we make a pure culture in the laboratory we are thus merely taking a situation which may already exist in nature and magnifying it in order to study it conveniently.

The crucial point is whether or not we have altered the organism by placing it in laboratory culture. As Stanier (1953) has discussed, microbial variation is of two kinds, physiologic and genetic. Physiologic variation is induced by the environment, the culture medium, temperature, pH, and other factors. Other organisms may modify this environment (as will be discussed later), but they do this in predictable ways. Further, the environment of a cell is a microenvironment, and the events which occur past the narrow sphere of influence within which it rests have no effect on it. We may look at an agar plate and say that the environment of a cell on that plate is different from its environment in the soil. What we really mean is that from the human scale an agar plate differs from a soil particle. Yet within the limited sphere of interest to the cell, the two environments may not be grossly different. If we imagine the cell in the soil, we can conceive that at two different moments in time the environment surrounding that cell may be violently different, as for instance during a severe drought and then immediately after a hard rain. Indeed, our agar plate may more closely resemble the cell environment after the rain than does the soil particle before the rain.

If we consider genetic variation, we meet the same considerations. Genetic variation in microorganisms is due mainly to mutation, and a mutant may be either selected for or against by the environment. Ultimately

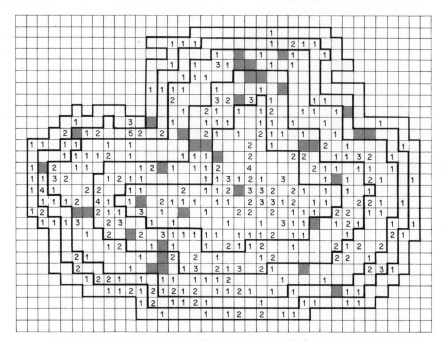

Fig. 3-1. Map of a section through a soil crumb showing the distribution of bacterial colonies (after Jones and Griffiths, 1964). Each square on the map corresponds to a 70μ square on the soil section. The figures indicate the number of bacterial colonies seen in each square. Shaded squares represent either empty spaces without soil or areas where debris prevented detailed observations. This figure emphasizes the fact that microorganisms live in microenvironments and that each such environment may have only one or a few kinds of organisms. Thus the diversity and heterogeneity seen in macroscopic studies disappear when the true microenvironment of the organism is studied.

then, the environment controls genetic variation. But, as Hungate (1962) has pointed out, with a mutation rate of 1×10^{-8} there is little chance that if a small inoculum of cells is used, any mutants will be present. The cultures obtained from natural samples will most likely be similar genetically to the bulk of the population. Hungate concludes: "*Unless there are indications to the contrary,* it is justifiable, and operationally necessary, to assume that in most characteristics pertinent to the habitat the pure cultures resemble their progenitors in nature."

Can we relate our laboratory isolates to strains in nature? First, unless an organism already exists on a macroscopic scale in nature (and this is rare), it is impossible to determine any of its physiological or biochemical properties there. Thus to compare laboratory isolates with organisms in microenvironments in nature, we must rely on morphology. We must then consider whether morphological characteristics correlate with the nutritional and physiological characteristics which are of ecological interest.

In the large and structurally complex organisms, such correlations may be quite good. The strains of *Leucothrix mucor* isolated by Harold and Stanier (1955) in California, by Pringsheim (1957) in Europe, by Lewin (1959) at Woods Hole, and by myself in Puget Sound, Narragansett Bay, and Iceland all appear similar morphologically and behave quite similarly in the laboratory. We may thus be safe in inferring something about the ecology of *Leucothrix* in the field in a new environment from what we know about the behavior in the laboratory of isolates from other environments, although we should always remember that the organism in the new area might be different in some ecologically important way. In the algae, protozoa, fungi, and the larger bacteria we are probably on fairly safe grounds in attempting to correlate morphology with ecologically relevant characteristics. It is when we turn to the small bacteria that we run into serious difficulties. Organisms like *Pseudomonas, Bacillus,* and the enteric bacteria are morphologically simple, and isolates from different locations may differ widely in physiology and nutrition so that it is almost impossible to relate laboratory isolates to organisms in the field. An especially pertinent case involves studies by Sieburth (1964) on marine arthrobacters. In pure culture, a single strain will show two temperature optima, and the morphology of the organism is entirely different when grown at these two different temperatures. At a low temperature (0-10°C) the organism grows as a gram-negative mycelioid form, whereas above 20°C the organism grows as a gram-positive coccoid bacterium, and Sieburth has been able to observe the transformation from one form to the other by shifting the temperature of the culture. Thus, if we were to observe this organism microscopically in nature, we might see either the coccoid or mycelioid form and not realize that they are identical organisms merely growing under different environments. Such considerations demonstrate more clearly than any other the crucial necessity of pure cultures in studies in microbial ecology.

Even with larger organisms some caution is necessary. Microscopic structures which appeared on glass slides immersed in sea water could not be cultured but were classified by Kriss as a completely new group of microorganisms; Sorokin (1964a), however, has shown that these structures are not microbial but are in reality tentacles of ctenophores. Kubiëna (1938) has found that fungus fruiting bodies, protozoal cells, and diatom frustules are usually smaller in soil than in culture. For instance, Figure 3-2 shows a comparison of the sporangiophores of *Mucor glomerula* as found directly in the soil and as they look in culture. Although similar in

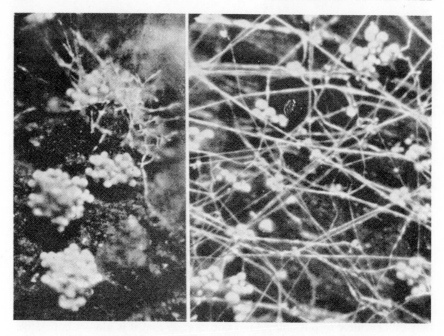

Fig. 3-2. Photomicrographs of *Mucor glomerula* growing directly in soil, LEFT, and in culture, RIGHT (Kubiëna, 1938), 43×. The sporangiophores are 50-55μ in diameter in the soil and 100-120μ in diameter in culture but are morphologically similar. In other cases, differences in morphology may be so great between the same organism in soil and in culture that they would be classified as different species.

morphology, the size is different, averaging 50-55 μ in soil and 100-120 μ in culture. "The differences in morphology of the same organism in soils and on artificial media may be so great that it becomes difficult to classify them under the same species or even the same genus" (Kubiëna, 1938). Algae which in nature differed so markedly as to have been classified as entirely different species have been reduced to synonymy when it was shown that they looked identical in laboratory culture (Hutner and Provasoli, 1964).

But the crucial point is whether or not the genotype of an organism changes in culture, since if it does not, then there is no a priori reason why we cannot create in the laboratory an environment nearly identical to that occurring in nature and thus obtain the organism as it was in nature. Since there is no evidence that the genotype does change, the criticism of cultural studies is not so much that they are done in the laboratory, but that no attempt has been made in the laboratory to recreate the natural environment. As Provasoli (1963) has stated, the observation that the form or morphogenesis of an organism in culture is altered should not be an excuse to reject culture methods out of hand: "To impute these events to the artificiality of *in vitro* experimentation is to reject the opportunity of finding the cause. . . ." And indeed, culture studies on algae by Provasoli and others have already proved their worth in ecological work, having revealed, for instance, a widespread vitamin heterotrophy of algae which had been previously unsuspected since it could hardly have been discovered by field observations alone.

Thus we may conclude that pure culture studies are essential in any autecological investigation, but that it should always be recognized that these cultures MAY differ in ecologically significant ways, so that the laboratory observations should always be correlated with field observations.

Taxonomy

and Ecology

Frequently statements made about the distribution or ecological role of an organism embody in them certain taxonomic assumptions. In microbiology, the basic unit of taxonomy is the strain or clone, which is a population of genetically identical cells. Each strain is distinguished from all other strains by its collective set of properties. Two strains are related when they have in common most of their properties. The more distantly related two strains are, the fewer properties they have in common (or vice versa). To the ecologist, however, relatedness does not refer to any common origin between two strains but rather to the fact that the two strains would be expected to behave in similar ways ecologically.

It is almost axiomatic that every strain isolated from a natural environment is different from all other strains, provided one looks hard enough for differences. What we really wish to know is whether two strains differ in a property which we consider ecologically important. Two gram-positive sporogenous aerobic motile rods which have been isolated from soil may differ in fermentation patterns or in growth factor requirements, but these differences may be of little ecological concern if we are interested in the ecology of the sporulation process. Alternatively, two morphologically diverse organisms may both oxidize alkylbenzene sulfonates, and if we are interested in this oxidation process, then the morphology of the organisms may not specifically interest us. However, if we are interested in why a certain strain, and no other, is found in a specified environment, then we will probably have to consider all of the properties of the strain, and we may have recourse to certain properties of this strain which are of little ecological importance, but which are so highly specific that they instantly identify it. Thus bacteriophage typing, bacteriocine typing, and immunological classification are very useful procedures, even though the properties studied may be only indirect manifestations of ecologically significant primary characteristics. Therefore we should always be careful to distinguish between characteristics which are useful to us in our studies and characteristics which are useful to the organism in its natural environment.

TAXONOMIC GROUPS

The segregation of strains into species, genera, families, orders, classes, and phyla is a matter of personal judgment rather than of scientific operation. Basically, what is being done is deciding that certain strains have a group of characteristics in common and thus can be thought of together, WITH RESPECT TO THESE CHARACTERISTICS. Usually when we use the words "bacteria" or "algae," we have a collection of properties in mind. Do such broad taxonomic groups have any ecological significance? For instance, blooms in fresh water lakes are not caused by all Chlorophyta but only by certain strains. If these strains are well characterized, then no new ECOLOGICAL information is provided by the statement that they are members of the Chlorophyta. In fact, it would be misleading to state ONLY that the blooms were due to Chlorophyta, since this division covers such a diverse group of organisms.

Of course, generally the more restricted the taxonomic grouping is, the more likely it is to have some ecological significance, although only rarely does any taxonomist take ecology into consideration. Thus one bacterial family (e.g., Athiorhodaceae) may be composed of a relatively homogeneous group ecologically, whereas another family (e.g., Enterobacteriaceae) may contain ecologically highly divergent organisms. As our ecological knowledge of microorganisms develops, it will perhaps be interesting in the future to examine the correspondence between ecology and taxonomy. At present we can use only the groupings which the taxonomist has given us.

Identification
of the Habitat

If one discovers a certain microorganism in a locality, its existence can be explained in either of two ways: (1) the organism has multiplied and developed in the locality, or (2) the organism has been transmitted to this locality from elsewhere. In the first case, the organism is said to be autochthonous, endemic, or native, and in the second case the organism is said to be allochthonous, foreign, introduced, or accidental. The habitat of an organism can best be defined as the place in nature where it actually grows. The actual definition of a habitat is not uncomplicated. If the organism is attached to a permanent substrate, such as a rock, or an attached plant or animal, then it can usually be assumed that it has actually grown in this location and that this is its habitat. For instance, filaments of *Leucothrix mucor* (Brock, 1966) are usually found attached to seaweeds (*see* Figure 3-3), and we have shown by radioautographic procedures (Brock and Brock, 1966a) that they do indeed grow in this location in nature. However, organisms which are free living may move either under their own power or passively, so we cannot conclude that a particular location is an organism's habitat because it is found there. Especially in aquatic situations wind, waves, and currents may combine to concentrate into one area individuals which have grown in widely separate regions, and this may complicate any autecological study. Even in terrestrial environments active or passive movement is possible, although here the problems are much less complicated. For instance, an animal which has just died in the soil will be populated by bacteria which it has brought to this location from elsewhere, but the organisms in question grew within the animal and thus are autochthonous as far as the animal is concerned.

In each locality, mutation, recombination, and selection will act to create a group of local strains which are best adapted to that particular

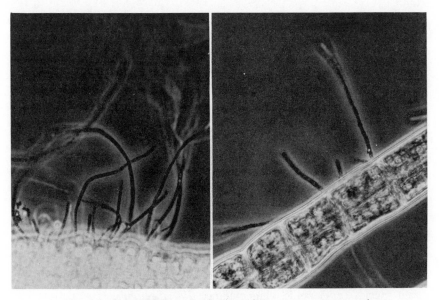

Fig. 3-3. Epiphytic growth of *Leucothrix mucor* on seaweeds in nature and in the laboratory (Brock, 1966), 980×. *L. mucor* growing in nature on *Callophyllis haenophylla*, LEFT, and in pure culture in the laboratory with a pure culture of *Sphacelaria* sp., RIGHT, phase contrast.

locality. On the other hand, dispersal mechanisms will spread these locally bred strains to distant parts, promoting outbreeding and an increase in uniformity. Thus evolution and dispersion tend to counteract each other, the one leading to specialization, the other to uniformity (Gregory, 1961). In discussing the microhabitats of protozoa, Bamforth (1963) has said:

"The composition of microhabitats may be disturbed by diurnal movements and chance migrations. Most non-photosynthetic protozoa show little reaction to sunlight, and tend to remain in their microhabitats, but chlorophyll-bearing forms may exhibit diurnal movements, rising to the surface shortly after sunrise and descending again after sunset. If the latter are in large numbers, they may displace the colorless forms, which return again at night (Bamforth 1960). Such phenomena can occur not only in open water, but under plant cover and in algal masses. Chance migrations may also disturb the composition of microhabitats: suddenly by rain, wind, and large animal movements; or less noticeably by transport of organisms attached to moving gas bubbles and detritus.

"Despite these disturbances, microhabitats often contain special types of populations. Just as plains, forests and mountains favor different and special types of vertebrate fauna, so different types of microhabitats favor different and special types of protozoan communities, seen in the following examples:

"1. The bottom furnishes a substrate rich in organic matter and bacteria for creeping organisms such as *Sarcodina* and flattened ciliates (small hymenostomes, many hypotrichs), motile ciliates that may glide (gymnostomes), and sessile *Stentor, Suctorida* and *Peritrichida.*

"2. Submerged structures can support a variety of communities (aufwuchs), depending on the nature of the substrate. Broad surfaces usually support low numbers of peritrichous and flattened motile ciliates; whereas finely branched substrates such as algal masses or grass leaves, not only provide increased surface area for flattened creeping forms (e.g., *Glaucoma, Aspidisca, Chilodonella*), but numerous spaces for rounded and cylindrical forms (most flagellates, gymnostomes, some heterotrichs) to swim and glide. The dangling roots of floating aquatic plants, such as *Lemna* and *Azolla,* provide similar microhabitats, in which swimming and interface populations mix. In these habitats, swimming forms often take on the gliding habit.

"3. Open water (below surface and above bottom) favors rounded forms (most flagellates, *Heliozoa,* many *Holophryidae*) and active cylindrical species (euglenoids, gymnostomes, *Paramecium*).

"4. The water surface film receives organisms from open water below and provides a substrate for flattened ciliates to dart along. Formation of surface scum furnishes a firmer substrate, and creeping ciliates, and *Sarcodina,* and sessile *Stentor,* peritrichs and *Suctorida* appear. . . . Examination of the community structure of microhabitats may furnish greater understanding of protozoan ecology, and provide additional clues to protozoan evolution."

Physiological
Ecology

CHEMICAL COMPOSITION OF CELLS

The chemical composition of cells is summarized in Giese (1962) and Spector (1956). Some materials are invariant and are found in all cells, whereas others are found only in certain groups. From organism to organism the concentrations of cell constituents can vary tremendously, either genotypically or phenotypically. All the elements of a cell ultimately come from the environment, but most elements are extensively reworked by the cell into its own framework. It is obvious that if an element is absent from the environment it cannot be present in the cell. If an element is present in the environment, it may be excluded from the cell, or it may be concentrated within the cell in amounts in excess of those in the environment. Table 3-1 shows the relative concentrations of various elements in sea water as compared to their concentration in marine organisms. Certain elements such as Na, Cl, and Mg are excluded from the organism, but most elements are concentrated in the organism far above those concentrations found in the environment. Note especially the exceedingly high concentration factors for the biologically important elements N, P, Fe, and Co. Thus, the richest source of nutrients essential for growth of an organism will be the bodies of other organisms. It should also be noted that just because an element is present within a cell, it cannot be concluded that this element is required by the cell; it may merely be passively or nonspecifically taken up.

Table 2-1 listed a variety of physical and chemical factors which influence the growth and activity of organisms. Four of the physical factors—

TABLE 3-1. CONCENTRATION FACTOR FOR VARIOUS ELEMENTS IN LIVING ORGANISMS

10^{-2}	10^{-1}	10^0	10^1	10^2	10^3	10^4	10^5	10^6
Na	Mg	Ba	Ca	As	C	Mn	N	Au
Cl	Br	I	S	K	Zn	Se	P	Co
	Li	Sr	F		Cu	Ag	V	Fe
		B	Al		Ni	Si		
					Rb			

From Baas-Becking (1959). Figures indicate ratio of concentration of the elements in sea water to that in marine organisms.

temperature, hydrostatic pressure, osmotic pressure, and visible radiation—
are especially relevant in controlling the distribution of organisms, whereas
all of the chemical factors are important. It should be recognized of course,
that occasionally the decision as to whether a factor is physical or chemical
is purely arbitrary. Indeed, in some cases (e.g., NaCl concentration) the
same variable probably acts in both manners simultaneously. It should
also be remembered that a factor which is harmful to one organism may be
beneficial to another. Thus H_2S is toxic to most aerobic organisms but is
an essential nutrient and energy source for certain sulfur bacteria; some
organisms are killed by high acidity, whereas others can grow under no other
conditions.

The quantity of any factor can vary over wide limits, but it is usually
found that a given organism can grow and function over only a limited
portion of this range, so that it is possible to establish a minimum, an
optimum, and a maximum value at which growth will occur. In general,
the optimum for any factor is closer to the maximum than it is to the
minimum, and typical temperature response curves are shown in Figure
3-4. Any organism can be tested for its ability to grow in the presence of

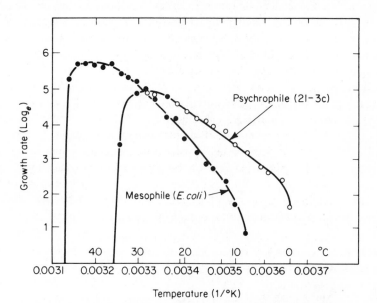

Fig. 3-4. Relationship between growth rate and temperature for
a psychorophile (strain 21-3c) and a mesophile (*Escherichia
coli*) (after Ingraham, 1962). This figure is an Arrhenius plot,
pressing $\log_e$ of growth rate versus reciprocal of absolute temperature. It is characteristic of temperature relationships that
the optimum temperature is much nearer the maximum than
the minimum.

varying amounts of each environmental factor, and thus characterized ecologically. It is therefore possible to group organisms arbitrarily with relation to various factors and give names to these various groups, such as thermophilic, auxotrophic, etc. It should be remembered that any classification of this sort is quite arbitrary, and that in practice living organisms will not fall into neatly defined groups. The main function of such a classification is to focus attention on the ways in which organisms can differ in environmental requirements and how these differences will influence the distribution of organisms in nature. All taxonomic groups show ecological diversity, although the bacteria are the most diverse.

Garrett (1951) has provided an ecological classification of soil fungi, distinguishing saprophytic sugar fungi (i.e., those unable to use insoluble polysaccharides as nutrient sources), root-inhabiting fungi, lignin-decomposing fungi, coprophilous fungi, and predaceous fungi. It happens that the sugar fungi are mainly Phycomycetes (especially of the Order Mucorales) and the lignin fungi are Basidiomycetes, but many Basidiomycetes are not lignin utilizers, and many Phycomycetes are not sugar fungi, while some sugar fungi are Ascomycetes. The role of these various ecological groups in the decomposition of leaf litter is discussed on page 252.

Lochhead and Chase (1943) developed a nutritional classification of the predominant bacterial flora of the soil, recognizing the following groups: (1) bacteria showing no growth factor requirements and growing on a simple glucose-nitrate-salts medium; (2) bacteria requiring one or more amino acids; (3) bacteria requiring one or more B vitamins; (4) bacteria requiring amino acids plus vitamins; (5) bacteria requiring unidentified substances in yeast extract; (6) bacteria requiring unidentified substances in soil extract; (7) bacteria requiring unidentified substances in both yeast extract and soil extract. This work led to studies showing that many bacteria in the root zone of plants (the rhizosphere) required vitamins for growth, whereas others synthesized vitamins (Lochhead, 1958). At least one of the unidentified growth factors in soil (the terregens factor, a growth substance for *Arthrobacter terregens*) was shown to be an iron-containing substance similar to ferrichrome, a natural iron chelate which probably functions as a source of biologically available iron (Lochhead, 1958). The incidence of soil bacteria requiring various vitamins is shown in Table 3-2.

In earlier years, workers hesitated to place organisms under widely varying environmental conditions to see how they behaved. Such experiments were rigorously proscribed by Winogradsky, who called this "forcing the species." Yet, microorganisms live in nature in changing environments, and if they are to survive they must be able to adapt to these changes. It is no more unreasonable for an organism to be subjected to different environments in the laboratory than for it to be subjected to different

TABLE 3-2. INCIDENCE IN A FIELD SOIL OF BACTERIA REQUIRING SPECIFIC VITAMINS

Vitamin required (either alone or with others)	Vitamin-requiring bacteria	
	Percentage of total isolates	Approximate no. (millions/g)
Thiamin	19.4	10.2
Biotin	16.4	8.6
Vitamin B_{12}	7.2	3.8
Pantothenic acid	4.6	2.4
Folic acid	3.0	1.6
Nicotinic acid	2.0	1.1
Riboflavin	0.6	0.3
Pyridoxine	< 0.2	< 0.1
p-Aminobenzoic acid	< 0.2	< 0.1
Choline	< 0.2	< 0.1
Inositol	< 0.2	< 0.1
One or more factors	27.1	14.1

From Lochhead (1958).

environments in nature. For instance, many phototrophic algae can grow in the dark if provided with an appropriate organic energy source (Pringsheim, 1959), but it might seem that this is forcing the species to do something it would not ordinarily do. However, it is now known that algae may grow heterotrophically in nature (Rodhe, 1963), so that the laboratory studies are now of more than academic interest.

LIEBIG'S LAW

An important physiological concept, widely used in ecology, is Liebig's Law of the Limiting Factor (Odum, 1959). Briefly, this law states that the rate of growth or activity of some processes in an organism is controlled by the environmental factor which is limiting. If the limiting factor is changed so that it is no longer limiting, then another factor becomes limiting, and so on. This concept is ideally suited to experimental ecology since it means that even though most factors of the environment are continuously varying, fluctuations in all factors which are not limiting can be ignored, and attention can be directed to the limiting factor, greatly simplifying the analysis. Liebig's Law can also be extended to include factors which affect organisms because they are in excess and thus become toxic or inhibitory. High temperature or high CO_2 concentration might also act as a limiting factor.

Work on the nutrition of algae (Provasoli, 1958a; Hutner and Provasoli, 1964) has provided some insight into limiting factors for algal development in nature. This work has revealed the surprisingly large number of algae which have absolute requirements for certain vitamins (a vitamin B_{12} requirement being very frequent in marine isolates), and at least certain aspects of algal distribution can be explained by the variability of vitamins in the environment. "Ideally, one hopes to discern why each alga fits its niche—a stupendous task. . . . If one begins by attacking the nutrition of ecological indicator species especially from habitats exemplifying extreme conditions, ecological information can guide laboratory work. . . . Bloom organisms, too, are likely to respond sharply to few variables or even to a single one . . . and so their niches may be easy to find" (Hutner and Provasoli, 1964).

GRADIENTS

In nature gradients frequently exist for various environmental factors, and the distribution of organisms along these gradients may provide clues to ecologically limiting factors. Gradients exist for such factors as temperature (thermal springs, *see* Figure 3-6), light (Crossett et al., 1965) and hydrostatic pressure (vertical descent in an aquatic environment), nutrient concentration (sewage effluents), and oxygen concentration or oxidation-reduction potential (aquatic sediments, flowing springs). Occasionally there are countergradients, and an organism will occur only in a district stratum which provides the optimum balance of two critical factors. For example, as discussed by van Niel (1955), the sulfur bacterium Thiovolum accumulates in a region of a liquid culture where the concentrations of H_2S and O_2 are optimum. These concentrations may be achieved by the diffusion of O_2 into the liquid from the surface and by the diffusion of H_2S into the liquid from the sediment. At a precisely balanced point within these two gradients, Thiovolum finds its optimum environment and grows as a thin veil (see also La Rivière, 1963). Similar stratification has been observed for the sulfur photosynthetic bacteria in freshwater lakes (Kuznetsov, 1959), and two examples are shown in Figure 3-5.

MULTIVARIATE ANALYSIS

Although Liebig's Law provides a useful simplification for experimental work, it should be noted that Liebig himself did not accept this law without question, as is shown by the following quotation: "I have often thought, in my long practical career . . . how much pains and how many researches are necessary to probe to the depths a rather complicated phenomenon. The greatest difficulty comes from the fact that we are too much accustomed to attribute to a single cause that which is the product of several, and the majority of our controversies come from that" (letter from Liebig to Duclaux, *in* Duclaux, 1920).

In environments which are not extreme it is the interaction of all environmental factors that is important, and we cannot say a priori that any

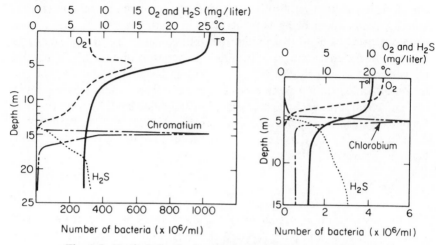

Fig. 3-5. Vertical distribution of temperature, oxygen, H₂S and photosynthetic sulfur bacteria in two freshwater lakes (after Kuznetsov, 1959). LEFT, Lake Belovod, showing sharp stratification of the purple sulfur bacterium *Chromatium*. RIGHT, Lake Bolschoje-Kutschejer, with the green sulfur bacterium *Chlorobium*. Note that in both cases the bacterial layer exists at the balance point of two gradients, light and H₂S concentration.

factor is more important than any other. Thus ideally it would be better to perform a multivariate analysis of the simultaneous influence on the growth and function of the organism of variations in temperature, pressure, pH, oxygen concentration, concentration of nitrogen source, of carbon source, of phosphate source, etc. The difficulty of such an analysis, however, is that if each variable were allowed to assume several levels and then all were tested in all possible combinations, the number of separate tests becomes enormous. For instance, in a simplified analysis with only four variables at three levels, 81 separate tests are required! Given the will, it is feasible to carry out such a multivariate study and with computers the data could be analyzed. Since organisms are sometimes subjected to wide variations in temperature, pH, nutrient concentration, etc., such an analysis could be important. For instance, ZoBell (1958) has considered the interaction of hydrostatic pressure with other variables for a sulfate-reducing bacterium. As the pressure was increased, the temperature optimum of the organism increased, and at 1000 atmospheres the organism grew even at 104°C! Meyer et al. (1962) studied the microbiology of an unfrozen saline pond in Antarctica. This pond varied in temperature from −24 to −5°C, but because of the high salinity (14 times greater than that of sea water), the water never froze. Even though the organic content was low, bacteria grew well in this water, forming colonies visible in the liquid. The organisms from this pond included *Bacillus megaterium,* a *Micrococcus,* and a *Corynebacterium,* all of which would grow well in ordinary laboratory media of low salinity and high organic matter content at 20°C. The authors suggest that there may be a ". . . relationship between high salt concentration and the ability to grow at low temperatures and in an environment of low organic content."

ENVIRONMENTAL EXTREMES

Vallentyne (1963) has reviewed the environmental limits for certain physical factors, as determined both by observation in the field and by experimentation in the laboratory, and his conclusions are summarized in Table 3-3. In extreme environments microbes are the only living organisms found. Note that most of the data were derived from monovariate analyses. If several variables had been allowed to fluctuate at the same time, even more extreme limits might have been discovered.

Vallentyne concludes: "The microorganisms referred to in this paper are peculiar in that they grow in environments that are lethal to most other forms of life. One can instructively reverse the point of view that has been taken here and ask why it is that most organisms live under 'common' conditions. The answer is, of course, because life as a whole is selectively adapted to growth in common environments. If the waters of the earth were predominantly acid, growth at neutral pH values would be regarded as an oddity. Thus, the fact that most living species conform physiologically and ecologically to average Earth conditions should not be taken to indicate any inherent environmentally based physicochemical conservatism of living matter. Adaptation has taken place.

"Environments of the Earth that are sterile or nearly so mostly fall into one of two categories: nonaqueous environments, and noncirculatory aque-

TABLE 3-3. ENVIRONMENTAL LIMITS FOR GROWTH AND REPRODUCTION OF MICROORGANISMS

Factor	Lower limit	Upper limit
Temperature	−12°C (fungi, bacteria)	104°C (sulfate-reducing bacteria at 1000 atm)
E_h (at the prevailing pH)	−350 to −450 mv at pH 8 to 9.5 (sulfate-reducing bacteria)	+850 mv at pH 3 (iron bacteria)
pH	0 (*Acontium velatum, Thiobacillus thiooxidans*)	13 (?) (*Plectonema nostocorum*)
Hydrostatic pressure	Essentially 0	1400 atm (deep sea bacteria)
Salinity	Double distilled water (heterotrophic bacteria)	Saturated brines (*Dunaliella,* halophilic bacteria)

Adapted from Vallentyne (1963) and Vallentyne (personal communication).

ous environments. . . . In small enclosed systems extinction becomes increasingly probable with time because of the small numbers of organisms involved, the accumulation of metabolic waste products, and the general decrease in free energy of the system as a function of time. Continuous circulation negates these factors and in addition permits occasional injections of diverse microorganisms into new environments, to which they may become adapted over many generations. Given the presence of circulating water, it seems rather unlikely that any aqueous environment could remain indefinitely sterile over geologically long periods of time."

Table 3-4 lists examples of natural habitats providing extreme environments in which microorganisms can be regularly found.

TABLE 3-4. HABITATS PROVIDING ENVIRONMENTAL EXTREMES

Factor	Lower limit	Upper limit
Temperature	Frozen foods, snow fields, glaciers	Hot springs, volcanoes, laundry waters
E_h	Deep aquatic sediments, anaerobic sewage digesters	Atmosphere
pH	Acid mine waters, acid springs	Alkaline lakes, certain industrial waters
Hydrostatic pressure		Deep sea
Salinity	Oligotrophic lakes	Saline lakes
Light	Caves, ocean floor	High altitudes

TEMPERATURE

Probably no environmental factor can be measured as easily and precisely and with as minimum a disturbance to the system as temperature, and consequently we have considerable knowledge of the relationship of temperature to growth and ecology (Precht et al., 1955; Ingraham, 1962), Organisms will grow at any low temperature at which liquid water still exists, so that the lower limit for biological development is that temperature at which not even microscopic pockets of water exist. Much of the environment of the world exists at fairly low temperatures. Only rarely do oceanic temperatures get above 40°C, and most of the waters of the world are below 30°C (Hedgepeth, 1957). Terrestrial environments fluctuate in temperature more than aquatic regions, and at the soil surface temperatures greater than 40°C are easily reached in midsummer, but because of the absence of convection even here the temperature a few inches beneath the surface will be much cooler (Russell and Russell, 1950). Microorganisms have no specific means of regulating their own temperatures, although a crude temperature regulation might occur where high population densities develop, as in compost or sewage digesters. Many microorganisms are able to grow rapidly at low temperature, but it seems surprising that organisms which spend their entire lives at temperatures below 10°C still often show temperature optima for growth of around 20-25°C. This suggests that there are intrinsic factors limiting growth at low temperature (probably diffusion), which even the most perfectly evolved organism cannot overcome. Typical curves relating growth rate to temperature for a psychrophile and mesophile are shown in Figure 3-4.

The main environments with temperature in the range of 35-40°C are the bodies of warm-blooded animals, and microorganisms have evolved which have their optima precisely in this region, growing poorly or not at all at lower or higher temperatures. Of organisms adapted to warm-blooded animals, the greatest diversity is found in the bacteria. The fungi, for instance, do not show much ability to adapt to this environment, although there are important fungal representatives associated with animals.

High temperatures are fairly uncommon in the world, thermal springs and volcanoes usually being so rare as to become tourist attractions. The hottest waters in hot springs are usually sterile (Setchell, 1903; Kempner, 1963; Brock and Brock, unpublished). The highest temperature ·at which living organisms are found is affected by pH and other environmental factors, and in the most favorable conditions is in the range of 85-88°C (Setchell, 1903; Brock and Brock, unpublished) at which bacteria, but not algae, are found. The upper temperature limit for algal growth is about 73°C under the most favorable conditions (Kempner, 1963; Brock and Brock, unpublished).

We have made use of the thermal gradients created in the effluents of hot springs to measure the optimum temperature for biological development (Brock and Brock, 1966b). Quantitative cores of the blue-green algal mats were taken at various temperatures along the gradient and assayed for chlorophyll, protein, and RNA content. The results for a typical spring are shown in Figure 3-6, where it can be seen that a sharp optimum temperature occurs at 56°C. Since all other factors of the environment remained essentially constant, it can be concluded that the controlling factor in biological development in these springs is temperature. A number of studies have been made of the blue-green algae associated with hot springs (Copeland, 1936), but cultural studies have been quite limited (Dyer and Gafford, 1961). High temperatures also develop through certain microbial processes, such as composting and silage fermentation, so that thermophilic organisms are not restricted only to national parks and monuments. Indeed, most soils will yield at least a few strains of thermophiles.

It should also be noted that organisms may exhibit new nutritional requirements as their growth temperature is raised, so that the nature of the medium and other factors will determine the optimum or maximum temperature for growth. Most organisms grow in regions of fluctuating

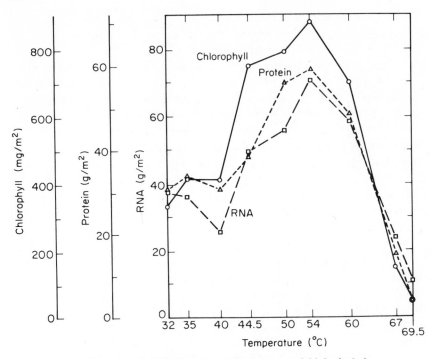

Fig. 3-6. Relationship between temperature and biological development in the thermal gradient created by the effluent of a hot spring in Yellowstone National Park (after Brock and Brock, 1966*b*). Quantitative cores were taken of the blue-green algal mats developing at different temperatures and assayed for various biochemical parameters. The sharp optimum at 54° is noteworthy.

temperature, so that it would seem reasonable to assess the effect of various temperature regimens on growth. For the photosynthetic algae the day and night temperature optima for growth are likely to be different if these organisms are similar to higher plants. But even heterotrophic organisms might thrive better with fluctuating than with constant temperatures. So far as I know, systematic experiments along these lines have not been performed with microorganisms.

SALINITY

Although many factors may affect osmotic pressure, the most important natural factor is salinity. Natural waters vary from those as dilute as rain water to those essentially saturated with salt (Brown, 1964). Most fresh waters vary considerably more in salinity both seasonally and yearly than do oceanic waters, although the salinity of inshore waters in many areas may be markedly affected by surface runoff and river drainage. The salinity of soils is affected by rainfall and drought, but ion exchange and other factors probably modify these fluctuations considerably. The environment with the most constant salinity would be experienced by organisms which live within the bodies of those animals which have precise ion regulatory mechanisms.

A frequent error is the assumption that marine organisms are exceptionally salt tolerant or halophilic. Rather, it is usually found that marine organisms are quite precisely adapted to the range of salinity of the water in which they live (usually equivalent to about 3.5% NaCl) and grow poorly at salinities both above and below this value, although there are always a few organisms in a marine environment which will grow in dilute media, just as there may be fresh water organisms which will grow in sea water. For extreme halophilic organisms, sea water is as harmful as distilled water. Ingram (1957) has shown that halophiles are in ionic equilibrium with their environment and possess the same concentration of salt within their protoplasm as is found externally. Both marine bacteria (MacLeod, 1965) and extreme halophiles (Larsen, 1962) have a specific requirement for sodium ions. The relationship between sodium ion concentration and growth for selected organisms is shown in Figure 3-7. Extreme halophilic bacteria use sodium ions to help maintain their rod-shaped structure, so that both sodium ions and a cell wall are necessary if the organism is to remain rod shaped (Brown, 1964). Halophiles also use sodium ions to help stabilize or activate certain enzymes. Presumably during their evolution extreme halophiles have made use of the ever present sodium ion to carry out certain biochemical functions which are performed in other organisms in different ways. Note, however, that some organisms (e.g., *Escherichia coli*) can show physiological, but not genetic, adaptation to increased salt concentration (Ingram, 1957).

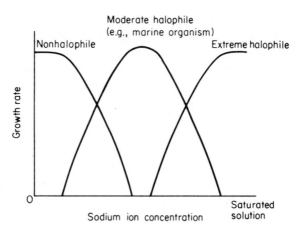

Fig. 3-7. Idealized diagrams of the growth rates of three kinds of organisms as a function of Na$^+$ concentration.

SPECIALISTS AND GENERALISTS

Some organisms are able to grow under a wide range of physical and chemical conditions, whereas others are highly restricted. An organism like *Pseudomonas fluorescens* is quite adaptable, and a single clone can oxidize a wide variety of organic substances. Such an organism grows in a wide variety of environments, and because of this an autecological study is of low interest, since it is difficult to make restrictive statements about the distribution and function of the organism. On the other hand, specialized organisms such as parasites and many sulfur and iron bacteria grow only in restricted environments, and autecological investigations are more satisfying. Knowledge of the nutritional and environmental requirements of a specialist frequently leads to the possibility of predicting the distribution and function of the organism in nature. The purple photosynthetic sulfur bacteria (Thiorhodaceae), for instance, can be quite precisely described ecologically. Perhaps it is for this reason that bacterial ecology is more closely identified with the study of these specialists. Not surprisingly, the generalists are easier to culture in the laboratory than the specialists. The trials and tribulations of obtaining cultures of the iron bacteria are well documented by Wolfe (1964).

NUTRITION

Nutrients can be divided into two classes: (1) necessary nutrients, without which a cell cannot grow, and (2) useful but dispensable nutrients, which can be used if present but which NEED not be present. In the latter case it is assumed that the cell can synthesize the substance or its equivalent if it is lacking from the environment.

It is useful to distinguish between those nutrients which are incorporated into the protoplasmic mass of the cell and those which are used and acted upon by the cell but which are subsequently disposed of. In the former class would be most of the carbon, nitrogen, sulfur, and phosphorus compounds and most of the metals. In the latter class would be: (1) substances which function as electron donors or energy sources, such as water (photosynthetic organisms), ammonia (nitrifying bacteria), glucose (lactic acid bacteria), and H_2S (colorless sulfur bacteria), and (2) substances which function as electron acceptors, such as oxygen (most aerobes), nitrate (denitrifying bacteria), sulfate (Desulfovibrio), etc. In some cases a substance may function in both ways, either in different cells or in the same cell. Thus oxygen gas functions mainly as an electron acceptor but in some organisms is also a direct reactant in the biosynthesis of unsaturated fatty acids, sterols, tyrosine, and other compounds (Goldfine and Bloch, 1963).

It is also useful to distinguish between macronutrients, those substances required by cells in large amounts as precursors of or as direct building blocks of the cell structure, and micronutrients, such as vitamins, hormones, and trace elements, which are required in amounts so small as to be difficult to detect analytically. The distribution of an organism in nature may be controlled by the absence from an environment of either a macronutrient or a micronutrient and one cannot say that either group is more important than the other, but since it is more difficult to measure the presence or absence of a micronutrient, these micronutrients become experimentally more important. Also, the macronutrient requirements of many organisms will be similar or identical, whereas the micronutrient requirements are more likely to differ from species to species. Thus the distribution of micronutrients may play a great role in determining whether or not a given species will develop in a given environment.

The nutritional requirements of an organism are determined mainly by its genotype but may be modified significantly by variations in environmental factors such as temperature or pH. Thus, it is essential in any autecological investigation to determine the nutritional requirements under a range of physical conditions. For instance, *E. coli* will grow on a simple medium containing only glucose and salts, yet in nature it grows almost exclusively in the nutritionally complex environment of the intestinal tract. In *E. coli* nutritional requirements may represent only one small facet of the properties which must be considered together in any ecological investigation. Nutritional requirements of bacteria, fungi, and algae have been reviewed by Guirard and Snell (1962), Cochrane (1958), and Hutner and Provasoli (1964), respectively.

Cultural studies reveal the potential nutrients which an isolate can utilize, but they do not reveal which nutrients the organism was actually able to use in nature at the time it was isolated. We have recently (Brock and Brock, 1966a) developed a radioautographic technique which permits a study of the nutrition of an organism directly in nature. We have chosen for this work the bacterium *Leucothrix mucor,* because it is a large morphologically distinct organism which can be identified directly microscopically, and because it occurs in very high numbers as an epiphyte on seaweeds. From extensive direct microscopic observations (Brock, 1966) I have determined that this organism is always present on filamentous red and green algae which live in areas with much water flow due to wave action or tidal current. Thus I can confidently select algal fronds which I know will be colonized with *L. mucor.* Preliminary studies have been performed with C^{14}-glutamate and H^3-glucose, since these are common nutrients which we know from cultural studies can be used by *L. mucor.* Samples of algae are taken and placed in vials of sea water containing a known amount of

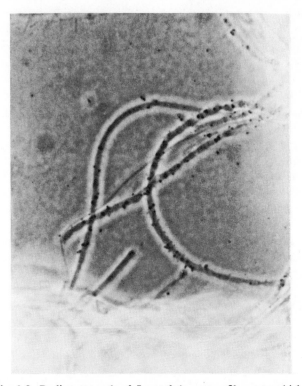

Fig. 3-8. Radioautograph of *Leucothrix mucor* filaments which had incorporated glucose-H³ directly in nature, 810×. *L. mucor* epiphytic on red alga growing in Narragansett Bay, Rhode Island. Incubated in situ for one hour with 1 μC/ml glucose-H³, then fixed and processed. The marked heterogeneity in ability to incorporate the isotope should be noted.

radioactive material and incubated in the ocean for various periods of time. The algae are then fixed in formalin, affixed to slides, and the slides dipped in photographic emulsion and exposed as in usual radioautographic procedures (Prescott, 1964). Figure 3-8 shows typical results obtained with H³-glucose, and it can be seen that many of the *L. mucor* filaments are covered with silver grains and hence have incorporated the glucose. This technique allows one to observe the microheterogeneity which occurs in most natural populations; although most *L. mucor* filaments may incorporate the compound, some may be dormant or are not adapted to the substrate.

This technique has wide potential use in microbial ecology, since it allows one to carry out observations of a biochemical sort directly at the microenvironmental level (Brock and Brock, 1966*a*).

NUTRIENT CONCENTRATION

The importance of the adsorption of nutrients to surfaces in altering the ability of organisms to grow in dilute media is discussed on page 73. Nutrient concentration may play as much of a role in ecological relationships as nutrient quality. If the concentration of a nutrient is low, many organisms will not be able to grow, as they are unable to concentrate the nutrient sufficiently, although many aquatic organisms seem to be able to develop in extremely low concentrations of nutrients. If the concentration of a nutrient is too high, it may be toxic, either for osmotic reasons or because of some specific inhibitory property. Many substances toxic in high concentrations (e.g., phenol, pyridine) may be used for growth if they are added in small amounts. Some organisms have specific transport mechanisms (permeases) which enable them to use more efficiently the specific nutrients transported by these permeases.

When the nutrient supply is exhausted, the organism may die, or it may become dormant. Dormancy is due either to sporulation or to an ability to maintain cellular structure by means of a low rate of endogenous metabolism using endogenous reserves. The behavior of an organism at nutrient exhaustion is probably determined both genetically and by its prehistory and may greatly influence the distribution of an organism in nature. Aquatic and soil microorganisms which live in environments where nutrients may become suddenly depleted may be more likely to tolerate nutrient deficiencies than microorganisms associated with the rich nutrient sources of plants and animals.

NUTRIENT PREFERENCES

When an organism is supplied with two functionally equivalent nutrients it may use one in preference to the other. For instance, if an organism is supplied with nitrogen in the form of NH_4^+ and NO_3^-, the former will usually be used first, and then the latter. Such preferences are of great ecological interest, since organisms frequently are presented with nutritionally equivalent substances, and it would seem reasonable that the ability to select one over another plays some role in the success of the species. Generally, the organism utilizes first the material on which it has to do the least amount of work before it can become a usable product for macromolecular synthesis or metabolic function.

Organisms also show preferences between exogenous and endogenous nutrients. For example if *E. coli* is provided with arginine in the medium, it stops making arginine internally until the external material is gone, a phenomenon called repression or feedback inhibition, depending on the mechanism of the inhibition. Pardee (1962) has discussed the evolutionary aspects of such phenomena, and it would be of great interest to study their ecological significance.

COMPETITION OF NUTRIENTS

Two substances may combine with the same cellular site and thus compete with each other for this site. For instance *E. coli* can use either O_2 or NO_3^- as an electron acceptor, but the affinity is so much higher for oxygen than for nitrate that the former is able to exclude the latter, and only under anaerobic conditions can nitrate be used (Pollock, 1946). Two substances may be transported into the cell by the same system but move into divergent pathways after they have entered. In streptococci (Brock and Moo-Penn, 1962), serine, alanine, and glycine are transported by the same system, and if one is present in great excess, the entrance of the others into the cell will be inhibited. Since both serine and glycine are required by the cell for growth, an excess of one inhibits growth probably by creating a deficiency of the other. Examples of growth inhibition due to amino acid imbalance are common and are reviewed by Guirard and Snell (1962). Interestingly, such an imbalance can be obviated if the amino acid in the minority is provided in a peptide which enters the cell by an alternate pathway (Kihara and Snell, 1960).

COOPERATIVE ACTION OF NUTRIENTS

The Stickland Reaction is the name given for the process by which certain clostridia are able to decompose rapidly appropriate pairs of amino acids, whereas neither of the amino acids supplied alone can be attacked. Decomposition can occur when any amino acid capable of serving as an oxidant and any amino acid capable of serving as a reductant are present together (Barker, 1961). Note that the clostridia are obligate anaerobes and thus must have available organic electron acceptors. The ability of many facultative aerobes to use nonfermentable organic compounds such as acetate and succinate is usually conditioned by the presence of O_2 as an electron acceptor.

UTILIZATION AND DISSOLUTION OF INSOLUBLE SUBSTANCES

Even the most insoluble substance has a finite solubility, and since solution is an equilibrium process, theoretically any material can be ultimately dissolved. An insoluble substance can usually be viewed as a polymeric material made up of subunits held tightly together by chemical bonds. Solution then results from the release of subunits from the polymer. Writing of organic polymers, Rogers (1961) has said: "It is . . . logical to suppose that if one chooses the right place and the right way to look one will always find some organisms which can decompose any naturally occurring substance, however intractable it may appear at first sight. This hypothesis has been many times tested and found to be true." (*But see* page 77.) Organisms can utilize insoluble substances in two ways: (1) by excreting enzymes or other substances which break the chemical bonds and release subunits, and (2) by adsorbing very tightly to the substance and utilizing the subunits which go spontaneously into solution.

The first method is the best understood. Extracellular enzymes are produced by microorganisms which will attack a wide variety of organic polymers: cellulose, starch, pectin, alginic acid, chitin, hyaluronic acid, chondroitin sulfate, various capsular polysaccharides and blood group substances, various proteins and peptides, nucleic acids, and bacterial cell wall substances. Many of these enzymes are constitutive, but some are inducible, although it is more likely that the inducer is a small oligomer derived from the polymer rather than a high molecular weight polymer itself.

Nonorganic substances are also dissolved by microorganisms, probably not through the action of enzymes but rather through the action of metabolites which bring about the dissolution. Thus 2-keto-3-deoxy-6-phosphogluconic acid has been implicated in the dissolution of silicates, and a variety of acids will dissolve calcium carbonate and calcium phosphate (Henderson and Duff, 1963).

In some cases dissolution occurs without the mediation of external products. Stanier (1942) has shown that cellulose is broken down by Cytophaga only upon direct contact of the organism with the substrate, no extracellular enzyme being produced. The molecular mechanism of such a hydrolysis is unknown, but it is possible that the initial breakdown occurs spontaneously to a very slight extent and that the close contact between organism and substrate makes it possible for the organism to utilize efficiently the oligomers, releasing more oligomers. Sulfur particles are also broken down only by direct contact between cell and substrate (Schaeffer et al., 1963); it is not likely that an enzyme is involved. In cases where extracellular enzymes are absent, adsorption of the cell to the particle has more than passive significance, and there may be specific affinities of cell to particle. Such systems, although difficult to study, may provide much interesting information. The dissolution of clay minerals by adsorbed diatoms has been reported (Hutchinson, 1957), although nothing is known about the mechanism. Here the diatom liberates the silica and uses it for cell wall synthesis, while the alumina is left behind and precipitates as an insoluble product. See page 72 for a discussion of the ecological significance of adsorption to particles which are not dissolved by the cell. The geochemical significance of the insolubility of many organic compounds has been discussed by Vallentyne (1962).

ENERGY

Energy for the growth and function of living organisms is derived either from light or from the oxidation of certain organic or inorganic compounds. The amount of energy available from different materials is shown in Table 3-5. The amount of protoplasm which an organism can make with a given substrate is roughly proportional to the amount of energy available to it from that substrate (Gunsalus and Shuster, 1961). Organic substrates are relatively rich in energy as compared to inorganic substrates and thus can support heavier growth. Most organisms oxidizing inorganic substrates are obligate aerobes and must have O_2 as an electron acceptor. Many heterotrophic organisms use O_2 as an electron acceptor, although many organic compounds can be oxidized anaerobically in the absence of an additional electron acceptor (fermentation), in which case some of the carbon atoms are oxidized and others reduced, the latter accumulating as metabolic products. Sedlaczek (1964) using calorimetric techniques has shown that aerobic bacteria are 40-50% efficient in converting organic substrates to cell material. The energy yield in fermentation is considerably lower than that in oxidation (efficiency of 5-10%), and therefore the organism makes considerably less protoplasm from the same substrate anaerobically than aerobically. This inefficiency is compensated for by the fact that the organism is able to grow in environments where aerobic organisms cannot grow.

One question of interest is the manner in which the organism is able to make adenosinetriphosphate (ATP) from available energy sources. In aerobic processes, ATP can be made by oxidative phosphorylation, but in fermentative processes substrate level phosphorylation is required, and there are only a limited number of reactions in which this can occur. While many simple organic substrates (e.g., formate, acetate) are fermented with

TABLE 3-5. ENERGY AVAILABLE TO LIVING ORGANISMS FROM VARIOUS SUBSTANCES

$H_2S + \frac{1}{2}O_2 \rightarrow H_2O + S + 41$ kcal[a]
$H_2O + S + 1\frac{1}{2}O_2 \rightarrow H_2SO_4 + 118$ kcal
$HNO_2 + \frac{1}{2}O_2 \rightarrow HNO_3 + 17$ kcal
$NH_4^+ + 1\frac{1}{2}O_2 \rightarrow 2H^+ + H_2O + NO_2^- + 66$ kcal
$H_2 + \frac{1}{2}O_2 \rightarrow H_2O + 56$ kcal
Red light   40 kcal per mol quantum
Glucose $+ 6O_2 \rightarrow 6CO_2 + 6H_2O + 690$ kcal
Ethyl alcohol $+ 3O_2 \rightarrow 2CO_2 + 3H_2O + 327$ kcal[b]
Glucose (anaerobic) $\rightarrow 2C_2H_5OH + 2CO_2 + 20$ kcal

[a] Data from Lees (1955)
[b] Data from Giese (1962)

difficulty and are relatively stable anaerobically, other substrates (e.g., amino acids) can be fermented by only a few organisms. Thus under anaerobic conditions, many organic molecules are relatively resistant to biological attack and may accumulate in the environment. Since sugars are readily fermentable they rarely accumulate even in anaerobic environments (Vallentyne, 1962).

The ability of different organisms to derive different amounts of energy from the same substrate is determined by their enzymatic equipment and thus ultimately by their genotypes (Gunsalus and Shuster, 1961). The efficiency of energy conversion controls the maximum amount of proto-plasm obtainable from a given substrate but has little to do with the rate of growth on the substrate. Growth rate is influenced by factors intrinsic to the organism (*see* Table 5-1) and by physical and chemical factors of the environment.

It might be asked how an organism which can make only one mole of ATP per mole of glucose could ever survive in nature in the face of com-petition from organisms which can make 2 moles of ATP? The answer to this question undoubtedly lies in a consideration of all of the factors which influence the development of the organism, of which energy yield is an important factor but not the only one.

LIGHT

The primary source of energy for the living world is the sun. The energy in a quantum of radiation is greater in the short than in the longer wave lengths, therefore short wave length radiation is more active photo-chemically and photobiologically. Certain chemical substances (dyes or pigments) are able to absorb radiation at specific wave lengths, the precise wave lengths at which absorption will occur being determined by the struc-ture of the specific molecule. When a photon is absorbed, electrons of the pigment are raised to higher energy levels (activation) and these excited molecules can then undergo chemical reactions in which the energy is stored in a form which can be utilized later.

The photobiologically effective wave lengths can be determined by an action spectrum in which the rate of the photoreaction is measured when the organism is illuminated with different wave lengths of monochromatic light. This action spectrum can then be correlated with the absorption spec-trum of the cell as a whole, or with the absorption spectrum of isolated pigments, and in this way the pigments which are relevant to the photo-reaction can be identified.

Microbial pigments of main ecological interest are the chlorophylls and phycobilins, which function in photosynthesis and in certain phototactic and phototrophic responses, and the carotenoids, which may participate in the above reactions but which also function as photoprotective agents.

Different chlorophylls absorb at different wave lengths (Stanier and Cohen-Bazire, 1957) and a complementarity exists between the absorption spectra of algae and those of photosynthetic bacteria (Figure 3-9). Bacterial photosynthesis is an anaerobic process and in nature would be ex-

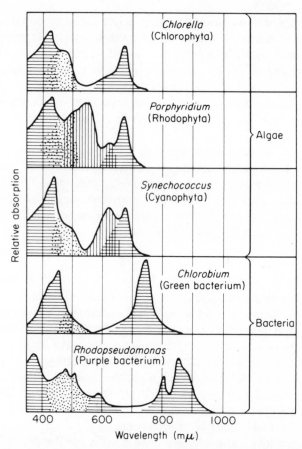

Fig. 3-9. Absorption spectra of representative photosynthetic microorganisms (after Stanier and Cohen-Bazire, 1957). The contributions of the various classes of photosynthetic pigments are approximately indicated as follows: HORIZONTAL LINES, chlorophylls; STIPPLING, carotenoids; VERTICAL LINES, phycobilins. This figure shows that the green and purple sulfur bacteria have their main chlorophyll absorption peaks at wavelengths at which the algae do not absorb, and thus the bacteria would be able to capture light transmitted by the algae. The photosynthetic bacteria are frequently found in nature underneath the algae, where the main light available would be at the higher wavelengths.

pected to occur in deep waters and at the surface of muds where anaerobic conditions prevail. In algae, photosynthesis is an aerobic process; these organisms grow in surface waters and thus absorb much of the light in the blue and red regions so that the deep lying bacteria, if they are able to survive, have to use the light which the algae allow to pass—light mainly in the far-red and infrared. Thus the complementary absorption spectra have an ecological explanation. Water absorbs red light better than blue (*see* Chapter 2), and organisms which live in deep water may possess chlorophyll pigments best adapted to absorb blue light, although this idea of chromatic adaptation has recently been questioned by Crossett et al. (1965).

The fact that a chemical substance in an organism absorbs light does not mean that its ecological function is to absorb this energy, since its absorptive properties may be merely incidental as is apparently the case with cytochromes and flavins. In addition to their involvement in photosynthesis, pigments may function as: (1) photoprotective agents, absorbing light which would otherwise initiate a harmful effect (e.g., carotenoids), (2) primary absorption in phototrophic, morphogenetic, and sexual responses, (3) primary absorption in phototactic responses, and (4) coloring agents, in which the color is recognized by another organism, as in flower pigments, although I know of no evidence for this latter function for microbial pigments.

Organisms which live in the light frequently have evolved tactic responses which enable them to adjust to changing light conditions in ways most favorable for their reproduction and survival. Studies of these phenomena are well covered in the recent review by Clayton (1964). Light is a variable which can be very precisely characterized in physical terms and is precisely measurable in natural environments; hence it can be studied ecologically with considerable sophistication.

The work of Mathews and Sistrom (1959, 1960) and Stanier and Cohen-Bazire (1957) on the role of carotenoid pigments as photoprotective agents is of considerable interest. Mathews and Sistrom studied the role of carotenoid pigments in the nonphotosynthetic bacterium *Sarcina lutea,* and some of their results are presented in Figure 3-10. They found: (1) normal cells are not killed on exposure to sunlight in the presence of air; (2) carotenoidless mutants are quickly killed under the same conditions; (3) neither mutant nor wild type is killed if irradiated in the absence of air. These results suggested that the carotenoid pigment of *S. lutea* serves as a photoprotective agent and prevents killing by sunlight. Since *S. lutea* is an organism which is frequently isolated from the air, it seems reasonable that the presence of the carotenoid pigment enables the organism to be transmitted successfully through the air. The final proof of this conclusion would require an experiment on the comparative efficiencies of

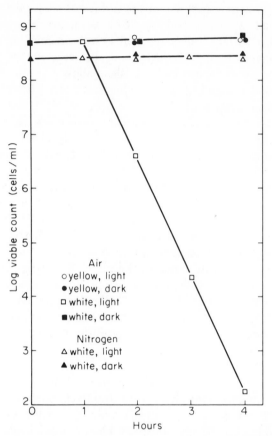

Fig. 3-10. Exposure to direct sunlight of normal *Sarcina lutea* (yellow) and pigmentless mutant (white) in air or nitrogen atmospheres (after Mathews and Sistrom, 1959). Cells suspended in phosphate buffer. Light intensities: 0 time, 12,000 ft-candles; 2 hr, 10,000 ft-candles; 4 hr, 5000 ft-candles. This figure shows that the white cells are killed in direct sunlight in air, presumably due to photooxidation. It may be concluded that the probable role of the yellow pigment is to protect the organism against photokilling during its dispersal through the air.

the transfer of the colorless mutant and the wild type through the air. Most nonsporeforming organisms, both bacteria and yeasts, isolated from the air are pigmented. Likewise, many aquatic bacteria isolated from surface waters are pigmented, and it seems reasonable that in many of these organisms the pigment functions as in *S. lutea*.

Stanier and Cohen-Bazire (1957) studied mutants of photosynthetic bacteria which lacked carotenoids but possessed normal chlorophyll. Photosynthetic bacteria grow photosynthetically only anaerobically and grow heterotrophically in air in the dark. Since photokilling is due to photo-oxidation, it requires the presence of both light and air. The carotenoidless mutant was thus not killed when grown photosynthetically, since this occurred under anaerobic conditions, but when the organism was trans-ferred to air, it was rapidly destroyed. The wild type, on the other hand, tolerated these conditions well, and it can thus be concluded that the carotenoid pigment probably serves as a photoprotective agent.

Photosynthetic organisms which grow in bright sunlight are frequently bright red, the color due to a carotenoid pigment which masks the green chlorophyll. Here again it seems likely that the red pigment has a photo-protective function. Examples of habitats revealing such organisms are glaciers and snow fields which contain red-pigmented Chlorophyceae (brilliantly visible to summer hikers in high altitudes) (Garric, 1965; Kol, 1957); the surfaces of sunny tropical seas which sometimes show blooms of the nitrogen-fixing marine blue-green alga *Trichodesmium erythraea* (Wood, 1963), hot springs in which blue-green algae develop in thin mats on top of the depositing sinter (Copeland, 1936), and bird baths and orna-mental urns which often reveal the brilliantly red-colored Sphaerella (Haematococcus) (Smith, 1950).

Cell Structure
and Ecology

The structure of an organism probably plays an important role in how the organism interacts with its environment.

Rigidity

Most microorganisms possess walls or membranes which help them to maintain definite shapes. Only a few protozoa such as the amoebae lack some element of rigidity, and even in the amoebae, species can be differ-entiated at least partially by their average shapes. The rigidity of other protozoa is under the control of the pellicle or test, whereas in the bacteria, fungi, and algae, it is the cell wall which determines the shape.

Interestingly, most microorganisms live in hypotonic media, which may account for their development of walls or pellicles which counteract the tendency to lysis. The hypertonicity of a cell is probably a reflection of the fact that it has concentrated from its environment various soluble materials and nutrients. Halophilic organisms are in osmotic equilibrium with their environment (Ingram, 1957), but their cell walls do not lack rigidity. Rather, the cell wall is stabilized in some manner by sodium ions, so that if the cell is transferred to a sodium-free medium, the wall structure is disorganized and there is the immediate formation of a protoplast and subsequent lysis (Brown, 1964).

The degree of rigidity of cells may vary and cells with thicker cell walls are probably more rigid than those with thinner walls. Within the fungi and bacteria, the organisms with the thickest walls usually stain gram positively, and Salton (1960) has shown that gram positivity is probably a function of the impermeability of the cell wall to the alcohol decolorizing agent. Gram-positive cells are usually more resistant to drying than gram-negative cells, and the asporogenous organisms isolated from the air are usually gram-positive yeasts or gram-positive cocci. The resistance of staphylococci to drying is notorious and may be a factor in the prevalence of hospital infections by this organism. Thus drouth resistance and cell wall thickness are probably correlated.

The sensitivity of the highly flexible spirochetes to drying is well known and probably explains why syphilis is a venereal disease, the causal organism being transmitted only through direct contact because it cannot withstand the drying influence of the open air. Free-living spirochetes are found only in aquatic environments not susceptible to drying.

Different organisms have acquired different chemical structures for maintaining rigidity, some of which are shown in Table 3-6. The chemical composition of the rigid layer may influence the degree of rigidity and associated functional features but is probably more important in affecting the resistance of the wall to attack by deleterious agents such as lytic enzymes and chemicals. Environmental factors will play an important role in the formation of the rigid layer. Thus, diatoms have a specific

TABLE 3-6. CHEMICAL SUBSTANCES FOR MAINTAINING CELLULAR RIGIDITY

Organism	Rigid layer	Structural substance
Radiolaria	test	silica
Foraminifera	test	calcium carbonate
Green algae	cell wall	cellulose
Some marine algae	skeleton	calcium carbonate
Diatoms	cell wall	silica
Many seaweeds	cell wall	mannan, xylan, complex polysaccharides
Fungi	cell wall	glucan, cellulose, chitin
Yeasts	cell wall	glucan, mannan, protein
Bacteria, blue-green algae	cell wall	mucopeptide
Iron bacteria	stalk	ferric hydroxide
Iron bacteria	sheath	ferric hydroxide, calcium phosphate

Data summarized from various sources.

requirement for silica, foraminifera are found in the marine environment which has a high calcium content, and stalked iron bacteria occur where iron is present.

SIZE

Microorganisms vary in diameter over at least a 10,000-fold range. The smaller the organism, the greater its surface-to-volume ratio. A tiny bacterium with its relatively enormous surface can absorb nutrients, grow, and metabolize at a much faster rate than can larger organisms, but a small organism is subjected to greater surface tension forces. The larger an organism, the more rapidly it will settle in a gravitational field, although the rate of fall will also be influenced by the density of the organism and the viscosity of the medium. Brownian movement (*see* page 9) is significant only for colloidal particles and small bacteria. Brownian movement will be a counterforce to gravitation, so that the particles may not settle out even after long periods of time unless the gravitational field is markedly increased, as by centrifugation.

SHAPE

In phagotrophic organisms, shape is controlled by the requirements for engulfment of solid particles. In the plantlike microorganisms, nutrients enter the cell as small molecules by diffusion through the cell wall. Since a high surface-to-volume ratio as in rod-shaped and filamentous organisms will increase the efficiency of uptake, it is interesting to note that most bacteria found in lakes and oceans, where the concentrations of organic materials are low, are filamentous or rod shaped, the cocci apparently occurring more commonly in the nutrient-rich sediments (ZoBell, 1946). Spherical cells are usually more resistant to drying than rod-shaped cells, possibly because of more uniform pressures on the cell during drying, cocci and yeasts being the most common asporogenous organisms isolated from the air.

Many of the larger nonmotile unicellular oceanic algae possess spines and large appendages which increase their surface area without increasing their density, thus slowing their descent through the water. Since such photosynthetic organisms can live only where light is available, it is reasonable to assume that such adaptations would have survival value in the open sea; littoral algae frequently lack these appendages.

One of the more fascinating shapes is the helix which occurs in spirochetes, spirilla, and the blue-green alga Spirulina. In the spirochetes the cell is flexible and the shape is created by the attachment and function of the axial filament (discussed later), whereas in Spirulina and spirilla the helix is rigid. The shape may be merely a consequence of the way in which the cell wall is put together and thus may play no ecological role, but it is interesting to consider the possibility that the helical structure is necessary to ensure a helical movement of the cell. For instance, the spirochete *Cristispira* is a large organism found in the crystalline style of bivalves (Noguchi, 1921); the material of the style is a quite stiff, almost agar-like substance, and yet the *Cristispira* cells are very actively motile. Possibly helical movement would enable these organisms to move through debris and viscous media which would impede organisms possessing straight filaments.

ECOLOGY AND MORPHOGENESIS

In many microorganisms form does not remain constant, and two or more distinct shapes may occur. In aquatic environments filamentous bacteria epiphytic on plants and animals show morphological differentiation between the basal and apical region. For instance, in *Leucothrix mucor* the basal region contains holdfast material and grows as a straight unsegmented filament, and the apex forms spherical or cylindrical cells which separate and colonize new surfaces (Harold and Stanier, 1955). Stalked bacteria (Poindexter, 1964) show a differentiation which serves ecological ends, the basal cell remaining attached to the substrate and forming flagellated offspring which swim away, settle down on substrates, and form new stalks. By definition, form is what we humans see, but it is the function of this structure which is relevant. Thus spores and cysts are of ecological interest because of their resistance to heat or drying, and the shape of the spore would be expected to be of ecological importance only if it somehow influences the efficiency of the dispersal process. However, it is well to keep in mind that structural changes may reflect ecological adaptations, and studies of such changes may be of value since the structure of an organism is one of its few attributes which we can recognize in nature and which may thus provide for us a bridge between the field and the laboratory. Starr and Skerman (1965) have recently provided a useful review of the morphologically unusual bacteria which emphasizes the wide variety of forms and structures produced.

MOTILITY

Most aquatic and many terrestrial microorganisms are motile, and this process has recently been thoroughly reviewed by Jahn and Bovee (1965). In phagotrophic microorganisms motility would seem to be of benefit for the capture of food, although there are a number of sessile forms such as *Stentor* and *Vorticella* which are only sporadically motile and have specialized cilia around the gullet which push liquid into the mouth and extract the food microorganisms from it. In other microorganisms motility is probably a means of distribution. The mechanism of movement has excited more interest than has its ecological role (Weibull, 1960). The existence of phenomena such as phototaxis and chemotaxis suggests that motility has adaptive value in enabling organisms to respond quickly to changes in environment. The high mutation rate between motility and nonmotility in bacteria (Braun, 1953) suggests that this is a characteristic which bacteria can discard lightly, although the selective advantage of motility can be readily seen when motile and nonmotile cells are embedded in a viscous substrate in which they must grow with the nutrients that reach them by diffusion: some of the motile cells swim away and their progeny soon spread throughout the medium and form a large number of colonies. The success of this common laboratory method for selecting motile strains suggests that motility does confer a selective advantage on an organism in certain natural conditions.

True bacteria and many algae and protozoa are motile by means of flagella and cilia but other mechanisms also exist. Amoebae and many metazoan cells possess amoeboid motion, moving by extension of pseudopodia; the protoplasmic streaming of plasmodial slime molds is an analogous process. Amoeboid movement usually occurs only when the cell is in contact with a solid surface, and a cell in suspension usually rounds up. Diatoms apparently move by a form of jet propulsion, while desmids probably move as a result of the secretion of gelatinous materials which then become hydrated and swell (Smith, 1950). The blue-green algae, their colorless relatives, and the myxobacteria possess a gliding motility and move only when in contact with a solid surface, but the mechanism of this movement is still under debate (Weibull, 1960). Cellulose-digesting myxobacteria align themselves parallel to the axis of cellulose fibers, suggesting again an ecological adaptation of movement (Stanier, 1942).

The interesting mechanism of motility in spirochetes has been described by Bradfield and Cater (1952). A bundle of contractile fibers (the axial filament) is wrapped around the flexible cell and is attached only at the poles. When the fibers contract, the cell is thrown into a helical shape. Motion apparently occurs as a result of the contraction and expansion of the axial filament with a concomitant coiling and uncoiling of the cell, the organism moving forward like a snake. A possible ecological advantage of the spiral shape was discussed earlier (*see* page 61).

Taxes are movements induced by external stimuli and may be either positive (towards the stimulus) or negative (away from the stimulus). Phototaxis occurs in a number of microorganisms; Weibull (1960), Manten (1948), and Clayton (1964) have analyzed this process in detail for bacteria. Bacterial cells do not recognize the direction from which the light is coming, but only whether it is light or dark. When a bacterial cell moves from a lighted area to a dark one, the cell stops and reverses its movement, thus effectively keeping it within the lighted area. The flagellated algae possess a photosensitive pigment, the "eyespot," which is NOT the photoreceptor (Halldal, 1962), but which is an auxiliary body casting a shadow on an underlying photosensitive region, thus enabling the organism to recognize both the intensity and direction of the light. It is felt that the true photoreceptor is a thickening near the flagellar base. The ability to recognize the direction from which the light is coming and to orient accordingly has been called topotaxis. Some gliding blue-green algae which lack eyespots and flagella are able to orient themselves with respect to the direction of light through an unknown mechanism. Little is known about the cellular control mechanisms involved in phototaxis, a field which should be susceptible to investigation with modern techniques. *Rhodospirillum rubrum* can exhibit either negative or positive phototaxis, depending on environmental conditions, the net result being that the organism places itself in the light when environmental conditions permit photosynthesis and in the dark when environmental conditions (e.g., high O_2 tension) prevent photosynthesis (Clayton, 1964).

Chemotaxis is also a widespread phenomenon in motile organisms and is most easily demonstrated by inserting a capillary pipette filled with the test solution into a suspension of motile cells, the organisms collecting at the tip of the capillary. Chemotaxis may be induced by a variety of organic and inorganic nutrients. In sexually reproducing organisms, chemotaxis may be an aspect of the mating behavior (*see* Chapter 5), and since in these cases specific attractions exist between mating types, this behavior should be distinguished from the more nonspecific attractions towards common chemicals.

Both chemotaxis and phototaxis were studied in detail by Jennings (1906), and this pioneering work still provides a great fund of descriptive knowledege on environmentally-directed movement. Unfortunately the molecular basis of neither phototaxis nor chemotaxis can be studied until the molecular basis of motility in general is understood.

PHAGOTROPHY

Phagotrophic organisms obtain their nutrients by the ingestion of particles or other organisms (Pringsheim, 1959). In the animal kingdom, phagotrophy occurs not only in protozoa but also in all higher groups where specialized cells (e.g., leucocytes) are present which can carry out this function. Phagotrophy also exists in some organisms which have chlorophyll, such as Chrysophyceae and Dinophyceae, as well as in swarm cells of certain Heterokontae and Chlorophyceae. In chloromonads, Cryptophyceae and Euglenophyceae, some species are phototrophic whereas others are phagotrophic. Although some information is available on the mechanics of ingestion, little is known about the physiological mechanism of ingestion. Seemingly, phagotrophic organisms benefit by being able to dispense with active transport mechanisms for the acquisition of nutrients from dilute environments, but at the same time they have given up the ability to live in dilute environments, since phagotrophs can flourish only where a rich supply of particulate food is available and are thus usually found where bacterial growth is heavy.

SURFACE STRUCTURES

SLIME LAYERS may be rudimentary holdfasts, or they may be incipient capsules. In bacteria, the slime layer is thought to promote resistance to drying by enabling the organism to retain moisture. Slime production is also involved in the formation of bacterial aggregates called zoogloea, which are found in sewage treatment plants, in the soil, and in aqueous environments. The slime layer may also make it possible for phyllosphere bacteria to adhere to leaves in tropical rain forests, thus resisting dislodgment by torrential rains (Ruinen, 1961).

CAPSULES are larger and more sharply bounded than slime layers and are produced by a variety of bacteria, especially pathogenic forms. The pneumococcus capsule has been shown experimentally to function in invasion and virulence (Wilson and Miles, 1957). Noncapsulated mutants are not invasive or virulent, whereas as few as 5-10 capsulated cells inoculated into the peritoneal cavity of a mouse will initiate a fatal infection. Genetic transformation of the ability to produce a capsule transfers at the same time the ability to initiate a fatal infection. The capsule enables the organism to evade phagocytosis, and noncapsulated forms are quickly consumed. In the group A streptococci the M protein, which is on the surface of the cell wall, plays a similar role in invasion. When this protein is removed from the cells by trypsin digestion, pathogenicity is lost without the loss of viability. If trypsin treated cells are allowed to resynthesize the M protein, virulence is regained (Wilson and Miles, 1957). Rarely can such sophisticated conclusions be drawn concerning the ecological role of microbial characteristics, and such experiments emphasize that medical microbiology is probably the most highly developed branch of microbial ecology.

The chemical nature of the cell surface may influence the electrokinetic and hydrodynamic properties of the cell and thus affect indirectly its ecological behavior. Some yeasts and molds form films on an undisturbed liquid surface, presumably because of the high lipid content and hydrophobicity of the cell surface, and surface tension forces thereby prevent the organism from settling out. Since these organisms are aerobic but nonmotile, the ability to form a pellicle or mycelial mat presumably affords them an advantage by enabling them to remain where the oxygen tension is high.

Some bacteria possess filamentous appendages (fimbriae or pili) which resemble flagella but which are shorter and do not function in motility. Some fimbriae play a role in adherence, enabling bacteria to adsorb to surfaces of other cells or to nonliving substrates. Other kinds of fimbriae may be involved in sexual reproduction in bacteria, either by enabling cells to stick together (Heumann and Marx, 1964) or by providing a channel by which the DNA may pass from one cell to another (Brinton et al., 1964).

Surface structures frequently possess specific macromolecular configurations which are useful in characterizing specific strains. Capsules and cell wall components are antigenic and induce specific antibodies which can then be used to detect these antigens again in natural isolates. The use of fluorescent antibodies even makes it possible to detect given antigens microscopically on single cells, providing a useful bridge between the organism in culture and the organism in the field. However, there are numerous pitfalls in the fluorescent antibody technique which must be considered. Certain surface structures also contain the receptor sites for specific viruses (Frank et al., 1963), and if these viruses are available they can be used as reagents for the detection of the receptor macromolecule. Note, however, that the primary function of these surface macromolecules is not to interact with antibodies or viruses, but is for some other (unknown) purpose.

STORAGE PRODUCTS

Since storage products are frequently visible under the microscope, they will be included here, although they could also be discussed in the section on nutrition. Certain storage products and the kinds of organisms producing them are: starch—algae; oil droplets—algae, bacteria, fungi; poly-β-hydroxybutyrate—bacteria; polyphosphate (metachromatic or volutin granules)—bacteria, fungi; elemental sulfur—purple sulfur bacteria, colorless sulfur bacteria.

As can be seen, most of these substances are polymers of simple building blocks and enable the cell to maintain in reserve a large supply of energy or cell building blocks without the osmotic complications which would arise if the material were retained as monomers. Since most of these products can be recognized microscopically either directly or after staining, they reveal some information about the physiological status of a cell in its natural surroundings. For example, well-fed sulfur bacteria will be filled with sulfur granules, whereas poorly-fed cells will have depleted these internal reserves.

FILAMENTOUS HABIT

The filamentous habit is very common in microorganisms. In fungi and algae filamentation results from growth occurring only by extension of the hyphal tips, with little or no growth taking place distal from the tip except at points of branching. Filamentous bacteria probably do not grow only from the tip, and in these organisms the filamentous habit is due to the absence of cross wall formation or to the absence of cell separation. We have used tritiated thymidine and radioautography (Brock and Brock, 1966a) to show that filamentous growth of the bacterium *Leucothrix mucor* occurs throughout the filament and not at one end.

In the fungi, the filaments may form a dense branching hyphal mat which will float on the surface of an undisturbed liquid. Many fungi are able to extend themselves very rapidly across surfaces, even when these are almost devoid of nutrients. Even on water agar, fungus spores may germinate and form a few hyphae which will extend rapidly to the edge of the plate. Presumably such a property would enable the organism to leave a poor medium and colonize an adjacent rich medium.

Basidiomycetes frequently colonize tree roots and form ectotrophic and endotrophic mycorrhizas (*see* page 213). In the former the filaments of the fungus extend from the root in radiating branches and tufts which increase greatly the absorptive capacity of the tree roots and make it possible for mycorrhizal plants such as pine to colonize soils low in inorganic nutrients. At the same time, the fungus obtains the nutrients it needs for its heterotrophic growth from the tree, with nutrients sometimes being transferred through the fungus filaments for long distances from the root. Frequently the hyphae form aggregates called rhizomorphs which translocate nutrients; the hyphal fruiting bodies, which eventually appear at the surface of the forest floor, are usually attached to rhizomorphs, ultimately receiving their nutrients directly from the tree.

In running streams filamentous algae usually grow attached to rocks, forming a dense tangled mat, while other filamentous algae are epiphytes on larger algae or on higher plants. The relationship between algae and current flow has been reviewed by Whitford (1960a, 1960b). Many filamentous bacteria such as *Thiothrix* and *Sphaerotilus* grow in dense mats attached to rocks in running water. The filamentous habit offers the maximum surface-to-volume ratio for the organism, probably enabling the most efficient utilization of the dilute nutrients available (Lamanna and Mallette, 1959). The ability to attach prevents the organism from drifting along within an unchanging water mass, allowing it to be continually bathed by fresh water. The filamentous Actinomycetes, which are almost exclusively soil organisms, presumably benefit in other ways from their cellular form, but as yet little is known about this aspect of their ecology.

Some filamentous organisms exhibit TROPIC RESPONSES, growing in a curved manner toward or away from an external stimulus (Manten, 1948). Phototropic responses of fruiting structures in certain fungi have been well known since the classical work of Buller (1934). This process is illustrated in Figure 3-11. Presumably the bending of the sporophore towards the light before spores are ejected helps to insure that the spores will be shot out into open spaces where winds would be expected to be

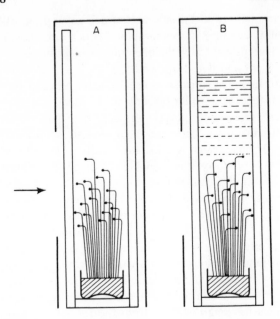

Fig. 3-11. Bending of sporophores of *Phycomyces nitens* during growth toward the light (LEFT, in air) or away from the light (RIGHT, in oil) (Buller, 1934). Arrow indicates direction of light.

stronger, so that the spores would be more likely to be carried to distant parts. Chemotropic growth of pollen tubes towards the ovary has been known for a long time. At the molecular level a tropic response is probably due to a differential synthesis of cell wall, the side of the filament on the outside of the curve growing faster than the inner wall.

RESTING STRUCTURES AND FRUITING BODIES

Resting structures of most microbial groups are of ecological as well as taxonomic interest. Resting structures probably have several functions: (1) to enable the organism to resist drying, (2) to enable the organism to survive for long periods of time under nutrient or other environmental deficiencies, (3) to enable the organism to withstand other adverse conditions such as high temperatures, ultraviolet radiation, and toxic chemicals, and (4) as the receptacle of the first product of sexual reproduction, the zygote. Although marked increase in heat resistance is found only in bacterial spores, the resting structures of algae, fungi, and protozoa are usually resistant to drying and sometimes to other noxious conditions. The longevity of certain spores and vegetative stages of a variety of microorganisms is given in Table 3-7.

Most resting structures are dormant and require special conditions for germination, an adaptation of obvious value since it means that germination usually will not occur during a transient appearance of favorable conditions, but only when conditions will continue to be favorable for growth and survival (Sussman, 1965). The frequent requirement of a cold period for the breakage of dormancy is an obvious result of evolution in temperate environments, the resting structure not germinating during transient warm wet periods of fall, but remaining dormant until spring. The physiological controls of germination are barely understood, except in the case of the bacterial spore (Halvorson, 1961) and the Neurospora ascospore (Sussman, 1965), and the relationships of germination requirements to natural situations are unknown. In the higher forms, the discovery of proper conditions for germination is a problem which usually falls to the

TABLE 3-7. LONGEVITY OF CERTAIN SPORES AND VEGETATIVE STAGES AND THE CONDITIONS UNDER WHICH THEY SURVIVE

Organism	Stage	Longevity	Conditions of storage
I. BACTERIA			
Bacillus anthracis	spores	47 yrs.	sealed vials and test tubes
Clostridium sporogenes	spores	46 yrs.	in alcohol
65 strains of non-spore-forming bacteria	vegetative	16-48 yrs.	room temp. in dark
Salmonella typhosa	vegetative	28 mos.	in ice cream ($-20°C$)
Rhizobium meliloti	vegetative	30-45 yrs.	autoclaved soil
II. FUNGI			
Hemitrichia clavata	spores	75 yrs.	herbarium collection
Lycogala flavofuscum	spores	68 yrs.	herbarium collection
Peronospora schleideni	oospores	3-4 yrs.	dry
Endoconidiophora fagacearum	ascospores	232 days	24°C, 10% relative humidity
Endothia parasitica	ascospores	1 yr.	dry in bark
Omphalia flavida	gemmae	26 hrs.	dry air
Cronartium ribicola	basidiospores	5-6 days	air-dried
C. ribicola	aeciospores	8 wks.	
Puccinia triticina	teliospores	2 yrs.	5-7°C
P. triticina	uredospores	44 days	-8 to $-9°C$ on plant
Tilletia foetida	basidiospores	25 yrs.	herbarium
T. foetida, T. caries	basidiospores	22 yrs.	room temp.
Ustilago nuda	mycelium	11 yrs.	in barley seed
Psilocybe natans	basidiospores	9 yrs.	herbarium
Schizophyllum commune	fruit body and spores	35 yrs.	0.1 mm Hg and 3 wks. at $-190°C$
Verticillium albo-atrum	micro-sclerotia	13 yrs.	in field or culture

From Sussman (1965).

geneticist, and methods which have been developed are mostly empirical. Indeed, in certain organisms such as the mold *Rhizopus nigricans,* the sexual spore, although a classical object of study in general botany classes, is difficult to induce to germinate in the laboratory. In the fungi, it is frequently observed that the sexual spore is more resistant to adverse conditions than the asexual spore. The asexual spore is usually nearly as sensitive to heat as the vegetative cell with its main function seemingly as a drouth-resistant structure which transports the species into new territories, and germination occurs readily, frequently even in distilled water. In the soil, however, germination of asexual spores may be inhibited by certain unknown factors; this inhibition is reversed by nutrients such as glucose (Dobbs et al., 1960). Thus if an asexual spore alighted in a nutrient-deficient soil it would not germinate but would behave as if dormant until the arrival of fresh nutrients. The sexual spore in fungi usually shows dormancy and resistance to freezing, heat, and other adverse conditions. It is the structure which tides the organism over the cold weather of winter.

The mushroom fruiting body is a spore-bearing structure with a unique role. The mycelium of most mushrooms obtains its nourishment from tree roots or leaf litter underground or from the depths of a tree trunk or fallen log. Under the control of conditions not understood, masses of mycelia aggregate and form a fruiting body primordium which then pushes to the surface of the ground or log and expands into the characteristic mushroom form. On the gills on the underneath surface of the fruiting body are borne basidiospores which are shed into the air and can be carried by wind currents to distant parts. Thus the fruiting body which so fascinates the mycologist or mycophagist for its structural and culinary properties plays an important ecological role in the life of the organism. The fungi are a group of organisms with tremendously interesting and complex structural adaptations which probably serve ecological ends.

The plasmodial and cellular slime molds and certain of the myxobacteria which live normally in the forest leaf litter and within logs also form characteristic fruiting bodies in which resting spores or cysts are formed. The fruiting of many of these forms requires light, and it seems reasonable that these fruiting bodies function by bringing the spores up into the atmosphere so that they can become airborne.

Resting structures are formed predominantly by terrestrial organisms and occur rarely, if at all, in forms which are exclusively aquatic. This is especially true of marine organisms which, except in the intertidal zone, are never subjected to drying or intense heat, and in which dispersal need not be through the air. The fungi constitute a group which is most highly developed on land and in which specialized fruiting structures are very common.

RHYTHMS

In fluctuating environments such as exist in nature, the rates of various physiological processes in microorganisms also vary. If the rate of a process varies in a predictable manner from day to day, it is called a rhythm (Sweeney and Hastings, 1962; Bünning, 1964). Exogenous rhythms are those which are controlled directly by the environment; thus the rate of photosynthesis rises during the daytime and falls to zero at night. Endogenous rhythms are those which are to some extent independent of environmental influences and seem to be under the control of an innate physiological process, although the periodicity may still be paced initially by an external factor. Endogenous rhythms may be characterized as diurnal, lunar, or tidal. Diurnal rhythms are known in algae for photosynthesis, luminiscence, cell division, phototaxis, and mating behavior. Tidal rhythms for phototaxis are known in several algae, the organisms becoming negatively phototactic at high tide, burying themselves in the mud, and coming out again at low tide, so that an organism with such a rhythm would be prevented from being washed out to sea at high tide. Lunar rhythms probably relate to the fact that the height of the tide is correlated with the phase of the moon; the green sea weed Ulva, which grows in tide pools, releases its gametes and spores at the time of the monthly low tide, thus insuring that a high concentration of gametes will develop in the relatively shallow waters and increase the probability of fertilization.

As noted, the periodicity of endogenous rhythms is relatively insensitive to environmental factors such as temperature, although the rhythm can be entrained (i.e., its phase shifted) by external influences. Little is known about the molecular basis of endogenous rhythms, but these rhythms obviously have considerable ecological significance and provide direct evidence of the profound adaptation of organisms to their environments. Although rhythms show aspects of purposeful behavior, since they usually proceed in anticipation of future events, the pace of the rhythm has been set by antecedent events, and the ability to respond rhythmically is itself a product of evolution. The existence of a rhythm gives a clue to processes in the organism which may be of significance in controlling the response of the organism to its environment.

ADSORPTION OF CELLS TO SURFACES

The prevalence of surfaces in the microbial environment was discussed in Chapter 2. The adsorption of cells to surfaces is also well known. A striking series of photos showing the attachment of an isolated mammalian cell to a glass surface was presented by Taylor (1962). Animal cells, which are flexible, can spread out readily and thus adhere to a surface over a wide area. As Taylor has shown, cells can attach to chemically clean glass including quartz glass and can also attach to methacrylate plastic. The attachment is inhibited by serum and various proteins but not by metal ions, chelating agents, or trypsin. Even formalin-killed cells attach to glass. There is no relationship between the hydrophilicity of the surface and the rate of spreading. Cell exudates can inhibit attachment so that cells can alter their own relationships to the glass. Attachment to surfaces is probably a significant factor in the human body where cells may attach to foreign particles, fibrin, collagen, and other substances. Weiss (1962) has shown how flexible mammalian cells can orient themselves along grooves in the glass substratum. The adsorption of bacteria and viruses to glass has been long known. Adsorption by these organisms and by other rigid organisms such as algae and fungi is much less firm than that of mammalian cells.

Some bacteria and many protozoa and algae produce structures called holdfasts which are responsible for their ability to adsorb to inert surfaces. These holdfasts are probably polysaccharides; they behave like glue, but their chemical nature and the basis for their adhesiveness is unknown.

Charge interactions between cells and surfaces lead to tight binding to materials such as clay minerals, sand, and other inorganic debris. This type of binding has been seen directly by Wood and Oppenheimer (1962) using a fluorescence microscope to observe chlorophyll-containing diatoms in situ.

Zvyagintsev (1962) has used ion exchange resins to study the specificity of adsorption of bacteria. After a resin had been saturated with one organism it could still adsorb another organism, and microscopic observations revealed that the two organisms adsorbed at different places on the resin. This observation suggests both a microheterogeneity of the resin and differences in microbial affinities. Because of their well-defined chemical compositions, resins might be useful model systems for the study of surface phenomena.

ECOLOGICAL IMPORTANCE OF ADSORPTION

Both cells and nutrients adsorb to surfaces, and when adsorbed the cell is able to grow more efficiently than when it is in free suspension. The biological importance of solid surfaces was first noted by sanitary bacteriologists who found that bacteria frequently increased in numbers in stored water and that the amount of increase was often related to the size of the bottle in which the water was stored (ZoBell, 1943). The increase in cell numbers under such conditions had been attributed to increased availability of oxygen, but ZoBell showed clearly that it was due to adsorption of organic matter onto the surface of the glass.

It is of interest to consider the problem of microbial growth in organically dilute solutions. There is probably a minimum concentration of organic material below which microorganisms cannot grow, possibly because of an inability to concentrate the nutrients within their cells. ZoBell (1946) has calculated that 1×10^7 bacteria/ml is equivalent in organic content to 1 mg/liter of organic matter. The organic content of sea water is 4-5 mg/liter, yet in the open sea the bacterial count is only 10^2-10^3/ml. There is sufficient organic MATTER for many more bacteria, but there apparently is not sufficient organic CONCENTRATION. If a sample of this sea water is now placed in a bottle and incubated for 24 hours at the same temperature at which it occurred in the sea, the bacterial count goes up to 625,000/ml, over a thousandfold increase; this is due to the fact that both bacteria and organic materials adsorb to the glass, thus raising the organic concentration. As the bacteria grow on the surface, many of the cells are sloughed off into the medium and are thus measured in the viable counting procedure.

Heukelekian and Heller (1940) showed a marked effect of glass surface on the growth of E. coli. At organic concentrations of 0.5-1.0 mg/liter E. coli did not grow unless glass beads were added to the bottle, but at organic concentrations of 50-100 mg/liter good growth occurred without glass beads, so that both control and experimental organisms grew to the same amount. As these authors point out, the organic matter content of natural waters, and even of sewage, is so low that solid surfaces may be essential for any significant microbial growth and function.

The stimulating effect of solid surfaces on bacterial growth in dilute solutions has been shown by various workers, and has been reviewed by ZoBell (1943, 1946). Substances which stimulate growth include: glass, plastics, porcelain, sand, clay minerals, kieselguhr, talc, asbestos, and calcium phosphate. Bigger and Nelson (1941) in particular showed that the growth-stimulatory effect of such materials was not due to nutrients contaminating the particles. They incubated the bacteria (E. coli) and talc on opposite sides of a dialyzing membrane and did not get stimulation but did get stimulation when the bacteria and talc were mixed. Incidentally, in their case the growth medium used was distilled water, showing that even this contains significant amounts of nutrients.

In most of the above work the bacteria studied did not become permanently attached to the surface. However, bacteria of the family Caulobacteriaceae normally live as epiphytes upon solid surfaces, attaching by means of a holdfast. Henrici and Johnson (1935) first studied the organisms which would attach to glass slides immersed in oligotrophic Minnesota lakes and found a large group of organisms that are usually missed in a survey of aquatic bacteria by cultural methods. Stark et al. (1938) later showed that organic matter from lake water would adsorb to glass slides and implied that this adsorption played a role in the attachment and growth of caulobacters. Both caulobacters and nonepiphytic bacteria probably behave in the same way, attaching to surfaces and then utilizing the adsorbed nutrients. The difference would be that caulobacters are permanently attached, whereas the other bacteria easily leave the surface. The fact that the true stalked bacteria have developed special asymmetrical processes for cell division (*see* page 62) suggests that they are more closely adapted to the epiphytic habit.

Since attachment of many bacteria occurs best when the liquid medium is low in organic matter and may be inhibited by higher concentrations, it is rarely a problem in the usual laboratory culture media with their more concentrated organic nutrients.

Little work has been done on the relationship of microorganisms other than bacteria to surfaces. Wood and Oppenheimer (1962) showed with the fluorescent microscope the attachment of algae to sand particles. Many protozoa form stalks and are sessile, although it is likely that these organisms benefit in other ways from their sedentary existence. The effect of solid surfaces on the action of antiseptics and disinfectants has been considered by Reddish (1954). Quaternary ammonium compounds are partially neutralized by glass, probably because they are adsorbed to the glass more readily than the target bacteria. This is apparently of some practical significance in the use of these compounds as sanitizers. The attachment of organisms to the surface of metals is an important step in corrosion, especially in the marine environment. The dissolution of the surfaces of rocks by microorganisms during weathering and soil formation is discussed in Chapter 9.

ATTACHMENT TO THE SURFACES OF LIVING ORGANISMS

The old rhyme about big fleas having little fleas is readily verified in any aquatic environment. The basis of the pyramid is usually a vascular plant rooted in the bottom to which various algae attach. Many diatoms seem to prefer an epiphytic existence, as do various blue-green algae. Bacteria, at the top of the pyramid, attach to everything, especially to the filamentous algae. In the marine environment I have rarely seen an algal filament which was not colonized by bacteria, frequently at very high density. The limnologist speaks of this development of epiphytes on higher plants as an "Aufwuchs."

More than likely the attachment of bacteria to algae or other plants is analogous to the attachment to glass slides, except that the living plant provides nutrients from within as well as those which adsorb to the surface. Unless there is an element of specificity in the attachment (e.g., a fungus which attaches to only a limited group of plants), the plant surface is analogous to an agar plate, a nutrient surface on which the organism can grow. A large proportion of the bacteria epiphytic on aquatic plants is composed of either stalked or filamentous forms. In the latter case a hold-fast may be only faintly visible. The filament grows perpendicular to the surface and may achieve some length, but usually there is a mechanism by which elements at the tip of the filament break free and alight at another spot to form a new filament. This is a structural adaptation made essential by the permanent epiphytic habitat (*see* page 62). Attachment of micro-organisms to terrestrial plants is probably less specific since the forces which might dislodge them are less strong than in aquatic environments. How-ever, in tropical rain forest plants the leaves (the so-called phyllosphere) often possess specific kinds of bacteria which fix nitrogen and which syn-thesize slimes in low nitrogen environments. These slimes probably help in enabling the bacteria to stick even to leaves which are subjected to heavy rains (Ruinen, 1956, 1961).

Alteration of the
Environment by the Cell

DEMONSTRATING THE ECOLOGICAL ROLE OF A SPECIFIC FUNCTION

The activities of living organisms cause profound alterations in the environment, some of which are listed in Table 3-8.

When we have isolated and characterized an organism, it is natural to speculate on the ecological roles of its various functions. In some cases a role may be obvious from the nature of the study; the slime formed by an organism isolated from zoogloea is easily explained, as is the cellulose-digestive ability of an organism isolated from rotting compost. But with many other properties an ecological role is not so easy to visualize, as for example with luminescence, tetanus toxin or penicillinase production, red color, or spherical shape.

TABLE 3-8. CHANGES IN THE ENVIRONMENT BROUGHT ABOUT BY CELLS

Loss or reduction in amount of specific chemicals (e.g., cell nutrients)
Loss or reduction in amount of gases (e.g., O_2, N_2, H_2S, CO_2)
Increase in amount of specific small molecules (e.g., cell metabolites)
Increase in amount of gases (e.g., O_2, N_2, H_2S, CO_2)
Appearance of specific enzymes (exoenzymes)
Appearance of other specific macromolecules (e.g., toxins, DNA)
Increase or decrease in pH
Increase or decrease in redox potential
Change in surface tension or viscosity
Increase in temperature
Change in osmotic pressure
Increase in turbidity
Absorption of light

We should remember that when we study a characteristic, there is a tendency for us to look for its function by reference to what we see, whereas in reality what we see and what the organism "sees" in the same characteristic may be two quite different things. Saz et al. (1964) have shown that the penicillinase produced by some bacteria is really a nonspecific peptidase which probably functions in the amino acid nutrition of the organism, and its action on penicillin is thus possibly fortuitous. This might explain why organisms which are never exposed to penicillin in nature might still produce the enzyme. In autecological studies we are mainly concerned with changes of a rather specific nature which are induced by an organism. For instance, O_2 depletion is brought about by many aerobic microorganisms, and rarely would we attempt to attribute this to a particular organism, whereas the production of H_2S is carried out by a more restricted group of organisms, so that we might seek for its production by a specific organism.

The proof that a particular chemical change is brought about by a specific organism follows the principles of Koch's postulates which were enunciated clearly by Conn in 1917 with reference to soil microbiology:

"1. The organism in question must be shown to be present in active (not spore) form when the chemical transformation under investigation is taking place.
2. It must also be shown to be present in larger numbers in such soil than in similar soil in which the chemical change is not taking place.
3. The organism must be isolated and grown in pure culture.
4. The organism when inoculated into sterile soil should produce the characteristic change. This is in itself not conclusive, for sterile soils do not occur in nature. Theoretically the organism should be inoculated into a non-sterile soil and be found to produce the characteristic change, in practice, however, it is difficult to get an organism to grow vigorously in soil already stocked with a bacterial flora of its own, and difficult to interpret results" (Buchanan and Fulmer, 1930).

The above postulates can be suitably modified for environments other than soil.

In practice it may be possible to modify these procedures. Thus if the process in question is quite rare and highly specific, and if it can be shown that the organism is able to carry out this process in the laboratory in pure culture, it may be possible to avoid step 4. As noted, it is very difficult to successfully inoculate a new organism into a nonsterile environment. The success of Koch's postulates in their original form is due to the fact that the interior of an experimental animal is usually sterile.

A further difficulty arises if an organism is found to do something in the laboratory which it does not always do in nature. For instance, it is frequently postulated that antibiotic production is a laboratory artifact and does not occur in nature. Two questions are really involved here: (1) is ANY antibiotic at all produced in nature, and (2) is sufficient antibiotic produced to inhibit the growth of other organisms? Since it is possible to detect antibiotics in natural soils, to isolate antibiotic-producing organisms from these soils, and to reinoculate these organisms into sterile soils and get antibiotic production (Brian, 1957), the main criteria of Conn have been met. The real difficulty is that soil contains so many microenvironments that it is difficult to know if antibiotic production does or does not occur in a specific location in the soil. Further discussion of antibiotics will be reserved until a later chapter.

MICROBIAL VERSATILITY

There is a widespread appreciation among microbiologists of the versatility of microorganisms. Alexander (1964) has called this the Principle of Microbial Infallibility which states that all organic molecules, regardless of complexity, are ultimately degradable by microorganisms. As Alexander points out, however, even the power of the microbe has limits, since man has been able to synthesize toxic pesticides and unique detergents which even the microbe cannot cope with or can handle only poorly. And there are even some natural materials such as lignins and humins which, anaerobically at least, are highly resistant to attack.

But the fact remains that microbes are versatile. How is this explained? First, from a genetic viewpoint we can consider the enormous population sizes which occur in nature, especially for the bacteria, leading to increased chances for the development of mutants capable of performing specific tasks (see Chapter 5 for a further discussion of this point). Second, within a given microbial genotype there are many opportunities for adaptation through the production of induced enzymes and the use of alternate pathways. However, since an organism probably would not retain forever a gene which is not called into function we would expect an organism to have genes only for functions which are requisite for the environment in which it has evolved. Also, there need not be a different enzyme for every different function since some enzymes have quite broad specificities and thus may recognize a certain functional group when it occurs on a variety of substrates, no matter what else is present in the molecule.

An interesting example which contains elements of both of the above ideas has been recently reported by Mortlock et al. (1965). It is possible to select a strain of *Aerobacter aerogenes* which is able to use the rare C_5 compound xylitol. The initial enzyme involved in the utilization of xylitol is ribitol dehydrogenase, which acts on xylitol at only a low rate and converts it to D-xylulose, which is then acted on by other normal enzymes and is eventually converted to fructose-6-phosphate. However, the strain which utilizes xylitol differs from the wild type in that it is constitutive for ribitol dehydrogenase and produces this enzyme at excessively high rates. Thus even though the specificity of the enzyme for xylitol is low, utilization is still possible because of the large amounts of enzyme formed. Therefore, it is not necessary to postulate that the xylitol-utilizing mutant has acquired genetic information for a new enzyme.

Concluding Discussion

This chapter has dealt with some aspects of organism-oriented ecology, or autecology. In such studies, our goal ". . . is to discover the factors that ultimately determine the survival of a species" (Stanier et al., 1963). Organisms have evolved to cope with various environments, and organisms are thus in a sense products of their environments. In any autecological investigation our goals should be (1) to study and define the range of microenvironments in which an organism lives in nature; (2) to study in pure culture the growth and behavior of the organism when exposed to wide variations in physical and chemical environmental factors; (3) to study in pure culture the modifications which the organism makes in its environment; (4) to modify the natural environment in various ways and observe how the organism responds; and (5) to inoculate the organism into natural environments in which it is not found, and observe its responses.

The investigator in any autecological study should continually move from the field to the laboratory and back to the field, using the observations from one to complement those of the other. With sufficient will and ingenuity such studies should be capable of considerable sophistication and should provide interesting and useful information.

If we know something about the nature of the environment, then we can predict at least approximately the ecological attributes of the organisms we might find there. Alternatively, if we know something about the organisms we find in a given habitat, then we can perhaps predict something about the nature of this environment. Further, the information we have obtained might help us to predict the ecological attributes of the organisms which might develop in some new environment, either natural or man-made.

One essential point of this chapter has been that microorganisms exist in microenvironments which up until now have been only imperfectly defined. From the autecological point of view this difficulty is serious, since it is only after we can define the environment of an organism that we can begin to study its ecology. From a synecological point of view the problem is less disturbing, since in the study of microbial ecosystems we can frequently be satisfied with a definition of the macroenvironment within which the ecosystem exists. It is important to recognize the distinctions between the two types of studies.

CHAPTER 4

Dispersal

The macroecologist must take into consideration geological, historical, and geographical factors in his attempts to analyze the distribution of organisms in nature. Physical barriers such as mountain ranges and bodies of water play important parts in restricting distribution of higher organisms, and geological events such as continental glaciers may eliminate a species from an area. However, for the microbial ecologist historical and geographical factors are of minor importance. Because of their small size, microorganisms are not greatly restricted in distribution by weight limitations. Further, microorganisms occur in enormous numbers, and since each individual has the theoretical potential of colonizing a niche, any given strain or species has numerous opportunities for extending itself into new territory.

Finally, the rapid growth of microorganisms permits an organism which has found a new niche suitable for its reproduction to become established within hours or days. Thus geographical conditions are usually considered of little consequence in the distribution of microorganisms. Everything is everywhere; the environment selects. Gregory (1961), viewing the plant pathology literature, discounts this idea, but on logical grounds it is neither possible nor impossible to prove. To a first approximation this doctrine can be assumed to be true, since there is little to be gained by attributing unusual distributions of microorganisms to historical factors. The differentiation of autochthonous (native) and allochthonous (accidental) microorganisms should be kept in mind in any discussion of dispersal.

The structural and physiological adaptations in microorganisms which promote dispersal are listed in Table 4-1. Some of these features have been discussed in Chapter 3, and it is sometimes difficult to separate the role of a structure in dispersal from its other roles in the ecology of an organism.

TABLE 4-1. STRUCTURAL AND PHYSIOLOGICAL ADAPTATIONS AIDING DISPERSAL OF MICROORGANISMS

Medium of dispersal	Adaptation
Air	Structures resistant to drying: spores, cysts, drought-resistant vegetative cells (e.g., gram-positive bacteria)
	Spore discharge mechanisms in fungi
	Light weight, small size of organisms
Water	Flagella, cilia
	Gliding motility
	Phototactic and chemotactic behavior
	Resistance to starvation in dilute media
Animals	Pathogenicity
	Sexual cycles (e.g., malaria)
	Ability to survive digestive enzyme attack
Inanimate objects	Drought-resistant structures
	Adhesive properties (e.g., slimes)

Air
Dispersal

The book by Gregory (1961) should be sought for details regarding air dispersal. Because of the importance of air dispersal for plant and animal disease agents, aerobiology has been mainly an applied subject.

It is likely that little or no growth of microorganisms occurs in the air itself, the air functioning only as an agent of dispersal, although some workers have suggested that a true aerial plankton exists, living and reproducing at great heights. Airborne microorganisms may occur individually, but they more frequently occur in clusters or "rafts." In either case they are heavier than air, but their gravitational fall is opposed by turbulence and thermal convection. "Estimation of the microbial content of the air is particularly difficult because, although microscopic, the particles are often large enough to demand attention to the aerodynamic design of the sampling equipment. . . . Single bacterial cells in aerosols are small enough to be handled in the manner of a gas, without regard to their inertia; but larger organisms (and bacteria on 'rafts') impact on surfaces, stick on corners, slip out of streamlines, and settle under the influence of gravity. . . . The basic study of the airspora must be by visual methods under the microscope" (Gregory, 1961).

All kinds of microorganisms are found in the air: bacteria, algae, yeasts, fungus spores, viruses, and protozoa, as well as the spores and pollen grains of higher plants. Fungus spores appear to predominate, although this may be merely because they are more easily seen microscopically than bacterial spores. Brown et al. (1964) have reported recent studies on airborne algae in Texas, which suggest that the numbers and diversity of these organisms are greater than previously suspected. These workers showed that airborne algae are derived primarily from soil, and that in dusty air extremely high counts (3000 algae per cubic meter) may be obtained, frequently exceeding the fungus and pollen counts, whereas in nondusty air the algal counts are lower than the others. As many as 15 different algal genera were recorded on a single day. A summary of 28 consecutive days of quantitative sampling for algae, fungi, and pollen is given in Figure 4-1.

Although spore concentration decreases with distance from the source, the distribution does not follow a normal curve; there are fewer spores at intermediate distances than further from the source (Gregory, 1961). The concentration of spores decreases with distance from the source because of diffusion and also because of deposition. Curiously, the longer a spore has remained aloft, the farther it is yet likely to travel (Gregory, 1961).

Spore concentration over the land is greater close to the ground than at higher altitudes, although vertical currents may carry spores to great heights. The clearing of spores from the air by rain results in uneven distributions. At sea, the airspora concentration is less immediately above the water than at higher altitudes, suggesting that microbes are cleared from the atmosphere by the oceans. This implies, therefore, that microbes from the land are continually being added to the sea. It also implies that the air microflora has its source mainly in terrestrial environments, marine organisms either not entering the air at all or lacking the ability to survive in the air. Curiously, the growth habitats of many organisms which are found frequently in the air (e.g., black yeasts, pigmented cocci) are only vaguely known.

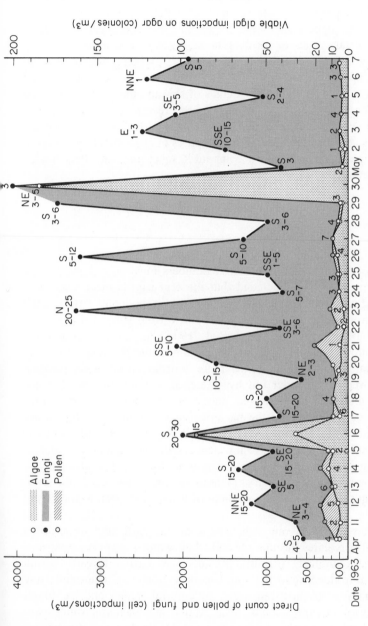

Fig. 4-1. Summary of 28 consecutive days of quantitative sampling of fungi, pollen, and algae obtained 25 m above the ground at the University of Texas, Austin (after Brown et al., 1964). Quantitative counts for fungi and pollen are expressed as direct observations of cell impactions per cubic meter (LEFT AXIS), while algae are expressed as viable impactions, counted as colonies per cubic meter, on agar (RIGHT AXIS). The data near the markers for fungi indicate the wind velocity and direction for all collections made on that date. Numbers adjacent to the markers for algae indicate the number of different algal genera obtained from a given collection. Copyright 1964 by the American Association for the Advancement of Science.

83

The number of spores formed by a single fungus fruiting body may be enormous; values of 10^9-10^{12} are not uncommon (Wolf and Wolf, 1947). Many fungi possess specific structural adaptations which forcibly expel the spores. Sporangiophores of *Pilobolus* and other Phycomycetes orient themselves toward the light (*see* Figure 3-11), and the sporangia are ejected violently for distances up to 20 ft. (Buller, 1934). The logic of such a mechanism for a forest-dwelling fungus is clear; by being ejected towards the light, the sporangia are most likely to travel out into the open where air currents would be stronger. For details of this and many other dispersal methods in fungi, the reader is referred to the review by Ingold (1953). As Gregory (1961) notes, a second important role of dispersal, especially in the fungi, is gene transmission. Fungus spores may germinate more readily if they come in contact with a compatible mycelium, and thus hyphal fusion and heterocaryosis are promoted.

Water
Dispersal

As discussed in Chapter 7, bacterial numbers must be at least 10^6/ml or 10^6/g before it can be concluded that the organism is making any significant contribution to the ecosystem. Except in polluted waters, such counts are rarely obtained in open water away from soils, sediments, or the bodies of living organisms. As ZoBell (1946) has shown, the number of bacteria found in sea water is far lower than would be expected on the basis of the amount of organic matter there. Further, most of the bacteria do not exist free in the water but live attached to plankton and detritus, and if these materials are removed, the bacterial counts are quite low. Thus it must be assumed that the bacteria found free in open waters are rarely autochthonous, but are merely on their way from one place to another, and therefore marine and fresh waters can be viewed mainly as means of dispersal in the same way that the air is a dispersal medium. Phytoplankton in open waters are autochthonous, on the other hand, but even for these organisms the water is a medium of dispersal as well as a medium of growth.

Fresh water begins as rain, which falls on the earth and forms lakes and rivers and percolates through the soil. This water transports organisms from one place to another. Airborne organisms are carried to earth in rain and thus are introduced into the soil. Visser (1964) has determined the microbial content of tropical rain water by cultural studies and has found a wide variety of microorganisms, algae, fungi, and bacteria, which generally resemble those found in soil (Table 4-2). In this way freshwater lakes could receive inoculum from terrestrial environments. Ground water

TABLE 4-2. MICROBIAL COUNT OF TROPICAL RAINWATER

Kinds of organisms	Numbers/ml
Total count	3.2×10^5
Actinomycetes	1.4×10^5
Fungi	2.1×10^4
Algae	10
Aerobic N_2 fixers	0.21
Anaerobic N_2 fixers	1.1×10^2
Ammonifiers	2.6×10^6
Nitrifiers ($NO_2^- \rightarrow NO_3^-$)	0.53
Denitrifiers	2.6×10^6

From Visser, 1964. Values are average of seven determinations over one year. Total count is that obtained on nutrient agar and is not the summation of the separate counts.

From the kinds of organisms found, it is likely that the organisms in rainwater are derived from the soil, carried to great heights on wind.

is depleted of its microbial population as it percolates downward, so that the microbial count of water from deep wells is considerably lower than that of surface water (Gainey and Lord, 1952).

Surface runoff will carry organisms from the soil into streams and rivers, depositing these organisms in other locations. Waves and currents will carry microorganisms long distances in large bodies of water. Microbial cells are denser than water and will eventually sink to the bottom, although this process may be counteracted by vertical currents and upwellings. Many aquatic microorganisms are motile and can move under their own power through the water, but this movement is probably significant over only short distances, long-range movement occurring by passive transport with the moving water. Although zooplankton are able to move vertically hundreds of meters in response to diurnal changes in light intensity, it is unlikely that small organisms such as bacteria can move more than short distances under their own power.

Microorganisms in marine environments are distinctly different from those in fresh water so the organisms transported to the ocean from land do not become established and eventually disappear. This is well described by ZoBell (1946). The oceans are a unique aquatic environment which is interconnected throughout, so that organisms from any part could be transported to any other part without the necessity of air dispersal over an intervening land barrier. I have compared strains of *Leucothrix mucor* isolated from Pacific and Atlantic waters and have not found any significant differences in nutrition or temperature optima for growth, which suggests that the various strains are quite closely related.

However, barriers do exist in the oceans in the form of temperature, salinity, light, and pressure boundaries, and thus local habitats are probably frequently created. Kriss (1963) has used bacterial counts at various stations and depths to aid in plotting oceanic currents.

Freshwater environments are less extensively interconnected, so that transmission from one body of water to another is usually through another agency, normally the air. In this respect, as in others, freshwater microorganisms seem to have more in common with terrestrial than with marine organisms.

Growth as a
Dispersal Method

Growth itself leads to dispersal into new environments, especially for filamentous microorganisms. The well-known ability of filamentous fungi to spread across poor media into rich media illustrates this point. Even though dispersal by growth can be over only short distances, it may still be of considerable importance, especially in the extremely heterogeneous soil microenvironments where these fungi are frequently found. Evans (1954) has described a special soil tube for studying the recolonization of sterilized soil by microorganisms.

Animal
Dispersal

No animal in nature is sterile, and microorganisms are frequently present in huge quantities, especially on the skin and in the intestinal tract. Because animals move, often long distances, they are a most important means of dispersal. In the human, 30% of the weight of the fecal matter is due to bacterial cells, and a human voids about 10^{11} bacterial cells per day as well as smaller numbers of fungi and protozoa. Some fungi, called coprophilic, are specifically adapted to fecal transmissal. Their spores are swallowed by the animal, and during passage through the intestinal tract the spore dormancy is broken. Growth then occurs on the dung, sporulation occurs, and the sporangia are shot away, adhere to vegetation and await ingestion by another animal (Buller, 1934) (Figure 4-2). Animal dispersal is of most significance with regard to disease-causing organisms, and detailed discussions can be found in books on medical microbiology (Wilson and Miles, 1957).

In the soil, microorganisms are undoubtedly dispersed both vertically

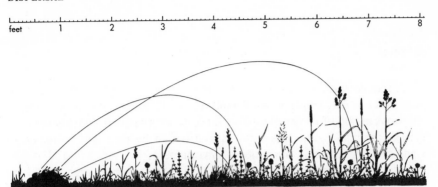

Fig. 4-2. *Pilobolus longipes.* Diagrammatic representation of the discharge of sporangia in a meadow (Buller, 1934). To the left is a horse dung plat, deposited about five days ago and now bearing fruit bodies. It is noon and the fruit bodies are beginning to discharge their sporangia. The trajectories of three discharged sporangia are indicated. Owing to the resistance of the air, the sporangia, like spent bullets, have descended more steeply than they rose. As may be seen by reference to the scale of feet, the sporangium shot farthest traveled horizontally about six feet.

and horizontally by the action of animals. Earthworms, nematodes, and other animals ingest plant remains and their attendant microbes and void these in fecal matter at other places. In aqueous environments, animals conceivably play a considerable role in dispersal, but to date little work has been done, although aquatic animals frequently have extensive intestinal microbial floras. Floating animals and plants could transport adherent microorganisms long distances.

Man is involved in transmissal in much the same way as are other animals, but he also provides unique modes of transmission derived from his peculiar "human" activities. The importation by man of exotic flowers, fruits, trees, pets, livestock, foods, and inanimate objects provides for the importation of adherent microorganisms which otherwise might not have been able to pass across geographical barriers. Again, this is most important in reference to disease-causing organisms. Man's scientific activities may also lead to microbial dispersal; for instance, the myxomatosis virus was imported into Australia to effect control of the rabbit. It can be safely assumed that except for the open oceans and the polar regions, no place on earth has escaped the influence of man. However, as far as microbes are concerned, man's role as a dispersal agent is probably less important than his role in altering the environment in ways which will greatly influence the growth, survival, and evolution of microorganisms.

Inanimate
Objects

Although a rolling stone may not gather moss, it does gather microbial cells which it may transport to distant places. This, however, is scarcely an efficient method of dispersal, and as far as terrestrial environments are concerned, inanimate objects, except as transported by man, are probably insignificant in dispersal. In aqueous environments it is otherwise. Floating objects, such as logs and fishing floats can carry adherent organisms long distances. It would seem possible that transmissal would be more certain for an organism attached to such an object than for a microbial cell existing free in the ocean. Many organisms are undoubtedly transmitted on the bottoms of ships, although this might be considered a human agency rather than an inanimate one.

Conclusion

To a first approximation geographical barriers to microbial dispersal probably do not exist, either in aquatic or terrestrial environments. In terrestrial environments, isolation mechanisms do not exist in so far as organisms capable of air dispersal are concerned, and since drought resistance is most likely a necessary adaptation for terrestrial existence, most terrestrial organisms can probably be dispersed through the air, so that the terrestrial environments of the world are essentially in microbiological equilibrium. For freshwater environments the situation is less clear. Many freshwater organisms have definite affinities with terrestrial forms (and fewer affinities with marine forms), and thus may be derived from the adjacent land. If there are unique freshwater microorganisms which cannot be dispersed by air, they have probably evolved in situ from terrestrial counterparts, although the relatively short duration (in geological terms) of any lake or river would mean that evolution has occurred only over a limited time.

CHAPTER 5

Population
Ecology

"There is good reason for considering population and community ecology the unique part of ecology. Some, at least, of the principles [of ecology] might be considered as being a part of chemistry or physics, or an extension of physiology. The study of group organization, however, is exclusively in the realm of ecology and could hardly be considered a part of any other fields as now conceived."   ODUM, 1959

When is a cell really alone?

Let us imagine a single cell immersed in the center of a large volume of nutrient medium. Now it may interact with its environment; nutrients will flow in; metabolites will flow out; interesting and complex functions will occur. As nutrients are removed from the immediate vicinity of the cell, new supplies can move in by diffusion, and as metabolites are released, they

89

can move away from the cell by diffusion. In a large volume of medium, equilibrium may be easy to achieve, and the cell lives in a constant environment. Now let us place another cell of the same kind, identical in all respects, near the first. The second cell is also using nutrients, releasing products, functioning. As we move the two cells closer together, they begin to interact. In the space between the cells the nutrient supply is reduced, the metabolite concentration increases, and diffusion processes may no longer be able to occur quickly enough to maintain a constant environment. The cells compete. Each cell is no longer alone.

We do not really need to do this experiment; the cell does it for us when it divides, producing two daughter cells which are together at least initially and can interact. No cell is an entity apart by itself. It must always contend with the existence of other cells, of its own or other kinds.

A group of cells all of the same kind is a population. How close must cells be before they cease acting as individual cells and become a population? We do not know. We can say, however, that a crucial factor in any situation is the CONCENTRATION of cells. At high concentrations cells will obviously interact among themselves more extensively than they will at low concentrations. And as the concentration increases past a certain point, the cells cease acting as individuals and become a population.

In microbial ecology we have a dilemma. Most microbes are individual cells, but any pure culture is a population. If we admit that ecology is the study of populations, then the study of microbial pure cultures is microbial ecology. Yet this is a field which has traditionally been considered microbial physiology. However, there is an important distinction between what the physiologist and the ecologist might do with the same pure culture. The physiologist looks inward from the cell membrane and studies the function of a population as if he were studying the function of an individual cell. He requires that the cells of the population behave identically in every way so that he can measure changes in the population and assume that they represent changes in the individual.

The ecologist, on the other hand, looks outward from the cell membrane and is interested in the integrative properties of a population. He wishes to know how the cells of the population interact with and influence each other and whether or not the cells when they are collected together in a population acquire any new properties which they did not possess as individuals. Even though these studies may be strictly laboratory endeavors without any attempt to relate the findings to nature, they are still ecological and thus of interest here. Studies of this type may provide new insights, especially at the chemical level, into the means of communication between the units of a population and therefore may be of interest to macroecologists as well. Further, it is likely that the information used may aid the understanding of the ecology of microorganisms in nature, since in nature microbes rarely exist as individual cells but usually as populations.

The Colony.

Macroformations

On solid or semi-solid surfaces motility and Brownian movement are hindered, and as growth and division proceed a very high cell concentration develops, and a colony is formed. Most microorganisms form colonies, but the most interesting and characteristic are those formed by unicellular organisms. Since the days of Robert Koch (Brock, 1961), the colony has played a crucial role in the methodology of microbiology and still provides the main basis for the isolation of pure cultures.

A colony is more than merely a collection of cells all in one place. A colony has shape, form, texture, structure, size, and color. It is the collective expression of the wonderfully complex processes of cell growth, division, and interaction. It is a thing in itself, worthy of study. As Koch noted, and as has been noted many times since, different organisms produce different kinds of colonies. Even organisms differing by as little as single genes may produce entirely different types of colonies, as illustrated in the smooth-rough transformation, which is often due to differences in capsule production by different strains (Braun, 1953).

In earlier years there was interest in colony structure and function as a study in itself (*see* Knaysi, 1951), but in recent times only the geneticist has been particularly concerned about the colony (Braun, 1953). The view that the colony is a biological entity which undergoes differentiation in a manner analogous to a higher organism was held by Legroux and Magrou (1920) who studied microtome sections of colonies and detected differences in morphology of cells in different parts of the colony. Although it may appear obvious that cells at the surface of the colony would differ from those in submerged positions, this does not mean that these differences are trivial or without interest. Indeed, even if all the cells in a colony were identical, the colony would still be of ecological interest, since it has form and structure which it derives from the characteristics of its cells, but which cannot be predicted from a study of these cells in isolation.

Colonies which develop from cells which are submerged in agar are usually lenticular in shape and lack the species-specific structural characteristics of surface colonies. As cells divide within the agar they are probably induced to orient more in one direction than another because of the fibrous nature of the agar gel.

Bisset (1955) has considered a variety of bacterial aggregates under the term "macroformations." He includes here the myxobacterial fruiting body, the myxobacterial swarm, aggregates of sheathed filamentous bacteria, and typical bacterial colonies. Expanding this, we could include the colonial algae such as *Volvox* and the fruiting bodies and asexual fruiting structures of fungi. Macroformations have two attributes: (1) they possess definite macroscopic structures, and (2) the units of which they are composed are still able to exist independently of the colony.

MOTILE COLONIES

Some motile bacteria form colonies in which the individual cells possess characteristic movement in one direction only (either clockwise or counterclockwise), and a rotating motion is conferred on the whole colony. The colony wanders over the surface of the medium, leaving in its wake stray cells which then form small colonies and thus create a track which reveals where the colony has moved. Some migrating colonies follow elaborate curved or spiral paths. Eventually the colony stops moving and may rotate in place (Salle, 1961). Such mass migrations of bacteria reveal that these simple creatures are capable of cooperative action. Is this merely a laboratory artifact, or do colonies move in nature as well?

COLONIES AND MACROFORMATIONS IN NATURE

In medical practice, foci of infection are well known and occur in many tissues and organs. These foci are probably colonies, and it is conceivable that cooperative effects occur which alter the outcome of infectious processes. The circular growths of dermatophytic fungi on the skin are quite analogous to colonies on agar. Colonies of pathogenic fungi occur on plant tissues, especially the leaves. Circular colonies of lichens occur on many rocks, and indeed the growth rate of a lichen can occasionally be determined by measuring the yearly increase in diameter (Hale, 1961) (Figure 5-1). Bacterial zoogloea are basically analogous to colonies, although these structures may be composed of either a single type of organism or a mixture, all held together by secreted slime. Many aquatic bacteria form zoogloea, e.g., *Thiodendron* (Lackey and Lackey, 1961), and these may achieve macroscopic size. Zoogleal aggregations are also found in the dental plaque which exists on the surface of teeth (Hoffman, 1964). Microtome sections of soil crumbs (Jones and Griffiths, 1964) reveal that most bacteria occur in microcolonies of a few hundred cells (Figure 3-1). Hoffman (1964) has emphasized some of the technical problems in studying colonies both in nature and in the laboratory.

Colonies do occur in nature, but because of the technical difficulties involved in visualizing them they are rarely sought, and colony formation

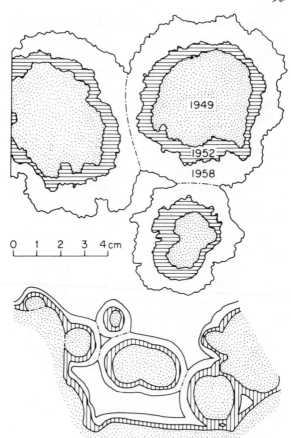

Fig. 5-1. Outlines of the colonies of the lichens *Parmelia conspersa*, TOP, and *Rinodina oreina*, BOTTOM, traced on plastic sheets in 1949, 1952, and 1958, and superimposed (Hale, 1961).

may be much more important in the ecology of an organism than we realize.

Population Growth
and Control

The growth of a cell is not the same as the growth of a population since population growth is a collective expression of the growth of single cells. That is, while a single bacterial or yeast cell increases in mass at an arithmetic rate (Mitchison, 1961), a population of such cells increases in mass at a logarithmic rate. The property of logarithmic or exponential growth is well discussed in most microbiology texts (e.g., Stanier et al., 1963) and by Hinshelwood (1946).

The growth rate of a population is a function of the rate of increase of mass in the individuals and of the growth habit of the organism. The analysis of growth rate is relatively uncomplicated for populations of unicellular organisms. Under constant conditions each unit cell increases in mass and size until a certain critical point is reached, and then cell division occurs and two unit cells are produced, each of which grows. Although there may be some functional differentiation within a unit cell so that growth is not proceeding equally in all parts, this is a minor factor and can be overlooked. Growth in unicellular organisms is said to be exponential or autocatalytic, but it should be emphasized that autocatalytic growth is a population phenomenon, not a cellular process.

Population growth is quite different in filamentous organisms from that in unicells. In filamentous fungi, for instance, growth usually occurs only at the tips of filaments; in the absence of branching, population growth is an arithmetic function rather than an exponential function. Most fungi do branch, however, but it is possible experimentally to keep the number of branches constant by forcing the fungus to grow on agar down a long straight tube, the so-called race track (Ryan et al., 1943) and thus induce arithmetic growth. A fungus usually spreads out radially on an agar plate, so that the number of branches present at any time is proportional to the uncolonized area at the hyphal front into which the hyphae will grow next. Since area increases as the square of the diameter, radial growth of fungi is a square root function of time (Worley, 1939). In liquid media, in the absence of extensive shearing forces, growth of fungi is a cube root function of time (Emerson, 1950).

CONTROL OF POPULATION GROWTH AND SIZE

The growth of many types of populations can be expressed in the form of the so-called logistics equation:

$$\frac{dN}{dt} = kN - \frac{k}{G} N^2$$

where N is the number of individuals, G is the maximum population attainable as controlled by environmental factors, and k is the growth rate constant. The first term in the equation expresses the growth rate during the exponential phase of growth, whereas the second term accounts for self-crowding effects (Odum, 1959). The factor kN expresses the intrinsic growth rate which is the most rapid rate at which the population can grow under the conditions used.

Even under optimal environmental conditions, different organisms grow at different rates, and some representative values are given in Table 5-1. It is generally found that growth rate increases as cell size decreases, and this relationship has been related to the surface-to-volume ratio (Fogg,

TABLE 5-1. GROWTH RATES OF SELECTED MICROORGANISMS (DOUBLINGS/DAY)

Organism	Growth rate	Temp. (°C)	Conditions
Blue-green algae			
Anabaena cylindrica	0.96	25	saturating light, synthetic medium
Anacystis nidulans	11.5	41	saturating light, synthetic medium
Schizothrix calcicola	3.4	30	saturating light, synthetic medium
Red algae			
Porphyridium aerugineum	1.4	21	saturating light, synthetic medium
Diatoms			
Asterionella formosa	1.9	18.5	saturating light, nonsynthetic medium
Navicula minima	1.4	25	saturating light, nonsynthetic medium
Phaeodactylum tricornutum	2.4	8	nonsynthetic medium
Tabellaria flocculosa var. flocculosa	1.4	20	saturating light, nonsynthetic medium
Euglenoid			
Euglena gracilis	2.2	25	saturating light, synthetic medium
Green algae			
Chlamydomonas reinhardtii	3.8	25	saturating light, synthetic medium
Chlorella ellipsoidea	3.6	25	saturating light, synthetic medium
Scenedesmus obliquus	2.2	25	saturating light, synthetic medium
Photosynthetic bacteria			
Chloropseudomonas ethylicum	3.3	30	synthetic medium
Chromatium D	2.6	37	synthetic medium
Rhodopseudomonas spheroides	10.1	34	synthetic medium
Rhodospirillum rubrum	4.5-5.2	25	synthetic medium
Heterotrophic bacteria			
Bacillus megaterium	46	30	broth
Escherichia coli	85	37	broth
Lactobacillus casei	38	25	milk
Rhizobium meliloti	13	25	complex medium
Streptococcus hemolyticus	45	37	broth
Treponema pallidum	0.7	37	rabbit testes
Protozoa			
Didinium nasutum	3.6	21	Paramecium
Paramecium caudatum	2.3	26	bacteria
Stentor coeruleus	0.6-0.9	19	ciliates
Tetrahymena geleii	5.7-10.9	24	
Fungi			
Saccharomyces cerevisiae	12	30	liquid shaken culture
Monilinia fructicola	0.8	25	liquid shaken culture
Basisporium gallarum	0.45	25	liquid shaken culture

Data from Hoogenhout and Amesz (1965): photosynthetic organisms; Spector (1956): bacteria and protozoa; Lilly and Barnett (1951): fungi; Brock (unpublished): *Saccharomyces cerevisiae.*

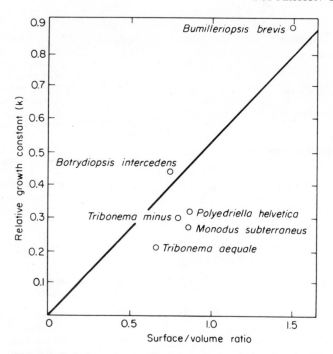

Fig. 5-2. Relation of growth rate to surface/volume ratio for
six algae grown under standard conditions (after Fogg, 1965).

1965), as shown in Figure 5-2. However, with organisms as small as
bacteria, this relationship does not hold well (Lamanna and Mallette,
1959). The increased growth rate in smaller cells is probably related to
increased ability to take up nutrients by diffusion, and it is obvious that in
a large cell, diffusion of nutrients to the center might take considerable
time (*see* page 8). However, it does not necessarily follow that the
most rapidly growing organism is the most successful. By definition, all
organisms are successful; otherwise they would not be here.

In the above, we have been discussing growth as an increase in cell
number, but it can also be considered as an increase in cell mass. The
rates of increase of these two parameters are not necessarily related, and
a large cell, although taking a long time to divide, may increase in mass
at a considerable rate.

The factor G in the above equation, which expresses the population
size when growth has ceased, will be controlled in part by the environmental conditions used and in part by the genetic constitution of the
organism. 'Population limitations have been explained in three ways: (1)
physical crowding, (2) exhaustion of an essential nutrient, and (3) production of toxic substances. The limitation of population size by physical

crowding received considerable discussion in earlier years, but as Henrici (1928) has pointed out, this hypothesis is in disagreement with the fact that on solid media organisms will grow at rapid rates in colonies where the crowding is much more severe than has ever been observed in liquid media.

There is good evidence that both explanations 2 and 3 are correct, and which of the two applies to a given case will depend on the organism and on the conditions. The most recent and sophisticated analysis of the mechanism of population limitation is that of Freter and Ozawa (1963) with *Escherichia coli*. By experiments using dialysis sacks and genetically marked strains, they showed that growth was limited by the exhaustion of a nutrient under anaerobic conditions or oxygen under aerobic conditions. In the bacterial chemostat (Novick, 1955) growth limitation by nutritional means not only can be readily demonstrated but is used to control population growth rate and density.

In natural environments population size may be frequently limited by the availability of an inorganic nutrient, but as Fogg (1965) points out, direct evidence of this is scarce. One example, discussed by him in detail, is presented in Figure 5-3 in which growth cessation and subsequent

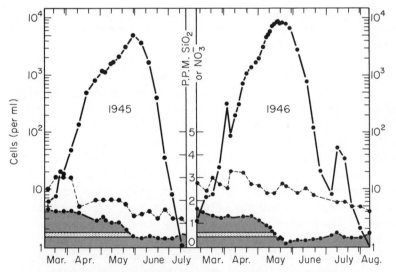

Fig. 5-3. Numbers of live cells of *Asterionella formosa* in Windermere, North Basin, during parts of 1945 and 1946, plotted logarithmically against time (SOLID LINE) (after Lund, 1950). Interrupted line, nitrate nitrogen in parts per million, values multiplied by 10 for convenience in representation; TINTED AREA, dissolved silica in parts per million with the 0.5 parts per million level STIPPLED. These data show that growth ceases and population decline begins when the silicate concentration drops below 0.5 mg/liter.

population decline in the diatom *Asterionella formosa* coincided with a drop in dissolved silica concentration below 0.5 mg/liter. Analyses of a variety of other factors showed none except dissolved silica whose decline correlated with the growth cessation. These results in nature agree with cultural studies which show that diatoms cannot multiply if the silica concentration is below 0.5 mg/liter. Other nutrients may be limiting with other organisms or habitats, and nitrogen and phosphorus are most frequently implicated (Fogg, 1965; Harvey, 1957). As another approach to this question, several workers have studied biological activity (such as $C^{14}O_2$ fixation) in natural waters which were experimentally enriched with suspected limiting nutrients. In this way Ryther and Guillard (1959) showed that silicate and one or more metal ions were limiting photosynthesis (and presumably phototrophic growth) in waters of the northwestern Atlantic and the Sargasso Sea.

Population limitation due to accumulation of toxic factors is also well established. Lactic acid bacteria cease growing when the production of lactic acid causes the pH to drop. If the pH is adjusted by periodic neutralization or by the use of highly buffered media, much higher population densities can be obtained (Toennies and Shockman, 1958). Yeast growth is frequently limited by the accumulation of alcohol, a problem of some practical interest since it sets a limit on the concentration of alcohol ultimately developed in wine or beer. Given a medium in which two types of organisms might grow at the same rate, one of these may achieve a higher population density because of an ability to store materials for use when the food supply is exhausted, because it can utilize the available food more efficiently, or because it is less affected by toxic metabolites. Fogg (1965) feels that there is no evidence of any role of autoinhibitors in limiting phytoplankton growth, and in view of the relatively low population densities under most conditions, this may be reasonable. However, algal populations may be very dense in favorable situations such as mineral springs, polluted streams, sewage oxidation ponds, eutrophic lakes, etc., and it would be here that the production of toxic metabolites might be significant. The production by algae of fatty acids which inhibit the growth of other algae is discussed in Chapter 5.

However, the exhaustion of a specific nutrient may not eliminate all biosynthetic processes. Toennies et al. (1959) have shown that in *Streptococcus faecalis* the exhaustion of an amino acid needed for protein synthesis but not for cell wall synthesis resulted in a population of cells which ceased dividing and making protein but which continued to make cell wall. Nongrowing algae may continue to photosynthesize and either store or excrete the reduced carbon compounds (Steeman Nielsen, 1963). Stationary phase cells differ in many ways from log phase cells. Changes can be expected in the amounts and kinds of enzymes, in permeability, in quantities of metabolites and coenzymes in the cell pool, in ribosome content, RNA content, cell wall thickness or composition, lipid content, and possibly even in DNA content (Lamanna and Mallette, 1959). The specific differences between log phase and stationary phase cells may be due to the nature of the nutrient which became limiting or to the nature of the metabolic product which became toxic and brought about an initiation of the stationary phase.

It should be noted that the above discussion introduces indirectly the element of competition. As a nutrient becomes limiting, the cells begin to compete for this nutrient, and not all cells will be able to acquire a sufficient amount to continue growing. Competition between units of a clone is just as important, although not as dramatic, as the competition between genetically dissimilar cells which is discussed in the next chapter. In some organisms the stationary phase is initiated or concluded by a morphogenetic process such as sporulation.

The logistics curve is a useful laboratory model in that it focuses attention on those factors which might control or limit growth, but it should be emphasized that growth of natural populations can rarely be expressed in this form. In nature, with open systems and population losses due to predation, sedimentation, or transport, quite different growth responses are usually seen, and population growth more resembles that seen in a chemostat (*see* Chapter 7).

POPULATION HETEROGENEITY

Not all the cells in a population are really identical. Henrici (1928) showed that cells of *E. coli* taken from a single point in the log phase showed wide variations in size and shape and that this variability was even greater in the middle of the log phase than later or earlier. Quantitative disinfection studies have also shown that log phase cells are heterogeneous (Rahn, 1945). Yet these are really microheterogeneities, of the type to be expected in any population of cells, probably arising as much from unequal distribution of cell materials in dividing cells as from any other cause. Of more importance are the differences which may be found between populations in different parts of the log phase. Thus *E. coli* cells are known to be very susceptible to cold shock in the early log phase and to become resistant in the middle log phase (Roeser, 1961), showing that early log phase cells are different from middle log phase cells in some way. The change in susceptibility to cold shock occurs when the population density is still quite low, around 3-5 × 10^7 cells/ml, and the population may go through many exponential doublings after this point, showing that the medium is not lacking in nutrients. The changes occur whether the medium is rich and complex or poor and simple. It can only be concluded that metabolic materials must be accumulating in the culture and bringing about the observed changes. In other words, the cells are interacting with each other and altering each other. We thus see that in this instance at about 3-5 × 10⁷ cells/ml the cells cease to become individuals and begin to become a population, doing things together which they could not do separately.

LAG PHASE

When log phase cells are transferred to a new medium lacking a factor previously provided, they will not grow until they have synthesized sufficient quantities of the missing factor. During this lag they may continue to respire, synthesize protein, and carry out many other processes, but they do not divide. Another cause of a lag is the transfer of stationary phase cells to a fresh medium of the same composition as that in which they were originally grown. Growth will not resume until the cells have produced all the enzymes or metabolites which had become depleted during the preceding stationary phase. Sometimes a lag under these conditions is more apparent than real. Many of the cells may be dead, and the remaining cells are able to begin growth immediately, but this growth is not apparent if only turbidity is measured, since the turbidity of the dead cells masks the small increment brought about by the few living cells.

The lag is probably of considerable significance in the success of a cell upon being transferred from one environment to another; if it exhibits a lag in the new environment it may be destroyed before it has had a chance to begin growth. A lag is most commonly seen when a low inoculum size is used and may be absent or greatly reduced with a large inoculum (Fogg, 1965).

POPULATION AND CELL AGE

Clearly there is no equivalence between an old cell and an old culture. With reference to a culture, age usually refers not to any time-dependent state but to the density of the population in the medium used. An old culture is one which is beginning to cease growing, and age is thus a population phenomenon. Age in reference to a cell has a different meaning. A yeast cell ages because it accumulates bud scars and eventually reaches a point where there is no more room on its surface for the formation of a new bud; it literally dies (Barton, 1950). In most diatoms, cell size diminishes through successive divisions and then is restored to maximum again through auxospore production (Smith, 1950). But most cells which reproduce by binary fission do not age, since the components of a mother cell become distributed amongst the two daughter cells more or less equally; in such organisms, it is not clear how old age should be defined, but it is usually population age and not cell age with which one is concerned.

The age distribution of a population is the frequency distribution of the ages of the individuals of the population. In most microorganisms, the age distribution would be impossible to determine, although in yeasts it could be measured by counting the number of bud scars per cell, and in diatoms by measuring cell size. In most populations it would be expected that the spread of ages would be widest in the late lag phase and at the beginning of the stationary phase and would be narrowest in the middle log phase.

A related phenomenon to population age is the so-called degeneration which occurs in Actinomycetes and ciliates when they are forced to divide only vegetatively for long periods of time (Reusser et al., 1961; Sonneborn and Schneller, 1960). In the Actinomycetes such degeneration may be due to a segregation of nuclei from an initially heterocaryotic myselium and a consequent loss in hybrid vigor. In ciliates, degeneration seems to be related to nuclear changes, and vigor can be restored by a cycle of sexual reproduction. Aging is clearly a property of considerable ecological interest, but one which has been rarely studied in microorganisms.

COOPERATIVE EFFECTS WITHIN A POPULATION

It is occasionally observed that a large number of cells can begin growth in a medium in which a small number of cells cannot grow, suggesting a cooperative interaction amongst the cells. Several explanations for this phenomenon exist. (1) There may be a constituent of the medium which is toxic when present above a threshold amount per cell. With many cells present, each one may adsorb a small amount of the material, but not enough to be inhibited, thereby removing the toxic material from the medium. Thus Hofsten (1962) showed that copper ions inhibited the anaerobic growth of E. coli from small inocula but not from large inocula, but if the medium was purified to remove the copper or if dead cells were added to adsorb the copper, then small inocula could grow. Many reports of chelating agents promoting the growth of small inocula probably can be explained in this way. (2) The chemical or physical properties of the medium may be altered by the cells. The best example of this arises from work on animal cell cultures. Eagle and Piez (1962) have shown that the amino acid serine is required by human cells when they are inoculated at low but not at high cell density. The reason for this is that there is a minimum concentration of serine that is needed in the EXTERNAL medium before the cells can begin to grow. Each cell synthesizes some serine which accumulates in the medium and at high cell densities enough is synthesized to bring the concentration up to the required amount. At low cell densities, it is impossible for enough serine to accumulate before the cells die. Some examples of cooperative effects in algae, leading to reduction in the lag phase, are discussed by Fogg (1965).

If such cooperative phenomena are requisite for the initiation of growth in a natural environment, then cells which arrive as individuals in this new environment will not become established. However, it is sometimes observed that single cells can initiate growth on agar, whereas they cannot in liquid medium of the same composition. Conceivably, on agar a few divisions occur using reserve materials stored in the cell, and because all of the progeny remain together on the agar, cooperative interactions begin immediately. Thus, growth occurring on the surface of a soil particle may be analogous to growth on agar, and cooperative effects may occur.

Cooperation is also seen in the self-protective phenomena observed when organisms are subjected to freezing; at high but not at low population densities the cells can withstand freezing (Kohn and Lion, 1961). Since the population density even in a microcolony is very high, it is conceivable that microcolonies on soil particles or organic debris might be able to survive freezing or some other deleterious influence to which the same cells as individuals might succumb. Cooperative effects may also occur in starving populations. For instance, Postgate and Hunter (1963) have discussed what they call cryptic growth; 50 organisms die and the nutrients released from the lysing cells are able to support the doubling of one survivor. Thus, as the population density increases, the rate of death due to starvation decreases.

Cooperation is also seen in experimental pathology, when an experimental infection can be initiated by a large number of cells, but not by a small number (Wilson and Miles, 1957). Although this is sometimes due to the presence of virulent mutants in the larger population, it may also be due to physiological cooperation, as in the production by the population of sufficient toxin to neutralize the host's defenses, or in the creation by the population of a favorable redox potential. In the infection of the mouse with *Salmonella typhimurium,* Stocker (1959) has shown using genetically marked strains that infection is not a population phenomenon but is initiated by single cells.

The distinction between cooperative and competitive interactions in populations can be seen in Figure 5-4. In (a), the cells of the population compete, so that growth and survival will be best when the population is smallest. In (b), the cells cooperate and grow better together than separately, but even here competition eventually is seen as the population density becomes high.

POPULATION DENSITY AND POPULATION CONTROL

The ecologist distinguishes two major kinds of population controls (Odum, 1959):

1. In DENSITY DEPENDENT control the rate of the event in question (e.g., growth, function) increases in proportion to the increase in population. Growth cessation in the stationary phase is density dependent, as are competitive and cooperative interactions between cells, including such processes as parasitism and sexual reproduction.

2. DENSITY PROPORTIONAL events affect a constant proportion of the population, irrespective of the initial density. In microbiology this is seen best in studies on disinfection; the rate of killing by an antiseptic is relatively independent of the population density, and in any given time unit a constant proportion of the cells is killed.

It should be noted that in density dependent events, the population control is biological, whereas in the density proportional events, the population control is environmental. This distinction is of importance in later considerations of ecosystems (Chapter 7).

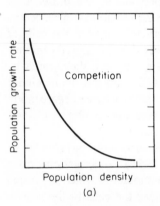 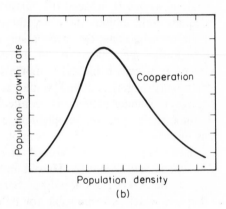

Fig. 5-4. Competitive and cooperative effects in populations (after Allee et al., 1949).

SPORULATION AS A POPULATION EVENT

As Halvorson (1962) has noted, chemostat experiments reveal that sporulation in bacteria does not occur during logarithmic growth, even after numerous generations. Sporulation is induced either by substances which accumulate in the medium or by the disappearance of nutrients that inhibit sporulation. These modifications in the medium are brought about by the cells themselves and are thus another example of a population dependent morphogenetic change. An interesting question which does not seem to have been asked is whether or not sporulation in natural conditions involves the same factors. Do high population densities occur in nature and bring about requisite changes in the chemical status of the environment, or are extrinsic factors involved in natural sporulation?

HOMOTAXIS

Individual cells of certain species may move towards each other and form aggregates. Although this is frequently called chemotaxis, I am calling this phenomenon homotaxis to imply that the movement is not directed to some extrinsic factor but to an intrinsic factor produced by the cells themselves. Homotaxis has been studied in the cellular slime molds. Each myxamoeba is able to produce a substance called acrasin which attracts other amoebae. Since acrasin also induces amoebae to produce acrasin of their own, an initial aggregate containing a few cells will increase its acrasin production, more cells will be attracted, and the process will continue at a rapidly increasing rate (Shaffer, 1962). Since the aggregating amoebae are genetically alike, homotaxis is a population phenomenon and is the result of the interaction of cells of the population. The aggregation of the amoebae is induced by starvation, and presumably the presence of adequate food inhibits the biosynthesis of acrasin. Homotaxis also occurs in the myxobacteria; the mechanism may be similar to that in the cellular slime molds, since depletion of the medium provides the initial stimulus. Obviously if cells exhibited homotaxis even when well fed, they would be perennially aggregated and would be in effect a primitive multicellular organism. Bonner (1959) has pointed out the analogy between aggregation in slime molds and similar phenomena in metazoa, and Hoffman (1964) has discussed some primitive examples in bacteria.

Homotaxis may be involved in the rosette formation by gonidia of *Leucothrix* and *Thiothrix* (Harold and Stanier, 1955). Aggregation occurs even in the absence of the polysaccharide holdfast material which is formed later and which is responsible for holding together the cells in the rosette (Brock, unpublished). Interestingly, the gonidia form when the medium becomes depleted (Pringsheim, 1957), and thus starvation provides the initial control of rosette formation, analogous to the aggregations of myxamoebae and myxobacteria. Since rosettes occur in nature and are relatively easy to observe microscopically, it might be possible to determine the factors involved in their formation.

It is possible that metabolic gases such as CO_2 can accumulate in the center of a cluster of cells, and such gaseous substances may be involved as controlling elements in morphogenetic changes.

Aggregation phenomena occur widely in microorganisms in both sexual and asexual interactions. Such clustering is obviously advantageous to the organism in nature, since it makes possible the acquisition of functions which the individual cell could not perform. At the same time, however, by reducing the number of independently active units aggregation reduces the efficiency of the selective processes in the adaptation of the organism to changing environments and also reduces the opportunity for dispersion into new environments. Thus aggregation and unicellularity are competing states in the life of the microorganism.

Genotype
and Phenotype

It is not possible to examine an organism directly for the presence of a given gene and all that can be observed is the phenotype; the genotype can be inferred only from the results of breeding studies. Since in population genetics breeding studies frequently cannot be done, it is essential to keep in mind that the existence of a given gene in a natural population is usually being inferred from studies done earlier on other experimental populations. Indeed, in so far as it is relevant to our population studies, we need not talk about genes at all but can treat the phenotype itself. Thus, much of what has been called population or ecological genetics (Ford, 1964) is ecological phenetics.

Under most conditions, probably no organism expresses all of the characteristics which it is potentially capable of expressing. Haploid homocaryotic organisms possess inducible and repressible genes which are latent under many conditions, providing the opportunity for short-term adaptability, but this latency is not of significance in population genetics. Heterocaryotic and diploid organisms possess recessive genes which are masked and which can be expressed only after segregation. In heterocaryons, this segregation is asexual, whereas in diploid organisms it usually occurs by a sexual process. Gene masking in diploids and heterocaryons is important in population genetics because it provides for adaptability over one or a few generations, thereby enabling the race or clone (but NOT the individual) to cope to some extent with changing environments.

In addition, organisms can acquire new characteristics by mutation. In haploid organisms a mutation can be immediately expressed, whereas in diploid organisms the mutation may or may not be expressed, depending on whether it is dominant or recessive. Since mutations occur by changes in the existing gene pool of the organism, they may result in the alteration or loss of the characteristic which had been expressed by that gene before it mutated. This should be of special significance in haploids, since they may have only one copy of each gene. (NOTE: It is possible that organisms carry surplus DNA which serves no function except as a source of new genes [Smithies, 1965]).

Organisms can also acquire new genetic characteristics by genetic recombination, by which two genes which existed in separate organisms are brought together in one organism. The phenotype of the hybrid may express each of the genes separately, or the two genes may interact to lead to some completely new characteristic which did not exist in either of the parents.

NUCLEAR CONSTITUTION AND LIFE HISTORIES OF MICROORGANISMS

The details of sexual and asexual reproduction in microorganisms are extremely diverse, and the reader is referred to monographs of different groups for a recital of these facts. Some species are haploid in the vegetative state, others are diploid, and some grow vegetatively in both stages. Special gametes may be formed for sexual reproduction, or the vegetative cells themselves may act as gametes. Some cells are mononucleate, while others may have more than one nucleus. The ciliates have both a macronucleus and a micronucleus, the former controlling phenotypic expression and the latter involved mainly in sexual reproduction. Divergences in life cycles undoubtedly play a great role in the population genetics and adaptation of microorganisms, but solid information is lacking.

The existence in most fungi, algae, and protozoa, and in some bacteria, of sexual mechanisms which permit outbreeding suggests that genetic recombination occurs in nature, but this question has been tested experimentally only rarely. Siegel (1961) has made collections of *Paramecium bursaria* which contained conjugating pairs and newly formed exconjugants and has presented other evidence that conjugation occurs in nature. Conjugating algae can often be observed in natural collections. Ottolenghi and MacLeod (1963) have shown that genetic recombination via DNA-mediated transformation can occur in experimental pneumococcus infections in the mouse. Stocker (1959) doubts that genetic recombination plays any important role in evolution of virulent strains of bacteria, although it seems unlikely that microorganisms would maintain complicated sexual and parasexual processes merely for the interest of laboratory scientists. An important requirement in all natural recombinational processes is that a high population density of at least one of the two recombining forms should exist, otherwise the probability of contact between two genetically diverse cells would be insignificantly low. In *E. coli,* for instance, cell densities considerably greater than 10^7/ml are necessary before frequent mating occurs (W. Hayes, 1964). Therefore we might expect mating to occur in nature in habitats such as animal intestines, eutrophic lakes, and on decomposing plant and animal remains, but not in environments which contain only low microbial populations.

In nature, sexual incompatibilities frequently exist between closely related strains. An investigation of incompatibility in the mushroom *Schizophyllum commune* which has had far reaching significance has been prosecuted by Raper (Raper et al., 1958, 1960). This fungus is well suited for such a study, since it forms in nature macroscopic fruiting bodies which can be easily recognized by eye; pure culture monocaryotic isolates can easily be obtained in the laboratory; and compatibility between various isolates can be easily recognized in appropriate crosses by the formation of dicaryotic mycelium with characteristic clamp connections. *S. commune,* in common with many other basidiomycetes, exhibits tetrapolar sexuality, so that at meiosis progeny of four mating types are produced in equal frequency:

$$A^1A^2B^1B^2 \rightarrow A^1B^1 \quad A^1B^2 \quad A^2B^1 \quad A^2B^2$$

Diploid   Haploid spore types

The monocaryotic cultures obtained from the four spore types will mate only if they differ in both the A and B characters:

Compatible matings	Incompatible matings
$A^1B^1 \times A^2B^2$	$A^1B^1 \times A^1B^2$
$A^1B^2 \times A^2B^1$	$A^1B^1 \times A^2B^1$
	$A^1B^2 \times A^2B^2$
	$A^2B^1 \times A^2B^2$

Thus if two isolates are identical at one of the two loci, then a compatible cross will not occur, and identity can be readily determined. Common A and Common B matings can be distinguished on agar plates by the behavior of the mycelium during growth.

Raper et al. (1958) obtained fruiting bodies of *S. commune* from throughout the world, isolated from each fruit body a pair of strains which were compatible (and hence contained between them all four alleles at A and B) and then performed matings between the 114 distinct strains in all combinations. Amongst the 114 homocaryotic strains, there were 96 distinct, compatible A factors. Of these, 79 distinct A factors were found only once, 16 were found twice, and one was found three times. The distribution of identical A factors was quite random, as found statistically and as shown in the following list:

Same A factor found 3 times in:
    Massachusetts—Massachusetts—Gold Coast (Ghana)
Same A factor found 2 times in:
    Wisconsin—Massachusetts
    Massachusetts—Germany
    New Guinea—Czechoslovakia
    Massachusetts—Pennsylvania
    Massachusetts—Pennsylvania
    Massachusetts—England
    Massachusetts—Brazil
    Australia—Mozambique
    Wisconsin—Mozambique
    Massachusetts—North Carolina
    Brazil—Brazil
    Brazil—North Carolina
    Brazil—North Borneo
    Philippines—Czechoslovakia
    Costa Rica—Australia

For the B factor there were 56 distinct isolates among the 114 strains, and of these one occurred six times, one five times, 6 four times, 9 three times, 13 twice, and 26 once. Statistical tests showed that for both A and B factors, there was no more replication in a local area than world wide, and in fact the same frequency of replication was found in a 75-acre tract of forest at Lake Geneva, Wisconsin, as throughout the world.

They conclude: "The value of the multiple-factor incompatibility mechanism in promoting outbreeding in . . . the higher fungi . . . has been recognized [by others]. . . . In a tetrapolar form such as Schizophyllum, inbreeding is possible at a level of 25 per cent, but spore dispersal by wind is remarkably efficient, and the upper limit of inbreeding is probably seldom if ever approached. On the other hand, the limits of outbreeding effectiveness can be quite accurately stated. On the twin assumptions of random distribution and equal frequencies of the factors of the A and of the B series, both of which assumptions are consistent with the data given above, the number of distinct mating types is given by the product of the specific A and B factors in the population. The estimates of 339 A factors and 64 B factors [obtained by extrapolating from the data given above] would thus provide 21,696 specific mating types, between which pairing can occur in 235,697,360 different combinations. Of these possible combinations, the fraction that will oppose different A and different B factors, that is, will be sexually compatible, is . . . 0.9815. . . . [Thus] the outcrossing efficiency in the natural population is 98.15%." In other words, inbreeding would rarely occur.

The genetic aspects of this kind of incompatibility mechanism, as well as some biochemical speculations on how it might operate at the cellular level, are discussed by Fincham and Day (1963).

POPULATION GENETICS

The chemostat is a very useful device for studying population genetics in haploid unicellular organisms, since it maintains homogeneous growing populations for long periods of time, and factors affecting mutation rate can be readily determined. Novick and Szilard (1951) have used the chemostat to study mutation to phage T5 resistance in *E. coli* (presumably a nonselective mutation in the absence of T5 in the environment) and have found that the mutation rate was the same whether the growth was limited by nitrogen, by energy, or by phosphorus source, and that the mutation rate was independent of the growth rate for generation times from 2 to 12 hours. This result was somewhat unexpected, since it had been assumed that spontaneous mutation was due to an error in copying of the genome, and that at slower growth rates DNA replication should proceed more slowly and hence mutation should occur less often in a given length of time. This point has never been adequately cleared up in terms of modern genetic theory, but from an ecological point of view, its significance is that mutations can occur when the organism is growing very slowly or possibly even in the complete absence of growth. Thus mutants could accumulate in a population even under unfavorable conditions, and perhaps one or several of these mutants might be able to cope better with these unfavorable conditions and replace the parent.

Should a mutant grow in the chemostat more slowly than the parent (that is, be selected against), the percentage of mutant cells washed out will be greater than the percentage of parent cells, and at equilibrium a fixed proportion of mutants will eventually be achieved which will be a function of the mutation rate and of the flow rate. Alternatively, if the mutant is able to grow faster than the parent, it will eventually replace it.

A simple calculation will show how important mutation and selection are in microbial populations. Pardee (1962) has calculated that ". . . a mutant with a growth rate of 60 minutes, appearing with a frequency of 10^{-8}, would in theory overtake its parent strain with growth rate of 60.5 minutes in about 3 months."

As Novick (1955) has said: ". . . a culture growing in a continuous system is [not] ageless. As time passes, mutations will occur. . . . a population inhabiting the growth tube cannot continue to live there indefinitely. As evolution in the form of mutation and selection is a necessary consequence of growth, CONTINUED GROWTH OF A POPULATION MUST EVENTUALLY BRING ABOUT ITS OWN DESTRUCTION." (Emphasis mine.)

In the above discussion we have been considering a single mutant type. But in any large population there will be numerous types of mutants, any one of which will be rare, but which taken together will encompass a wide range of genetic types. Atwood et al. (1951) have calculated that if only twenty mutant types are considered, and if the forward mutation rate is 10 times the back mutation rate, at equilibrium the MOST FREQUENT genotype would have a frequency of 0.9^{20} or about 10%. Thus even in the absence of selection any population will become extremely heterogeneous.

However, it is common laboratory knowledge that populations are not this heterogeneous. A wide variety of strains can be kept for long periods of time on the same nutrient medium and remain true to type. Atwood et al.(1951) have shown that this is due to a phenomenon which they call periodic selection; it results from the fact that mutants arise which grow slightly faster than the parent. If these better adapted or more rapidly growing mutants arise randomly in the population, they will more likely come from the original parent type than from some other mutant types, because the parent type is present in larger numbers. Thus the genotype of the original strain will be propagated in the new faster growing type, and the other mutant types will be selected against and will eventually be lost. During periodic selection there is a progressive remodeling of the genotype. "This environmentally determined progression suppresses, but does not of course completely eliminate mutants which are not directly concerned with increase in adaptive value. Since the accumulation of mutations leading to superior performance in one environment occurs at the cost of inefficiency in others, strains invading new environments would rapidly diverge and soon reach a point where they could no longer coexist if returned to a common ecological situation. This would lead to profound strain differences which could not necessarily be detected by the usual criteria of bacterial taxonomy" (Atwood et al., 1951).

These facts show clearly the reason why organisms even of the same species when isolated from different but quite similar environments are always different, if they are studied closely enough. For instance, every animal species and every individual within a species probably harbors its own strain of E. coli, differing in small or large ways from all other strains.

So far, we have been considering situations where selection pressure is very weak, resulting in subtle population changes visible only after long periods of observation. Under strongly selective conditions the situation is much simpler. Thus, the addition of an antibiotic to a growing culture of a susceptible organism provides a violent challenge, and the outcome of this challenge is usually clear: an antibiotic-resistant population replaces the sensitive population. A point often overlooked in such a situation is that the antibiotic-resistant cells may not be able to grow as rapidly as the parent cells, and if reversions occur, the antibiotic-resistant organisms may soon be lost in the absence of the antibiotic from the environment. But both reverting and nonreverting mutants may arise, and in the latter case the mutant will remain stable indefinitely in the absence of antibiotics. In recent years we have witnessed an experiment in nature on the importance of mutation in population changes in microorganisms. Twenty years ago all strains of pathogenic bacteria isolated from nature were antibiotic-sensitive, whereas today many are antibiotic-resistant, and the appearance of resistant strains correlates closely with the use of antibiotics in medicine (Bloch, 1964). Sensitive strains can develop resistance in the test tube and in the experimental animal, and resistance has been observed to develop also in the patient (Finland et al., 1946) (Figure 5-5). The genetic nature of antibiotic resistance is well established as is the origin of resistance through mutation and selection. The conclusion thus seems inescapable that the types of genetic changes observed in the laboratory do occur in nature and that the genetics of populations is an important area of ecological research. Unfortunately, until now population genetics has been studied mainly to investigate the mechanisms of mutation. Braun (1953) has considered bacterial population genetics in some detail, and readers are referred to his book for further discussion. The

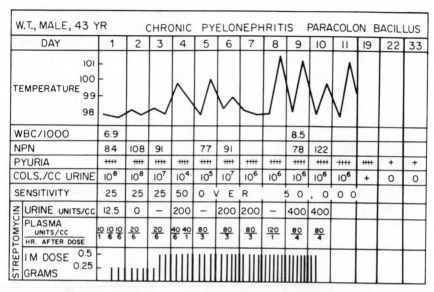

Fig. 5-5. Evolution of an antibiotic-resistant mutant in nature (after Finland et al., 1946). Clinical case of a urinary tract infection with a paracolon bacillus. Initial isolate was streptomycin sensitive, but after 4 days treatment the isolate was highly resistant. Note that the antibiotic concentration in both plasma and urine rarely reached an inhibitory dose. The urine later became sterile (on day 22) twelve days after antibiotic therapy had been stopped. Antibiotic sensitivity of the pathogen is expressed as the minimum inhibitory concentration of antibiotic in $\mu g/ml$.

principles he presents will probably hold also for other haploid organisms such as many fungi and algae.

Holzman (1959) has presented preliminary evidence on the fate of a genetically marked strain of *Paramecium aurelia* when added to a pond containing other strains of *Paramecium*. The introduced strain was able to maintain itself for several months but even in this time (short relative to the generation time of *Paramecium*) some segregation of the original heterozygote had occurred.

HETEROCARYONS AND HETEROZYGOTES

Many fungi are heterocaryotic, possessing several kinds of genetically distinct haploid nuclei in a common cytoplasm (Parmeter et al., 1963). The principles of population genetics may be applied here at the nuclear level, and we can talk about the selection of better adapted nuclei (Stanier, 1953). There is good evidence from the production of artificial heterocaryons in the laboratory that a heterocaryon may have survival value over a homocaryon. Since many fungi produce multinucleate spores and most fungi isolated from nature are heterocaryotic, it is likely that heterocaryosis is important ecologically. Saltation is an old term in mycology for the segregation under laboratory conditions of two or more distinct types from an original natural isolate, usually occurring because occasional hyphal tips arise with only one kind of nucleus. Nelson et al. (1955) have shown that heterocaryosis was responsible for the creation of a new race of the wheat rust fungus *Puccinia graminis* var. *tritici* which could infect a variety of wheat (Khapli) which neither of the homocaryons could infect.

Most diploid organisms in nature are heterozygous, and thus most natural populations are composed of genetically diverse members. If a clone is established in the laboratory from one unit, the properties of this clone may not necessarily represent the average properties of the natural population.

POPULATION DENSITY AND NATURAL SELECTION

Because of the rarity of mutations, the population density which an organism attains plays a great role in its ability to survive in selective environments. To a first approximation a given amount of nutrient will support the development of 10^9 small bacteria, 10^8 large bacteria, 10^7 yeast cells, 10^5 amoebae, and only 10^3 paramecia (*see* Table 7-2), and population densities in nature for different microorganisms generally vary in much the same way. Since the mutation rate is roughly constant throughout the microbial world, then in a given environment a requisite mutant will more likely occur among bacteria than among other microorganisms. For this reason, bacteria are much more adaptable to changing environments than are higher microorganisms and are able to evolve more rapidly.

If we were interested in isolating from a natural environment an organism which might perform a particular function, it might be wise to cultivate the natural population initially on a nonselective medium so that the population density could be greatly increased, thus magnifying our chances of finding a mutant which might possess the desired properties.

The Role of the Environment
in Molding Living Organisms

From the above brief discussion, it is clear that microbes are exceedingly adaptable and are indeed highly successful in the colonization of new environments. It is perhaps for this reason more than any other that microbes are the first to arrive at and the last to leave extreme environments and why microbiologists have faith that if a biochemical function can't be performed by a microbe, it can't be done at all (*see* page 77). Because of rapid and efficient dispersal, short generation time, high population density, and the severity of competition (to be discussed in Chapter 6), the organisms found in a given environment can usually be assumed to be the ones best adapted to that environment.

In one sense we can go even further and say that the environment "creates" the organism, since the environment provides the conditions for the selection and adaptation of the organism. Although this is most evident in extreme environments such as hot springs or acid mine waters, it undoubtedly occurs in all environments, although often only on a micro scale. It is for this reason that a microbial ecologist, if asked to provide a given kind of organism, can go at any time to the appropriate environment and be reasonably certain that the organism sought will be there.

However, as Stanier (1953) has pointed out, many microbial environments (e.g., soil) are discontinuous in time. The environment is constantly changing, both from external influences and from the actions of the organisms themselves. In such changing environments, one would expect evolution to be constantly occurring, the new replacing the old, and microbes in such environments must thus be adaptable. In an environment such as a sulfur spring, however, constancy is the rule, and one would expect a change of the sort described as periodic selection, but one would not expect radical evolutionary changes.

From the above considerations we can also see that although populations are composed of individuals, in a certain sense a population can be considered to be an entity, since it acquires functions and abilities which the individuals may not possess. These new functions are called integrative properties, since they could not be predicted from a study of the individuals alone. However, a microbial population is more a collection of units than it is an entity, and to a great extent we can treat the behavior of the population as a reflection of the independent behavior of its individuals, whereas in a higher animal or plant, the cells interact strongly and continuously, so that the integrative properties are of much greater importance.

When the integrative properties of microbial populations are studied in precisely defined laboratory situations, completely unrelated to any significance of the observation in nature, population ecology becomes more closely related to developmental biology than to traditional ecology. This, however, does not detract from its inherent interest.

CHAPTER 6

Interactions Between Microbial Populations

In thinking about the interactions between organisms it might be well to distinguish between two broad categories: (1) interactions between two microbial populations and (2) interactions between a microbial population and a macroorganism or macropopulation. This distinction is an important one and is essentially a matter of scale. Two cells which are of approximately equal size possess roughly equal numbers of molecules, their nutrient and space requirements are roughly equal, and if they come in contact, approximately equal proportions of the surface of each engage the other. Thus two bacteria are on the same scale, as are two protozoa, but a protozoon and a bacterium are on different scales.

This distinction is important experimentally as well as conceptually. With the magnifications used to study protozoa, bacteria vanish into the background and are frequently ignored. Alternatively, with the microscope used to study a bacterial population, protozoan populations cannot be easily studied, since one protozoon occupies the space of thousands of bacteria. Further, the techniques of isolating and handling the populations differ. If we now move up from protozoa to multicellular organisms, we find scale to be of even more significance. Thus a corn plant, a mouse, or even an insect is enormous in size when compared with a bacterium or even with a protozoon. This means that the protoplasmic mass of a microbial population is almost always vanishingly small when compared with the mass of a multicellular creature with which it may interact. Because of this, any perceivable effect of the microbe on a plant or animal is probably due to the production of specific highly active molecules by the microbe, whereas the effect of one microbe on another may involve less specific substances. In the present chapter we will discuss only the interactions between similarly scaled organisms and will reserve for a later chapter the interactions between organisms which are of different sizes.

The basic problem of population interaction can be expressed in the form $A \leftrightharpoons B$ where A is one population and B is the other. The arrows indicate the effect of A on B and the effect of B on A. Since for each arrow the effect can be either positive, negative, or zero, qualitatively nine different states are possible.

Relationships between organisms can be specific or nonspecific. As Dubos and Kessler (1963) have pointed out: ". . . specificity denotes the pattern of attributes of the two organisms constituting a symbiotic [or parasitic] association which allows them to interact with some degree of selectivity—the interaction taking the form of a relationship where each organism forms a more or less critical portion of the environment of its partner. In other words, specificity . . . is an expression of the complementariness of all their dynamically interacting attributes. The greater the number of factors which interact and the more selective any one of them becomes, the smaller is the probability of achieving the required combination for complementariness and hence the higher the degree of . . . specificity." The development of complementarity through genetic means is discussed in Chapter 8 (page 182), and the concepts developed there apply here with equal facility.

Intracellular associations provide the highest degree of specificity because the environments of the two organisms commingle, and because the actions of one organism so immediately and directly affect the environment of the other. In many cases these associations are obligatory, at least in nature. A less specific interaction occurs when one organism is an epiphyte on another and either remains completely outside or penetrates the host only with specialized growth processes (e.g., haustoria). In completely extracellular associations the organisms do not come in contact but influence each other only through their metabolic products, and consequently the association is generally less specific. Since intracellular interactions are not easily studied physiologically and biochemically, most of the following discussion is based on extracellular associations. Even with medically important intracellular parasites, only very little is known about the chemical basis of the association (Moulder, 1964).

There may be a tendency to view the interaction between two organisms (e.g., symbiosis, antagonism) as if it were the same under all conditions. However, it is clear (Dubos and Kessler, 1963) that relationships between organisms are not permanent and that environmental or other factors may convert a symbiotic relationship into an antagonistic one. Further, even under constant environmental conditions it is not always possible to classify a relationship distinctly as either beneficial or harmful, since even in symbiotic relationships there may be a struggle between the organisms. As Dubos and Kessler quote Caulery, in reference to lichens, "It is necessary to abandon the idea of a purely mutualistic association with equivalent reciprocal benefits. It is a conflict between alga and fungus" (*see* page 124).

Interactions between organisms have been categorized in a number of ways, and terminology is especially prolific and confusing (Odum, 1959). The terms chosen usually depend on whether a population is benefited, harmed, or not affected by an interaction, but often this decision is a matter of opinion or of the nature of the interest of the investigator. What we see and what the organism "sees" may be two different things. I do not believe that rigid criteria are useful or even possible; the important thing is to understand what is happening to the populations.

The classical work of Lotka and Pearl in the 1920's on the mathematics of population growth led to the elaboration of the equation for the logistics growth curve (Lotka, 1956) which was presented in Chapter 5 (page 94). This equation was then applied to interacting microbial populations by Gause (1934) in a work of far-reaching importance. Gause's work has greatly influenced animal ecologists (Slobodkin, 1962a; Bartlett, 1960) but surprisingly has been ignored by most microbiologists, even though the organisms Gause used for his experimental studies were yeast and paramecium. Gause modified the logistics growth equation by adding a term which expressed in density-dependent fashion the degree of influence of a second organism on the first one. Another equation was then derived for the growth of the second organism as modified by the first. Since the effect of one organism on another can be either positive, negative, or zero, it was possible to use the simultaneous differential equations obtained to express any type of relationship.

Gause then put his equations to experimental test by studying the interaction of two yeast cultures. Unfortunately, these experiments provided an unsatisfying exploration of the mathematical relationships, but this does not invalidate the equations themselves. Perhaps the most useful thing to be derived from the mathematical manipulations is that they reveal the complexity of the interaction between two populations during growth, and these complexities should be kept clearly in mind. Further, Gause's equations relate only to the effect of one organism on the maximum population size of the second organism. It is also possible that one organism will affect only the growth rate of the second organism without affecting its ultimate population size, or additionally, both the growth rate and the maximum population size may be affected. The mathematical relationships can become distressingly complex, and the investigator may be either driven away from the problem completely or may content himself with only an empirical approach to the problem. However, the empirical approach has provided many significant ideas, and the discussion which follows will be devoid of mathematical manipulation.

Neutralism

It is only rarely that two populations do not interact. Lack of interaction can be: (1) because the populations are too far apart, or (2) because the two populations are so different in environmental requirements that neither organism alters the qualities needed by the other. Since the absence of interaction has no drama or unusual interest, it has not been systematically studied, but it should be. It is perfectly valid to inquire as to what kinds of organisms can exist together and grow with undiminished vigor and reach population densities identical to those which they would reach when alone. It seems likely that neutralism would be exhibited more frequently by extremely diverse organisms than by closely related organisms, since two strains of a species would be so alike in nutritional and environmental requirements that they would compete for a common resource whereas diverse organisms might not compete.

Commensalism

In commensal relationships, one organism is benefited and the other is unaffected. For instance, one organism may alter the physical environment so that another can grow. Kadavy and Dack (1951) have shown that in bread which has a water content near the limit for growth of *Clostridium botulinum*, the growth of *Bacillus mesentericus* can raise the water content sufficiently so that the former organism can grow. In this case, the water content is raised because of the production of metabolic water by the bacillus. Osmophilic yeasts can grow in concentrated sugar solutions, and by fermenting or oxidizing the sugar they reduce the osmolarity sufficiently so that less osmotolerant organisms can grow (Mossel and Ingram, 1956). The cellular structure of a fruit often prevents the spread of yeasts, but this structure may be so altered by fruit-rotting fungi that the yeasts can now also grow. Similar phenomena may be involved in many other situations in which a primary pathogen paves the way for a secondary invader such as in the human respiratory tract, a plant leaf, or the trunk of a tree. The hyphae of the fungus *Rhizopus nigricans* grow rapidly across the surface of an agar plate and provide a transportation route along which motile bacilli are able to move, whereas on the agar away from the fungal hypha the bacilli are unable to swarm (Brock, unpublished observations). Neither organism affects the growth of the other. It is possible that filamentous fungi in the soil might perform a similar function for motile bacilli.

One organism may alter the physiological environment and make it suitable for the growth of a second organism. The fungus *Geotrichum candidum* consumes the lactic acid produced by *Streptococcus lactis;* the pH is thus kept high and the growth of *S. lactis* is not inhibited. On the other hand, the lactic acid bacteria may reduce the pH of a medium and thus make it favorable for the growth of yeasts (Elliker, 1949). The growth of aerobic organisms may lead to a reduction in the redox potential, permitting the growth of anaerobes (Mossel and Ingram, 1956). Alternatively, photosynthetic algae might produce oxygen and raise the redox potential so that sensitive aerobes could grow. It is frequently difficult to isolate obligate anaerobes in pure culture, although they can be carried indefinitely in mixed cultures with aerobes. This is probably because it is difficult to prevent traces of oxygen from getting into cultures, but these traces are rapidly consumed in the mixed cultures by the facultative contaminants. Such observations probably explain how it is possible for obligate anaerobes to persist and grow in apparently aerobic environments such as the soil; anaerobiosis is created in the microhabitat by associated organisms. A similar mechanism may be involved in the establishment of gas gangrene infections in man; the redox potential may be lowered sufficiently by contaminating bacteria that the clostridial spores can germinate and initiate infection (Wilson and Miles, 1957). Similarly, an anaerobic streptococcus could be induced to initiate an infection when inoculated together with an aerobic staphylococcus (Mergenhagen et al., 1958).

One organism may produce a nutrient essential for another. *Mucor rouxianus* when growing on potato hydrolyzes the starch to maltose by means of an extracellular amylase, and a micrococcus which itself is unable to digest starch can now grow (Buchanan and Fulmer, 1930). Interestingly, in this case the fungus becomes deeply pigmented only when grown with the micrococcus. On casein, *Pseudomonas fluorescens* is able to grow when *Bacillus cereus* is present to digest the casein (Buchanan and Fulmer, 1930). When fruit juices are fermented by yeast, ethyl alcohol accumulates, and this alcohol can now serve as a major nutrient for the growth of *Acetobacter*. This is, of course, a crucial step in the production of vinegar. Many algae excrete polysaccharides (Lewin, 1956), organic acids (Allen, 1956), and polypeptides (Fogg and Westlake, 1955; Fogg and Nalewajko, 1961; Fogg, 1962), and such materials undoubtedly are nutrients for the growth of bacteria. In several surveys of marine and freshwater algae, I have found that many forms which appear quite healthy are extensively colonized by epiphytic heterotrophic bacteria, and it seems likely that they are subsisting on products excreted by the algae. I have been able to grow *Leucothrix mucor* as an epiphyte on red and brown algae in pure culture for many months with no apparent effect on the algae, and indeed, the biomass of the bacterium is always less than 10% that of the alga.

Most of the transformations of sulfur, carbon, and nitrogen involve the production by certain organisms of nutrients which are used by others. Thus *Desulfovibrio* produces H_2S anaerobically, and this H_2S can move to aerobic environments and be oxidized by colorless sulfur bacteria or to photic environments and serve as an electron donor for purple and green photosynthetic sulfur bacteria (*see* Chapter 3). The ammonia released from amino acids by bacterial deamination can be oxidized by nitrifying bacteria. The methane produced anaerobically by methane bacteria can be oxidized aerobically by methane-oxidizing bacteria (Dr. J. Overbeck, Plön, Germany, personal communication). In all of these cases the relationship between the producer and consumer is a distant one, since they usually live under quite different environmental conditions; although such relationships are rarely viewed as examples of commensalism, they could be so considered.

We tend to think of cells as tight little compartments with strong barriers to the loss of soluble materials, but from sensitive permeability studies with radioactive materials it is known that materials do leak out of cells both actively and passively (Brock and Moo-Penn, 1962). Since the environment outside a cell contains substances like vitamins in only vanishingly low amounts, there is a tremendous concentration gradient for such substances from inside to outside the cell. Thus the leakage of such materials is reasonable, and no postulation of an active excretion mechanism is necessary. Because vitamins are active in promoting growth in very small amounts, it is clear that these products might play important roles in microbial associations; examples of this have been provided by Purko et al. (1951) and Challinor and Rose (1954).

One organism may destroy or neutralize an antimicrobial factor so that a second organism can grow. This process may be of considerable importance but has been little studied. The oxidation of lactic acid by the yeast *Geotrichum candidum* permits *S. lactis* to continue growth in milk, since without the yeast the bacterium is self-inhibited when the lactic acid concentration reaches about 1% (Elliker, 1949). Some bacteria and molds can oxidize phenols and benzoic acid, and certain yeasts can destroy SO_2, thereby enabling other organisms which are inhibited by these products to grow (Mossel and Ingram, 1956). Most of the classical antibiotics can be decomposed by bacteria or fungi, either by the production of extracellular enzymes (e.g., penicillinase) or by metabolism within the cell. In the case of the antibiotic nisin, the situation is even more complicated. This antibiotic is produced by certain dairy organisms, is active against other organisms, and is inactivated by a third organism, a *Lactobacillus* sp. (Mossel and Ingram, 1956). Certain pseudomonads produce a substance (N-heptyl-4-hydroxyquinoline-N-oxide) which does not inactivate streptomycin but which prevents this antibiotic from being active against other bacteria (Cornforth and James, 1956; Lightbown and Jackson, 1956). Antagonism occurs because streptomycin is much more active against aerobically than anaerobically growing cells, and the antagonist is an inhibitor of oxidative but not of fermentative metabolism. The antagonist essentially converts a sensitive aerobe into an insensitive anaerobe even in the presence of air. In addition to its inherent interest this discovery shows how an ecological observation can be of wider interest, since the antagonist is now available commercially for use as an inhibitor of cytochrome-mediated electron transport.

An interesting example of a commensal relationship almost at the macromolecular level involves a so-called plant satellite virus which is able to replicate in the host only when tobacco necrosis virus is also replicating (Bawden, 1964). Presumably the satellite virus lacks the information necessary to code for the production of a protein essential for its replication, and this information is supplied by the other virus.

Mutualism

Mutual interaction may lead to the production of a new metabolic product. During the 1920's there was a flurry of interest, mainly among sanitary bacteriologists, in the production of gas in fermentation tubes by two types of bacteria growing together, whereas neither could produce gas alone (reviewed by Buchanan and Fulmer, 1930). This phenomenon had practical considerations, since it led to false positives in water analyses. A detailed analysis of one case of this phenomenon was carried out by Holman and Meekison (1926) who termed it "bacterial synergism." To these workers, synergism was of great ecological importance, and they pointed out the analogy between the use of the word synergism in ecology and its use in theology: in theology synergism ". . . indicates 'the combined efforts of the human being and the divine grace in the salvation of the soul.' It is of interest to note that this culmination cannot be reached by the single effort of either factor." An example of such an interaction was shown by Gale (1940) between *E. coli* and *S. faecalis*. Putrescine could be produced from arginine when the two organisms grew together but not by either organism alone. This was explained by the following reactions:

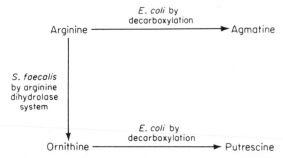

Since putrescine is a growth factor for certain strains of *Hemophilus* (Tabor et al., 1961), a possibility exists for a three-way mutualistic relationship. Interactions between *E. coli* and *S. faecalis* are of considerable practical as well as theoretical importance, because these two organisms are found together in the intestinal tracts of most warm-blooded animals. For instance, putrescine is produced in the intestinal tract of most animals and enters the blood stream. Since putrescine has a variety of pharmacological effects (Tabor et al., 1961), it is conceivable that the interactions between *E. coli* and *S. faecalis* described above play an important role in the life of the animal. Some other examples of mutualistic relationships of the above kind have been discussed by Buchanan and Fulmer (1930).

Bates and Liu (1963) have shown that two strains of *Pseudomonas* are able to produce a lecithinase when they are grown together, whereas neither strain can produce the activity alone. If each strain is grown separately and the culture supernatants are mixed, the enzymatic activity is obtained, suggesting that each strain produces one portion of the active enzyme, and that the separate portions combined in vitro.

In some mutualistic relationships, both organisms are benefited: ". . . all heterotrophs are genically insufficient, and depend for their subsistence on the biosynthetically expressed genic functions of other organisms. Thus it is possible to formulate a graded series of symbioses as genic interactions, from the co-habitants of a single chromosome, through heterokaryons and plasmids, to extracellular ecological associations of variable stability and specificity" (Lederberg, 1952).

Mutual interaction may exist in which the two organisms can grow, whereas each alone could not grow. Nurmikko (1956) showed that growth of *Lactobacillus arabinosus* 17-5 and *Streptococcus faecalis* could occur in a medium lacking phenylalanine (which the former requires) and folic acid (which the latter requires), each organism producing and excreting sufficient amounts of the factor required by the other so that both could grow (Figure 6-1). By using dialysis cells, Nurmikko showed that the organisms did not have to grow in intimate contact, but that the relevant factors could diffuse across the dialyzing membrane. An interaction of this type is frequently termed "syntrophism." A wide variety of syntrophic interactions have been shown to exist between mutants of a single organism which are blocked in the biosynthesis of an amino acid or other growth factor (Braun, 1953). One organism excretes a precursor of the requisite substance which the other is then able to convert into the final product.

Mutualistic relationships in the decomposition of cellulose have been frequently cited. Mutualism is usually suggested when a mixed culture is obtained which actively decomposes cellulose but the individual pure cultures will not perform the same task (Siu, 1951). Siu states: "As has been pointed out by Stanier, however, the so-called 'symbiotic effect' is merely an adjustment of the physical and chemical environment to a favorable level. With sufficient persistence and ingenuity a combination of factors can be obtained in the laboratory so that the mixtures of organisms can be separated into individual species." A pure culture is essential if one wishes to show that a specific organism is able to digest cellulose, but mixed cultures frequently digest cellulose more effectively than pure cultures, espe-

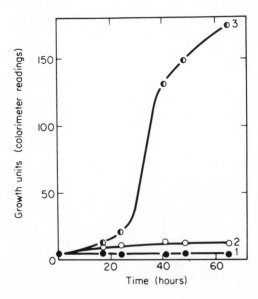

Fig. 6-1. Growth of *Lactobacillus arabinosus 17-5* and *Streptococcus faecalis R* in symbiosis (Nurmikko, 1956). Synthetic medium lacking phenylalanine and folic acid. CURVE 1: *S. faecalis* (folic acid-requiring strain); CURVE 2: *L. arabinosus* (phenylalanine-requiring strain); CURVE 3: both strains together.

cially under anaerobic conditions. Enebo (1949) isolated three organisms from an anaerobic thermophilic cellulose fermentation and then studied the process of cellulose decomposition in pure and mixed culture. Only one of the three organisms could digest cellulose, but the other two markedly altered the rate of this process, in addition to affecting the proportions of the various end products. Since all three organisms were anaerobes, it is probable that the organisms which could not digest cellulose altered the physicochemical environment in some way so that the cellulose-digesting organism could grow, probably by metabolizing a toxic product (e.g., lactic acid or ethanol) which accumulated as a result of the fermentation. The isolation of pure cultures of rumen bacteria which could digest cellulose presented many difficulties until it was found that many of them required growth factors present in rumen fluid, as well as a strict anaerobic environment, but now many pure cultures which digest cellulose are available (see Chapter 8, page 200). Since more organic matter is present in the world as cellulose than as any other product (Reese, 1963), and the decomposition of cellulose plays a crucial role in the nutritional economy of all ruminants and in soil fertility (Russell and Russell, 1950), the ecology of the mutualistic digestion of cellulose is of great interest.

Mutualistic interactions between algae and bacteria probably occur frequently in nature but have been little studied. In the marine environment many bacteria epiphytic on algae produce vitamin B_{12} (Ericson and Lewis, 1954) and since many algae require B_{12} (Provasoli, 1958a, 1963) the relationship between the organisms is probably a symbiotic one. A less specific type of relationship was described by Golueke and Oswald (1964). In sewage oxidation lagoons and in experimental biological gas exchangers for space vehicles, algae and bacteria living together form a mutualistic system. The bacteria oxidize complex organic materials to CO_2, and this gas is assimilated phototrophically by the algae with the production of O_2 which is then used by the bacteria in their oxidation processes. In such systems the bacteria rarely exceed 1-5% of the total biomass, but because of the intimate association of algae and bacteria, oxygen transfer from the former to the latter is very efficient.

GENETIC INTERACTIONS

In a certain sense, hybridization, heterocaryosis, and genetic complementation can be viewed as mutualistic interactions, since the offspring may acquire new properties lacking in both parents. An interesting case which demonstrates elements of both physiologic and genetic interaction was studied by Rowell and DeVay (1954). The corn smut fungus, *Ustilago zeae,* is obligately saprophytic as a haploid and obligately parasitic as a dicaryon. Thus the dicaryon acquires a new property not possessed by either haploid mating type (pathogenicity) but loses another property which the haploids possess (saprophyticity). This relationship has some elements of the fungal-algal association of lichens, discussed below. In addition, these workers showed that the nonpathogenic haploid lines could initiate infection on corn when paired with another fungus, *Sphacelotheca reiliana,* but in this case no hybridization occurred, and the two fungi could be reisolated later as unchanged haploids, thus showing that this second interaction was probably at the physiologic level.

Lichens

The following discussion is based on the recent reviews by Quispel (1959), Ahmadjian (1962, 1965), Hale (1961), Smith (1963), and Des Abbayes (1951).

The word lichen refers to any regular association between an alga and a fungus in which a functional relationship between the two partners seems to exist, independent of the morphological development of this association, and consequently refers to ". . . a rather heterogeneous group of associations in different degrees of development. This even is the case if we use the term . . . in its morphological and taxonomic sense. Therefore it has to be stressed from the beginning that generalizations are very dangerous" (Quispel, 1959).

The algae found in lichens are able to live separately also, and they belong to various genera of the green and blue-green algae. The fungi are mainly ascomycetes, some of which have also been related to free-living forms, but others of which, so far as is known, occur only in the lichen association. In many ways, it is preferable to look upon the fungus as parasitizing the alga. Des Abbayes (1951) states that fungi exist in all degrees of relationships to algae: (1) obligate lichen associates, which are never found free-living and which seem to undergo morphogenetic changes upon association with algae, (2) facultatively symbiotic fungi, which may grow either with or without the alga and do not exhibit any morphogenetic alterations, (3) fungi which are occasionally parasitic on algae, and (4) obligately saprophytic fungi. The parasitism by the fungus is most clearly seen in those cases where the fungus forms haustoria which penetrate into the algal cells; even if haustoria are not formed, it is thought that the intimate contact between fungus hypha and algal cell leads to nutrient exchange across the cell walls.

Environmental factors greatly modify the association between alga and fungus. In most cases, if the lichen is removed from nature and placed under favorable laboratory conditions (e.g., with organic substrates or high humidity), the fungus may proliferate and destroy the alga completely, or the alga may overgrow the fungus. Even if the relative growth rates are unaltered, the cellular contact between the alga and the fungus may become broken. It is just as difficult to grow a lichen thallus in the laboratory as it is to achieve a resynthesis of a thallus from the isolated components. The pure cultivation of either the lichen fungus or alga presents no special problems, and although their growth is usually slower than that of algae and fungi which do not form lichens, the nutritional and environmental requirements of the isolated components are not unique. Experimental resynthesis of the lichen thallus from the isolated components is difficult but has been performed unequivocally several times (Ahmadjian, 1962). Resynthesis never occurs in a medium in which the isolated components are able to grow: "Initial stages of lichen synthesis were achieved under laboratory conditions only on a completely inorganic agar medium, in which the fungal component was forced, as it were, by starvation into physiological union with its phycobiont" (Ahmadjian, 1962).

Only meagre data on the physiology of the lichen thallus are available. In nature the growth rate is exceedingly slow, the measured value of the radial growth increment varying from 0.33–4.0 mm per year (Hale, 1961) (see Figure 5-1). Indeed, lichens grow so slowly that they have been used by geologists to estimate the age of moraines near glaciers. Lichens are extremely sensitive to air pollutants and quickly disappear from urbanized areas; in Europe it has been possible to demonstrate a regular decrease in the extent of development of the lichen flora from the country through the suburbs to the inner city. It is felt that this great sensitivity is due to the fact that lichens absorb and concentrate elements from rain water and possess no means of excreting them, so that lethal concentrations of toxic air pollutants may be readily reached.

Many lichens produce characteristic pigments of unique chemical structure which are often used for taxonomic purposes. For a long time it was felt that the production of these products was a unique expression of the lichen symbiosis, but recently (Quispel, 1959), it has been shown that certain of these products may also be formed by the isolated fungus in culture. Interestingly, many of these pigments have antibacterial properties and conceivably function in nature as a defense against bacterial attack.

Lichens are remarkably resistant to desiccation, heat, and cold, and most lichens live in habitats exposed to direct sunlight where they are subjected to intense variations in these environmental conditions. A crucial consideration in characterizing a possible symbiotic relationship is whether or not the lichen is living autotrophically; that is, is there a net photosynthetic assimilation which exceeds respiratory losses? Since rain and rock do contain organic matter, and since lichens grow very slowly, it is conceivable that photosynthesis supplies only part of the organic carbon. Photosynthetic assimilation has been measured in the laboratory, and attempts have been made, from studying the effect of temperature, light, and moisture on photosynthesis, to estimate whether under the rather unfavorable natural conditions net assimilation could occur. The conclusion seems to be that in many species a net gain probably occurs (Quispel, 1959), but this rather unsatisfactory conclusion can be bolstered only by much more work. It has been clearly shown that lichens which contain blue-green algal associates fix gaseous nitrogen, whereas fixation does not occur when the associate is a green alga.

Is the lichen association a symbiosis? Clearly neither the alga nor the fungus NEED exist with the other under all conditions, since both partners are readily culturable. Also, it is clear that neither the fungus nor the alga acquires any new physiological properties upon association with the other, except possibly certain morphogenetic changes. However, the fact remains that IN NATURE, neither the fungus nor the alga is found growing in a free-living state in environments where the lichen grows. The two organisms ARE doing something together which they could not do separately, namely living and growing in excruciatingly severe environmental conditions. Thus, although a lichen may not be a symbiont physiologically, it is a symbiont ecologically.

Unfortunately the slowness of lichen functions does not encourage, in this fast-moving world, a concerted effort to study this problem. Perhaps the reputed existence of lichens on Mars will encourage a space-minded scientist to do such a study!

Competition

Organisms adapt not only to their environments but also to the presence and competitive influence of other organisms. Perhaps nowhere in the living world is competition more fierce than amongst the microorganisms. Population densities are high and generation times are short. This is why we can confidently postulate that the organism which we find in a given environment is probably at that time the best adapted to that environment.

Strict competition means that both organisms are after some common resource which is present in limited amounts. Although one organism may ultimately be less successful than another, neither attacks the other directly or indirectly. Since strict competition exists between cells of a single clone (see Chapter 5), the two competing organisms behave as if they were two parts of a single population; strict competition occurs most frequently between closely related organisms with similar environmental requirements. The outcome will depend on the relative growth rates; the organism which grows the faster will eventually replace the other, if a sufficient number of generations is available. Note that the environmental requirements for both organisms may be identical, but the growth rates may still differ, because growth rates are influenced by various intrinsic factors of the cell (see page 95). In microbiology strict competition is frequently seen on agar plates, where colonies which are close together are small, and well-isolated colonies are large. Talling (1957) found that in the mixed culture of two diatoms *Asterionella* and *Fragilaria,* both organisms grew at rates identical to their growth in pure culture, but the maximum population density of each was reduced by the presence of the other, presumably because the organisms competed for a common limiting nutrient.

Antagonism

It is perhaps human nature that we find great fascination in the antagonistic relationships between microbes so that we know quite a bit about such matters, at least in the laboratory. The alteration of the redox potential by one organism may inhibit the growth of another. Obligate aerobes may be inhibited by the growth of facultative organisms which consume all of the oxygen. This is an important phenomenon in population changes occurring in streams subject to sewage outfalls. Likewise, production of oxygen by photosynthetic organisms may hinder the action of anaerobes; Jannasch (1960) has shown that denitrification by *Pseudomonas stutzeri* (an anaerobic process) is inhibited when the organism is cultured with Chlorella (which produces oxygen).

Because changes of the above sort have a low specificity, they are rarely studied, yet such changes may be of great importance in natural environments, especially where population densities are high.

ANTIBIOTICS

Antibiotics are chemical substances which are produced by living organisms and which are able to kill or inhibit the growth of other living organisms. It is a common experience that antagonistic organisms occur very frequently in natural habitats. Antagonism has been found between pairs of the following organisms in all possible combinations with each other and with themselves: bacteria, fungi, algae, and protozoa (Waksman, 1945). In one survey of the occurrence of antibiotic producers in forest soils (Wallhäusser, 1951), 16 fungi and 123 bacteria were isolated and tested for antagonism in all combinations, with the following results:

Opponents	Number of tests	Number positive
Bacteria vs. bacteria	529	164 (31%)
Fungi vs. fungi	256	93 (36%)
Fungi vs. bacteria	368	161 (44%)

The proof that a given antagonism is due to the production of an antibiotic can be obtained only if the antibiotic is isolated and purified and the purified material shown to have the same kind of activity against the test organism as did the original antagonist. This criterion has now been met numerous times with relation to medically useful antibiotics, and there can no longer be any question that one of the most important factors in antagonistic relationships in laboratory tests is the production and action of antibiotics. Whether or not an antibiotic will be detected under a given situation depends on the intrinsic activity of the antibiotic against the test organism in the medium used for the test and on the amount of antibiotic made by the antibiotic producer; these two factors are sometimes confused. The antibiotic azaserine, for instance, is highly active against *E. coli,* yet it was missed for years in screening programs because the medium used for the test contained aromatic amino acids which reversed the antibiotic activity (Brock and Brock, 1961). Many antibiotics are irreversibly bound to soil, clay minerals, and other particulates (Brian, 1957) and are thus effectively inactivated.

Antibiotic activity is usually expressed quantitatively as the minimum amount of material which will bring about a given response with the test organism. On crude extracts and broth filtrates in which no knowledge of weight of material is available, the highest dilution of extract which produces a given response is used. A highly active preparation may contain large amounts of a weakly active antibiotic or small amounts of a highly active antibiotic. Conversely, a weakly active preparation may not result from a weakly active antibiotic, since the antibiotic may be very active but present in tiny amounts. Only after the antibiotic has been purified completely can its intrinsic activity against a given test organism in a given medium be determined.

If the antibiotic test is performed by allowing the antibiotic to diffuse in agar and measuring the size of the inhibition zone, an additional complication arises. The zone size, as well as being influenced by the intrinsic activity of the antibiotic and by the amount of it present, is also affected by the ability of the antibiotic to diffuse in agar. Diffusion rate varies with molecular size but is even more strongly affected by the binding of the antibiotic to the agar. This is especially a problem with antibiotics which are cationic in nature, such as streptomycin and neomycin. The diffusion rates of such antibiotics are strongly increased if the ionic strength of the medium is raised (Brock, 1956).

Many organisms produce more than one antibiotic and sometimes as many as five or six. The number of antibiotics and the amount of each is often influenced by the culture medium and by other environmental conditions. All of the antibiotics may be active against a single test organism, or different organisms may be sensitive to different antibiotics in the mixture. If the former is true, then it is obvious that the inhibition observed in an unfractionated preparation is due to the concerted action of the several antibiotics; this presents many complications. If the antibiotics can be separated, as for instance by paper chromatography, then it may be possible to assay for one in the presence of another. If the antibiotics cannot be separated, then the existence of multiple antibiotics may not even be suspected.

From the massive accumulation of data on the structure of antibiotics it is clear that widely diverse chemical substances may have antibiotic activity; the most recent compendium of such information is the book by Miller (1961).

A BACTERIOCINE differs from any other antibiotic only by the breadth of its spectrum of activity; a bacteriocine by definition acts on strains closely related to the producing organism. Although almost all groups of bacteria are now known to produce bacteriocines (Ivànovics, 1962; Hamon and Peron, 1963), the specificity of bacteriocines varies from strain to strain and species to species. Hamon and Péron (1963) considered briefly the function of bacteriocines and concluded that they probably serve as fertility factors, but although it is true that cell-to-cell contact is mediated in some enteric bacteria by bacteriocines, there is no prior reason why this should be so in all kinds of bacteria. Another role for bacteriocines may be in competition between closely related organisms. Hamon and Peron (1963) rejected this idea, but Pohunek (1961) postulated that streptococci which produced bacteriocines attacking vaginal lactobacilli may be able, because of this property, to invade the vagina and replace the resident bacteria. Since closely related bacteria are likely to have similar nutritional and environmental requirements, it is reasonable that they would often be competing for a common resource. Bacteriocines may thus be substances which aid in this competition. Macroecologists speak of competitive exclusion, which prevents two closely related organisms from occupying the same niche. Bacteriocine production may be a mechanism by which competitive exclusion exists in bacteria. The following quotation may be relevant to this point: "As the species of the same genus usually have . . . much similarity in habits and constitution, and always in structure, the struggle will generally be more severe between them, if they come into competition with each other, than between the species of distinct genera. . . . We can dimly see why the competition should be most severe between allied forms, which fill nearly the same place in the economy of nature; but probably in no one case could we precisely say why one species has been victorious over another in the great battle of life" (Darwin, 1859).

Substances analogous to bacteriocines are produced by many *Paramecium* strains, the so-called killer substances (Sonneborn, 1959). As shown by Mueller and Sonneborn (1959), killer paramecia, except in rare instances, have no effect on algae or protozoa other than paramecia. So far as I know, similar substances have not been demonstrated in algae and fungi, although the barrage phenomenon in incompatible matings in Basidiomycetes might be due to analogous materials. At least one intracellular particle in *Paramecium,* lambda, is not only involved in the production of a killer substance, but also is responsible for the synthesis of the folic acid growth factor required by the paramecium, so that the lambda particle carries out at least two mutualistic functions (Soldo, 1963).

THE ROLE OF ANTIBIOTICS IN NATURE

An interesting antibiotic relationship in a simple natural habitat has been reported by Smith and Marples (1964). The New Zealand hedgehog is frequently afflicted with a skin infection from which can be isolated two organisms, a penicillin-resistant *Staphylococcus* and a fungus, *Trichophyton mentagrophytes.* The penicillin resistance of the *Staphylococcus* is remarkable, since all natural isolates of staphylococci are penicillin sensitive in the absence of antibiotic therapy (to which the hedgehog had not been subjected!). The mystery was cleared up when it was shown that the fungus produces penicillin in its natural habitat, the hedgehog skin. This relationship is all the more remarkable when it is recalled that penicillin production in fungi is restricted mainly to the order Moniliales, whereas *Trichophyton* is in another group. We can thus infer that not only is penicillin produced in this environment, but that it is produced in concentrations sufficiently high to act as a selective agent against penicillin-sensitive staphylococci.

The role of antibiotics in soil has had considerable discussion (Waksman, 1961). The problem breaks down into two parts: (1) whether or not antibiotics are produced in soil; (2) whether or not they are antibiotically active in soil. Brian (1957) has considered these questions in detail. First, it should be remembered that there are at present no tests sufficiently sensitive to detect antibiotic molecules in microenvironments where they are likely to be active (but *see* page 17). Thus with soil one is forced to infer microevents from macroscopic observations. Even with these restrictions it can be shown that: (1) antibiotics can be extracted from nonsterile soil; (2) antibiotic production will occur in nonsterile soil which is inoculated with antibiotic-producing organisms and which is supplemented with organic enrichments such as straw; (3) antibiotic-producing microorganisms can be isolated easily from natural soils; (4) antibiotic-producing organisms are able under natural conditions to antagonize other organisms which are sensitive to these antibiotics; (5) conditions unfavorable for the accumulation of antibiotics reduce the antagonistic activity of the organism producing the antibiotic. Considering the enormously complicated nature of the soil environment, it is encouraging that even these observations can be made. Although unequivocal proof that antibiotics are active in nature is not available, the weight of evidence is in favor of this conclusion. Indeed, to postulate that antibiotics do NOT play roles in competitive relationships is to stifle any research on the ecology of these interesting substances.

MAJOR METABOLITES AS ANTAGONISTS

The distinction between a major metabolite and a true antibiotic is a matter of degree rather than of kind. Ethanol and its congeners are major metabolic products of yeasts and many filamentous fungi. Ethanol production is responsible for the self-limitation of yeast growth in many cases (especially where the initial glucose concentration is high). Since alcohol tolerance varies considerably, ethanol production by one organism may limit the growth of another. Gause (1934) in his classic work on competition showed that alcohol production by one of his yeasts probably limited the growth of the other.

Occasionally the pH of the medium is lowered by the excretion of hydrogen ions, but usually pH changes are induced by the production of organic acids. The production of lactic acid by many bacteria lowers the pH sufficiently to prevent other bacteria from growing. Thus in buttermilk, sauerkraut, and pickle fermentations, the acid-tolerant lactobacilli eventually predominate because the acid they produce has eliminated less acid-tolerant species.

Robbins et al. (1950) discovered that many of their fungus cultures were inhibited when they were cultured in the same incubator with *Penicillium funiculosum*. Since the inhibition occurred even when the two organisms were grown in separate tubes, they suspected a gaseous product and were able to identify HCN by chemical tests. Cyanide is also produced by other fungi and may accumulate in significant amounts in diseased alfalfa living under the snow (Lebeau and Dickson, 1955). The mitogenetic rays of early microbiologists were probably inhibitory gaseous substances (Lamanna and Mallette, 1959).

Fatty acids are important antibiotic agents in algae. Spoehr et al. (1949) showed that Chlorella cultures produced antibacterial substances and the material could be found in small amounts in culture supernatants. Considerably more material could be obtained by extracting whole cells, but it was found that these extracts had antibiotic activity only when they were exposed to light and air. Indeed, when whole cells were killed by heating and then were exposed to light and air, antibacterial activity developed through photooxidation. Further work showed that the substrates for the photooxidation were unsaturated fatty acids; saturated fatty acids subjected to photooxidation did not become antibiotically active. The exact nature of the photo products could not be determined, but it was felt that they were not peroxides (Spoehr et al., 1949).

It is also known that fatty acids which have not been photooxidized are also antibiotically active, the biological activity increasing with increasing degree of unsaturation (Kodicek, 1949). Unsaturated fatty acids inhibit mainly gram-positive bacteria, and the activity is antagonized by proteins, sterols, phospholipids, and other substances. It is a pity that the work with the photoproducts from Chlorella has not been pursued further. Since algae are normally grown aerobically and in the light, these antibacterial products may be of widespread occurrence and may be responsible for the well-known antibiotic properties of sea water (Saz et al., 1963).

Proctor (1957) has made a detailed study of an antagonism involving two algae in which the active agent is probably a mixture of fatty acids. He began by growing together in two-membered culture several species of algae and obtained evidence of antagonism in several cases. Because of the autotrophic nature of algae, most species, even if quite diverse, will probably have basically similar nutritional requirements; therefore it would be expected that competition for nutrients would frequently occur, especially if the two species in the pair differed significantly in size or growth rate. However, certain of the combinations studied by Proctor showed evidence of antagonism which could not be accounted for by strict competition. He selected for detailed study the couple *Haematococcus pluvialis* and *Chlamydomonas reinhardi,* since the latter completely prevented growth of the former. Since the haematococcus was five to ten times larger than the chlamydomonas, and the growth rate of the two organisms did not differ greatly, it was unlikely that the former was being eliminated by strictly competitive processes. Further, another species, *Chlamydomonas chlamydogama,* did not antagonize the haematococcus, but on the contrary was itself affected by the latter. Proctor attempted to find antibiotic activity in cell-free supernatants from the *C. reinhardi* cultures. Activity was detected in supernatants from older cultures (four to six days) but only when the pH was above 8.5. It is likely that the agent is active only at alkaline pH values, but Proctor did not eliminate the possibility that it was produced only when the medium became alkaline. The active material could be steam distilled and was soluble in organic solvents. Much larger amounts could be obtained from the cells than from the supernatant, a finding reminiscent of that of Spoehr et al. (1949). Proctor suggested that the active material found in the supernatant was derived from cells which had died and lysed, and he reinforced this idea with the observation that when the cells were grown under high light intensities and with nitrate as the nitrogen source, the pH rose rapidly and more death occurred than in low light intensities in medium with urea as a nitrogen source, where the pH was maintained at lower values. However, high light intensities would also be expected to lead to more photooxidized products (Spoehr et al., 1949). Proctor tested a variety of pure fatty acids and showed that *H. pluvialis* was markedly more sensitive than *C. reinhardi* to certain acids but not to others. Inhibition was greater at the more alkaline pH values, and the inhibitory activity was strongly antagonized by agar. This last fact should serve as a warning to those who would attempt to measure the ecological roles of antibiotics by the use of agar plates. Proctor has calculated from the sensitivity of *H. pluvialis* to fatty acids and from the concentration of fatty acids in *C. reinhardi* cells, that if 5-10% of the *C. reinhardi* cells died and released their unsaturated fatty acids, this would be sufficient to account for the observed inhibition of haematococcus. An extensive review of algal antagonism is provided by Hartman (1960), and further work in this area is urgently needed.

In the aquatic environment, experimentation on the role of antibiotics in antagonism might be easier than in soil, since the numbers and kinds of organisms are fewer, and there are fewer interfering substances to complicate analyses. Since antagonism of phytoplankton can be demonstrated in the laboratory (Proctor, 1957), it would be instructive to follow phytoplankton blooms in nature and test water samples at various times for antibiotic activity against pure cultures of the same organisms. Provasoli (1963) has discussed the meager evidence concerning the role of antibiotics in the marine environment. His words are perhaps of significance here: "The high solubility of many biologically active substances peculiar to the water environment permits rapid exchange of metabolites but it also limits their effectiveness through dilution; therefore, only substances active at extreme dilutions (10^{-15}), such as vitamins, are eligible for ecological importance. The antibiotics, at least those now known, are effective at much higher concentrations, (10^{-6}–10^{-9}); one wonders if they can play an important part in the *free* water environment. Their action may, however, be quite significant when the dilution factor is minimized, as in symbiosis, cohabitation and parasitism" (Provasoli, 1963). *"Das Wasser wird nicht mehr nur als Nährstoffmilieu, sondern auch als Wirkstoffmilieu betrachtet"* (Gessner, 1955). (Italics mine.)

LYTIC ENZYMES AS ANTAGONISTIC AGENTS

As noted in Chapter 3, many microorganisms have cell walls which confer rigidity, and if the cell wall is removed in some manner, the cell usually dies because of lysis resulting from osmotic imbalance. Cell walls in various microorganisms are composed of such substances as cellulose, chitin, mucopeptide, and β-1,3-glucan. In addition, many organisms have capsules, slime layers, or other surface components which are polysaccharides or proteins attached to the outside of the rigid layer or interdigitated with it, conferring additional rigidity and/or protection. Enzymes are known which will attack all of these polymers, and many of these enzymes are liberated into the medium by various microorganisms, either by excretion or by lysis of a small proportion of the cells producing the enzyme. An excellent review of the lytic enzymes produced by bacteria is given by Rogers (1961), whereas some of the enzymes produced by fungi are reviewed by Reese and Mandels (1963). In only a few cases have studies been made on the ability of such enzymes to lyse living cells (Rogers, 1961).

A study of an antagonism between the bacterium *Bacillus macerans* and the fungus *Fusarium roseum* was carried out by Park (1956). The bacterium was able to digest the fungal structures, and this lysis could be demonstrated readily in soil by the use of a soil slide method. Although extensive lysis occurred, the fungus was able to maintain itself by forming resting spores which were resistant to the lytic agent. Interestingly, on agar and in liquid culture the fungus was less severely antagonized than in soil, and eventually the fungus became dominant. Similar results were obtained if agar or excess liquid were added to the soil. The author suggests that a large, physically hard surface, such as soil or sand, is necessary for the development of the bacterial lytic action. Other examples of lytic action by soil organisms are reviewed by Alexander (1964). The lysis of the human pathogenic yeast *Blastomyces dermatitidis* in natural soil has been described by McDonough et al. (1965) and is apparently a factor in the elimination of this pathogen from contaminated soils.

TEMPERATE BACTERIOPHAGES

Lysogeny is the hereditary ability to produce virus particles without infection from the outside. A lysogenic cell possesses the genome of the virus in a state integrated with its own genome, and the virus genome (or prophage) is transmitted to all the progeny of the cell during the normal course of DNA replication and cell division. A lysogenic strain is immune to the virus it produces. Production of mature virus particles in uninduced cultures is a rare event, perhaps occurring in one cell in 10^2–10^5, and the cell which produces the virus particles lyses. Thus in a bacterial culture of 10^8 cells/ml which has not been induced, if the burst size were 100 virus particles per cell, there would be between 10^5 and 10^8 virus particles/ml. The small amount of spontaneous lysis which occurs would never be noticed, and since the organism is immune to the virus which it produces, lysogenic cultures containing many virus particles can be carried unsuspected for years.

Lysogeny is a widespread phenomenon, and almost every bacterial species which has been examined has been found to contain lysogenic strains. In certain species almost every strain is lysogenic, and in some cases a single strain may produce more than one virus (Adams, 1959). The viruses produced by lysogenic strains are called temperate viruses, to distinguish them from virulent viruses (to be discussed later) which never exist as prophages. A temperate virus is never active against the strain which produces it but is usually active against closely related strains. The host range of a temperate virus is determined by a number of factors and no general rules can be formulated. In the initial search for lysogenic strains, a sensitive strain is necessary with which to detect the virus; this is usually found by the blind testing of a large number of strains of the same species in all possible combinations. So far as I know, lysogeny has never been reported in microorganisms other than bacteria, but perhaps it has never been sought thoroughly. Phenomena analogous to lysogeny may occur in mammalian cells, especially in relation to tumor viruses.

A lysogenic strain possesses a very effective method of antagonism against closely related strains. Since the initially infected cells of the sensitive strain release virus particles which can attack other sensitive cells, the antagonism builds up in a progressive manner. Therefore even a few lysogenic cells introduced into a population of sensitive cells may replace the latter. In this way lysogeny differs from bacteriocinogeny, in that the bacteriocine is not a self-replicating particle, whereas the virus is. Note, however, that in this antagonism the lysogenic strain, by producing virus, sacrifices a few of its cells for the benefit of the population as a whole.

A further complication arises, however, in that a sensitive cell is not always lysed when it is infected with a temperate phage; it may be lysogenized. When lysogenization occurs, the phage genome becomes integrated into the genome of the sensitive cell; the latter now becomes immune to any further infection by that particular phage and becomes lysogenic itself. Further, the incoming phage may bring from the donor into the recipient genes which have nothing to do with the phage functions but which are normal donor genes. This process is called transduction. For reviews of the various genetic aspects of lysogeny and transduction see Stent (1963) and Jacob and Wollman (1961).

Unfortunately, there has been little consideration of the ecological aspects of lysogeny (Anderson, 1957). Perhaps the most interesting possibility concerns the toxigenic and atoxigenic strains of *Corynebacterium diphtheriae*. The former strains, which are responsible for the disease diphtheria because they produce diphtheria toxin, are lysogenic for a phage β, and when this phage is used to lysogenize atoxigenic strains, the latter now acquire the ability to produce diphtheria toxin. Toxin producing ability and phage producing ability always occur together. Thus, in such a case, the lysogenic strain may receive ecological benefit not because it is able to use the phage it produces in a competitive way, but because of another property which it has acquired as an incidental aspect of lysogeny.

Parasitism
and Predation

In many cases of antagonism, one organism is actually consumed by the other as a source of materials for cell synthesis. Predation is usually considered to be the actual ingestion of a smaller organism by a larger one, whereas in parasitism the consumer is smaller than the consumee.

PARASITISM WITHOUT CELL CONTACT

Myxobacteria are thin flexible rod-shaped organisms which show gliding motility and are widespread in soil and water (Stanier et al., 1963). A common method for isolating these organisms is to place a small amount of soil in the center of an agar plate which has been previously inoculated with a suspension of bacteria. The myxobacteria release lytic enzymes which digest the bacterial cells, and the myxobacteria spread across the plate consuming the nutrients which are released (Norén, 1960); they are also able to lyse and consume fungi. Myxobacteria are not obligate parasites, since they can be cultured on a variety of laboratory media.

PARASITISM WITH CELL CONTACT

The most interesting cases of parasitism and the ones most susceptible to quantitative experimental analysis involve cell-to-cell contact between predator and prey. It is to such interactions that Gause's well-known equations (1934) most aptly apply, leading to typical epidemic situations. Considering the ease with which predators and parasites can be studied in the microbial world and the difficulty of studying these matters in higher organisms (Flanders and Badgley, 1963), it is surprising that more work has not been done on them.

The recent discovery of *Bdellovibrio* emphasizes clearly a dilemma of microbial ecology; we have here a whole new group of microorganisms which are distributed widely throughout soil and sewage and which have a very interesting life history, and yet they were discovered only in 1962! How could we go so long not knowing *Bdellovibrio* existed? ". . . the organism has escaped discovery by microbial ecologists because it does not grow in culture media, because it is quite small and—most importantly—because there was no a priori reason to expect the existence of this unusual creature!" (Stolp and Starr, 1963). These unusual bacteria are very small monoflagellated vibrioid cells which are highly motile and which stick to the surface of their host cells, causing them to lyse. An electron micrograph of a *Bdellovibrio* cell attached to a host cell is shown in Figure 6-2. A number of strains of *Bdellovibrio* have been found, and each shows some host specificity; in general, gram-positive bacteria are not attacked. Lysis occurs only during attachment, and an extracellular lytic enzyme has not been found. On agar plates seeded with host bacteria, plaques are formed which more or less resemble bacteriophage plaques, but they develop more slowly and continue to enlarge during several days of incubation. A quantitative study showing the kinetics of appearance of *Bdellovibrio* and disappearance of the host is shown in Figure 6-3. Initial *Bdellovibrio* isolates will grow only in the presence of living bacteria and are thus obligately parasitic, but rare saprophytic mutants can be isolated which can no longer grow on living bacteria but will grow on heat-killed bacteria or on complex artificial media. From these saprophytic mutants, obligate parasites can again be selected by

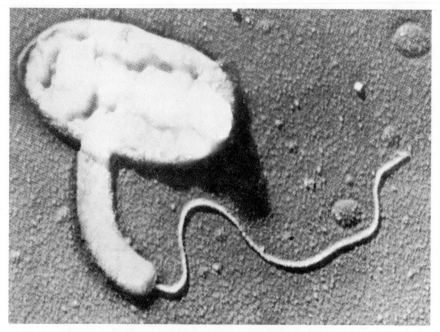

Fig. 6-2. Electron micrograph of a cell of *Bdellovibrio bacteriovorus* attached to a host cell of *Erwinia amylovora* (Stolp and Starr, 1963), 26,200×. The highly motile *Bdellovibrio* cell sticks to its host by a special region at the aflagellate end and subsequently induces lysis.

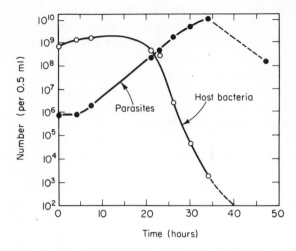

Fig. 6-3. Kinetics of development of *Bdellovibrio* on *Erwinia* (after Stolp and Starr, 1963). Although kinetically resembling a bacteriophage infection, the mechanism of attack and lysis is quite different.

using living host cells. Thus whether a population of *Bdellovibrio* cells at a given moment consists of parasites or saprophytes depends on the substrate offered to it.

Here, then, is an example of a parasite which attacks from the outside and can lyse its host only when attached to it, thus differing from myxobacters which can lyse at a distance and are not obligately parasitic. Because of the widespread distribution of *Bdellovibrio* strains, it can be assumed that these interesting creatures are ecologically significant. All varieties of bacteriolysis (e.g., by lytic enzymes, bacteriophage, bacteriocines, myxobacteria, antibiotics, and *Bdellovibrio*) have recently been reviewed by Stolp and Starr (1965).

PENETRATION BY THE PARASITE INTO THE HOST

Some fungi may be parasitic on algae or on other fungi, a property especially widespread in the order Chytridiales (Bessey, 1950). In the parasitism of an alga by *Phlyctochytrium hallii,* a motile zoospore comes to rest on the host and produces a protrusion called a haustorium which penetrates the host cell, while the portion remaining outside enlarges and becomes a zoosporangium. The mature zoosporangium ruptures and releases zoospores which move to other host cells and initiate a new cycle. This cycle is a simple one, but more complicated cycles involving sexual processes and extensive vegetative differentiation are known. The reader should consult Bessey (1950) or other mycology texts for details.

The parasitism of fungi on fungi has been reviewed in detail by DeVay (1956). Fungi from all taxonomic groups may act as parasites, and fungi from all groups may act as hosts. In some cases the parasitism results in the formation of haustoria which penetrate the host, and in these cases it seems reasonable that the fungus derives at least some of its nutrients from the host. In other cases the parasite does not form haustoria, but its hyphae may coil around the hyphae of the host and kill it, presumably by the production of a lytic enzyme. Because of the extreme diversity, few general statements can be made. The parasitism by fungi on nematodes has been reviewed recently by Pramer (1964).

VIRUSES AS PARASITES

Bacterial viruses have been studied for so long as model genetic systems that it may have been forgotten that most of the early studies by d'Herelle and others concerned the ecological role of viruses as possible agents in the lysis and elimination of pathogenic bacteria in intestinal infections (Stent, 1963). Among the microorganisms, viruses have been studied almost exclusively in the bacteria, although viruses are now known to attack certain fungi (Hollings, 1962; Hollings et al., 1963) and blue-green algae (Safferman and Morris, 1963; Schneider et al., 1964). Bacterial viruses are obligate parasites in the strict sense of the word, and from what is now known of them, it seems unlikely that any bacterial virus will ever be cultivated away from its host. In this way a bacterial virus differs from *Bdellovibrio* which, although parasitic, remains completely outside its host and uses the products of host cell lysis as its food. Because a bacterial virus is an obligate parasite, it can increase in numbers only when its sensitive host is available. In the absence of the host, however, the bacterial virus may not die but can remain latent for many years.

In many virus-host systems, a productive infection occurs every time a virus particle adsorbs to a cell. Thus the controlling factor in the host-parasite relation is the adsorption process itself. According to Stent (1963), phage adsorption follows the kinetics of a first order reaction and can be precisely described by a differential equation. The length of time required before a phage particle will adsorb to a cell is determined by the concentrations of both phage and cell. If both concentrations are low, infection will not occur, whereas if either one or the other is high, at least some infective collisions will occur.

Anderson (1957) has examined this problem experimentally, using Vi-phage A and Vi-type A of *Salmonella typhi*. Some of his results are shown in Figure 6-4. When low concentrations (about 100 cells and 100 virus particles per ml) were inoculated into broth, virus-host encounters could not occur and the virus concentration initially remained constant, while the bacterial count increased logarithmically. Only at a fairly high bacterial density was virus infection initiated, and the offspring from these first encounters infected other cells resulting in cell growth and phage growth occurring together in different segments of the population. When

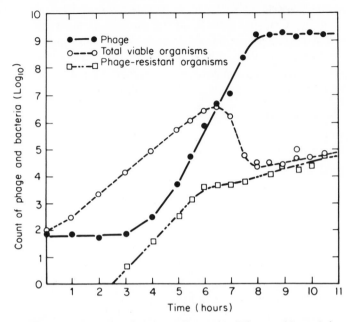

Fig. 6-4. Growth of *Salmonella typhi* (Vi-type A) and its phage when mixed together at small inocula (after Anderson, 1957). The phage do not initiate growth until the bacterial population has reached between 10^4 and 10^5 cells/ml. No detectable effect of the phage on the bacteria is seen until the bacteria reach 10^6/ml. Ultimately a mixture of phage-resistant and phage-sensitive bacteria is obtained.

the phage concentration became sufficiently high, a mass infection of the bacteria occurred and the host cell population then dropped sharply. Phage-resistant mutants which arose spontaneously increased in numbers so that later growth in the population was due only to them. As a result of this and other experiments, Anderson concludes: "These experiments show that, in order to exert a selection pressure sufficiently strong to eliminate a majority of sensitive cells so as to give a survival advantage to a phage-resistant mutant, high phage concentrations are necessary, and that, even under such conditions, total elimination of the phage-sensitive population is by no means certain, even in the static environment of a test-tube. . . . unless closed systems of a similar character are common in nature, the selection pressure exerted on bacteria by virulent phages is negligible." He considers the only closed systems in nature likely to exhibit these requirements to be cheese vats, where *Streptococcus lactis* phages are known to occur. Indeed, Collins (1955) has shown that bacteriophages do play a role in population changes in *S. lactis* dairy starter cultures, although Hunter (1947) has shown that sensitive strains of *S. cremoris* can replicate in milk in the presence of their phages. After adsorption and injection of phage nucleic acid, replication will occur if the environmental conditions are suitable. However, if replication does not begin immediately, host cells are able in many cases to destroy or inactivate the incoming nucleic acid, probably with nucleases. At low temperature or in a nutritionally inadequate medium, the sensitive cell may survive. Such a phenomenon is often seen in populations which have reached the stationary phase of growth; sensitive cells and virulent phages may exist side by side.

The recent ultra-thin sections of Fauré-Fremiet et al. (1963) (*see* Figure 6-5) reveal that bacterial viruses do exist in fairly high concentrations in microenvironments in nature. Hopefully more work along these lines will be carried out. Because of the highly developed state of the bacteriophage art, it should be relatively simple to study the ecology of the phage-host relationship in nature, as bacteriophage assay methods are

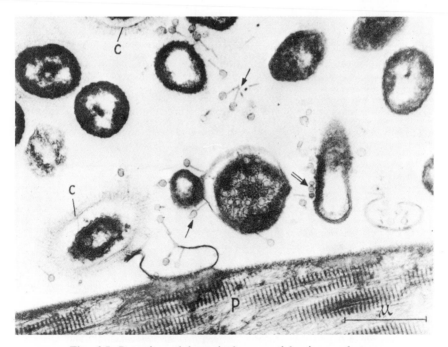

Fig. 6-5. Bacteria and bacteriophage particles in an electron micrograph of a thin section (Fauré-Fremiet et al., 1963). The bacteria are associated with a colonial protozoan, *Zoothamnion alternans*. Two kinds of phage particles can be seen (ARROW and DOUBLE-ARROW). Near the center of the picture, a bacterial cell seems to be full of nascent phage particles.

sensitive enough to detect a single phage particle in a natural microenvironment.

PREDATION

In the microbial world, predation is restricted to phagotrophic organisms which are so constructed that they can engulf particles and organisms. Microorganisms with cell walls, such as bacteria, fungi and algae, cannot be predators because the cell wall prevents the entry of particles and, indeed, in most cases even the entry of macromolecules.

An interesting analysis of a predator-prey relationship was performed by Gause (1934). He used two protozoan genera, *Paramecium* and *Didinium,* the latter preying on the former. Paramecia, of course, are also predators of bacteria, but in Gause's experiments the bacteria were kept in excess so that the interactions involved only the two protozoa. The food requirements of didinia are large, a fresh paramecium being consumed every hour. When its proboscis makes contact with a paramecium, the didinium paralyzes it with its trichocysts and then devours the paramecium whole. In the absence of a suitable food organism, the didinium will die unless it forms cysts, but in Gause's experiments cyst formation did not take place. A typical experiment is shown in Figure 6-6. The experiments were performed in small test tubes with about 0.5 ml of an oat decoction medium which provided the nutrients for the growth of the food bacteria. Into these tubes were placed five individuals of *Paramecium caudatum* which grew. Two days later, three individuals of *Didinium nasutum* were added. Soon the number of paramecia began to decrease

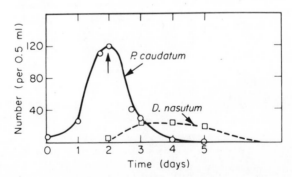

Fig. 6-6. Initial interaction between *Paramecium caudatum* and *Didinium nasutum* (after Gause, 1934). Nutrient medium is 0.5 ml of oat decoction containing bacteria as food for the paramecium. Values are numbers of cells per 0.5 ml. Initial inoculum, 5 paramecium at day 0. Three didinium added at day 2 (ARROW). Ultimately both paramecium and didinium are eliminated and bacteria remain unutilized.

and the number of didinia to increase, but in this limited universe soon the paramecia were exhausted and the didinia themselves died. A number of variations on this experiment were performed, and Gause concludes: "Thus we see that in a homogeneous nutritive medium under constant external conditions the system *Paramecium-Didinium* has no innate periodic oscillations in numbers. In other words, *the food chain:* bacteria → *Paramecium* → *Didinium* placed in a limited microcosm, with *the concentration of the first link of the chain* [the bacteria] *kept artificially at a definite level, changes in such a direction that the two latter components disappear entirely and the food resources of the first component of the chain remain without being utilized by any one."*

The above experiments had been done in a homogeneous medium without any sediment, so that the paramecia had no place to hide. If, however, an oat medium is used which contains a sediment, the situation is entirely different. Whether the didinia are present or not, the paramecia show a preference for the sediment, and because they are hidden, the didinia cannot find them. In such an experiment the didinia die and the paramecia proliferate. Many variations on these experiments were performed; Gause's book should be sought for details. In none of these experiments with didinia was there any evidence of periodic fluctuations in population levels, probably because the intensity of the predation was too fierce; either the didinia consumed all of the paramecia and then died, or the didinia died without consuming all of the paramecia. Because population cycles are well known in nature, Gause was naturally interested in creating a model system where cycles might be observed in the laboratory. To do this he needed a system where the intensity of interaction was lower, and he achieved this by scaling down the systems; he studied the predation by Paramecium on yeast cells. It would be extremely difficult or impossible for the paramecia to devour all of the yeast, since when the majority of yeast cells have been consumed, the probability of a paramecium finding a yeast cell is quite low. An experiment of this type is presented in Figure 6-7. Periodic oscillations were observed, the yeast cells increasing, then decreasing as they were consumed by the paramecia. The paramecia then increase until the yeast population has decreased to a point where the paramecia cannot maintain growth and die. Of course in a closed system such as this where the nutrient supply is restricted, the oscillations will gradually decrease until both organisms are dead. However, studies of this type are useful in that they reveal the limits to be expected in any interaction.

Curiously, microbiologists have shown little interest in the work of Gause, and it has been mainly the animal ecologists (Slobodkin, 1962*a*; Andrewartha, 1961) who have pursued this work. Mathematical analysis of epidemics and other population interactions (Bartlett, 1960) reveal

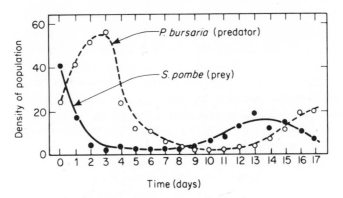

Fig. 6-7. Predator-prey relationship showing periodic fluctuations (after Gause, 1934). Mixed population of *Paramecium bursaria* and *Schizosaccharomyces pombe.*

marked similarities to the work discussed above. Bartlett's deterministic equation for the development of an epidemic is identical in form to Gause's equation and to the equation of Stent for phage adsorption.

Three-Organism Interactions

If we now add a third organism to a system, we find that the complexities are even greater. Thus, if we have organisms *A*, *B*, and *C*, we can have the following possibilities, where the arrow indicates that one organism is affecting the other, either in a positive or a negative way: $A \rightleftarrows B$, $A \rightleftarrows C$, $B \rightleftarrows C$. If we now consider the interaction of *A* and *B* as *AB*, of *A* and *C* as *AC*, and so on, we then have: $AB \rightleftarrows C$, $AC \rightleftarrows B$, $BC \rightleftarrows A$, in which each of the three organisms is shown as affecting the interaction of the other two, and the interacting pair is shown affecting the third organism. Finally, we have the product of all of these interactions, as:

$$A \rightleftarrows B \atop C \qquad A \rightleftarrows C \atop B \qquad B \rightleftarrows C \atop A \qquad = ABC$$

Since for each of the arrows, the effect can be positive, negative or neutral, the total number of possibilities in the above scheme is 81, depending on the characteristics of each of the three organisms. Then it must be remembered that this interaction is taking place in a single environment, with one set of nutrients, at a single temperature, pressure, pH, etc., and that in a different environment one or any of the possible interactions might be altered qualitatively or quantitatively. The mind reels when it considers the complexities that are possible.

Can we ever hope to understand nature, if even a three organism interaction is this complex? There is some hope. As the number of interacting organisms goes up, the chances of any organism drastically affecting another one goes down because there is a decrease in the probability of frequent and consistent encounters between the two organisms. Thus if we have 9 or 10 interacting organisms, all may live in a balanced state. We will discuss this problem further in the next chapter.

CHAPTER 7

Microbial
Ecosystems

An ecosystem (or biocoenosis) is usually defined as the
sum total of the interacting elements in a limited universe, including both biotic and abiotic (environmental)
components. Since the ecosystem concept is used mainly
as an aid in studying thermodynamic relationships and
biogeochemical cycles in nature, it is also useful to
define an ecosystem as an open system in steady state.
As discussed by Eyring et al. (1960), thermodynamics
can be applied to open systems only if they are in steady
state. Such a state is a time-independent condition in
which production and consumption of each element of
the system are exactly balanced, the concentrations of
all elements within the system remaining constant, even
though there is continual change. A crude example of
such a steady state is an adult human; the body remains

more or less constant in the quality and quantity of its elements from puberty to death, even though the cells and tissues of the body are turning over continuously. Food enters, wastes leave, yet everything stays the same.

On first thought it might be felt that no ecological system would exhibit steady state conditions. Yet it must be remembered that an important item is the time constant of the system. Although fluctuations in amounts of various elements may occur over a short period of time, if our view of the system covers a long enough period, we can ignore these fluctuations and concentrate on the overall stability of the system. Thus, although leaf fall to the forest floor occurs mainly in the autumn, on an annual basis the forest floor ecosystem is in steady state, since no net accumulation of leaves occurs (Ovington, 1962) and production (leaf fall) equals consumption (leaf decomposition). And, just as a small patch of forest soil is a steady state ecosystem, so also is the forest as a whole, since trees die and fall but are replaced by other trees and the forest goes on and on. Even the whole world is a steady state ecosystem, so that the concept is completely general and applies equally well to systems big and small.

The best laboratory model of such a system is a continuous culture device (Novick, 1955). In all continuous flow devices the volume and the population density remain constant, and nutrients are added and removed at constant rates. Two basic ways of achieving a steady state in such systems are by population density control and by environmental control. An example of a POPULATION DENSITY-CONTROLLED device is the turbidostat (Novick, 1955); a photoelectric device sensing the population density is coupled to a valve which controls the rate of flow of the nutrient (Figure 7-1). If the population increases, nutrient is added, the population is diluted, and the density is decreased. Growth then occurs and the process is repeated. As Novick has shown, the growth rate of the population in such a device is controlled by unknown factors in the population itself, since under the environmental conditions used all of the nutrient ingredients are in excess. An example of a population density-controlled microbial ecosystem in nature would derive from the self-shading effect (Fogg, 1965) of a bloom of phytoplankton in an excessively eutrophic lake or sewage oxidation pond; as the density of cells reaches a high level, light would be absorbed by the surface layers and could not reach underlying cells, so that the latter would cease growing. Then some of the cells would settle, the population density would decrease, and more light could enter the water, leading to a further increase in growth. Note, however, that even though this system behaves as a density-controlled device, it is the deficiency in an environmental factor, light, which essentially controls the population. Thus, if the intensity of light were increased, the self-shading effect could be reduced, and higher population densities

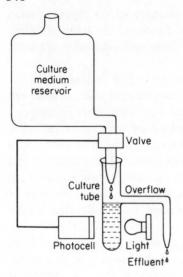

Turbidostat. An example of a *population density–controlled* continuous culture device. In such a device the density is arbitrarily controlled by the setting of the photocell, but the growth rate is controlled by unknown factors in the population itself, since all nutrients are in excess. A signal from the photocell controls the setting of the valve.

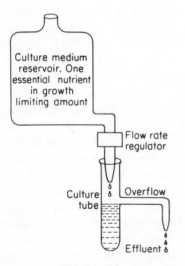

Chemostat. An example of an *environmentally-controlled* continuous culture device. In such a device the population density is controlled by the concentration of the limiting nutrient, and the growth rate is controlled by the flow rate, which can be arbitrarily set.

Fig. 7-1. Diagrams of two kinds of continuous culture devices.

could be obtained. A mature coniferous forest is a macroecosystem which is basically density controlled, since new trees spring up only when old trees fall and allow light to penetrate into the understory. Although Novick (1955) justly criticizes the population density-controlled device as a laboratory model for physiologic and genetic studies, it may be an important model for many microbial ecosystems.

The laboratory analog of the ENVIRONMENTALLY-CONTROLLED SYSTEM is the chemostat (Figure 7-1). This is also a constant volume continuous flow device in which the inflowing medium has an excess of all nutrients except one, the limiting nutrient. With this procedure the growth rate of the population is controlled by the flow rate, since the limiting nutrient will be used as fast as it is added. Thus the population is growing at a rate less than the maximum it is capable of attaining. As the flow rate is decreased, the growth rate of the population decreases, and there is a lower limit below which the population ceases to grow, enters a lag phase, or dies (Novick, 1955).

A good example of such a system is an activated sludge digester, discussed in detail by Wuhrmann (1964a) and shown diagrammatically in Figure 7-2. Sewage is passed continuously into a large tank where it is aerated. Microorganisms, mainly bacteria and protozoa, grow and form zoogloeal masses called flocs, deriving their nutrients from the sewage material. A food chain is set up (see page 178) and energy fixed at one trophic level is consumed at the next, so that ultimately most of the energy is dissipated within the system. In the clarifier, the sludge is allowed to settle, and some of the sludge is recycled to provide inoculum. The effluent with organic matter greatly reduced is then discharged. In the initial establishment of such a system, growth follows a typical logarithmic curve, but once the sludge is established, steady state conditions obtain, and the sludge concentration remains essentially constant. The rate of activity is a function of the flow rate and the organic concentration of the influent. If the flow rate were too fast or the organic concentration too high, digestion would not be complete, but in the conventional system these factors are controlled in order to achieve maximum possible digestion, and a true environmentally-controlled steady state exists. Whole domestic sewage is usually very dilute in organic compounds, although it contains an exceedingly complex range of substances. A typical sewage contained 94 p.p.m. dissolved organic carbon and 211 p.p.m. particulate carbon, and contained carbohydrates, amino acids, organic acids, surfactants and other compounds (Wuhrmann, 1964a). The importance of microbial growth

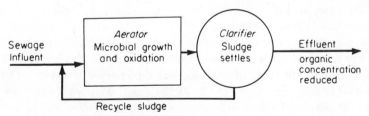

Fig. 7-2. Activated sludge sewage digester as a steady-state microbial ecosystem (adapted from Eckenfelder and O'Connor, 1961).

in the oxidation of sewage is shown by the fact that some industrial wastes (e.g., sulfite liquor of paper mills) are low in nitrogen and phosphorus and provide poor conditions for microbial growth, and to achieve optimum oxidation, these nutrients must be added. The ecosystem approach to sewage digestion may provide new insights in a field which has been primarily dominated by the engineer (Wuhrmann, 1964a; Eckenfelder and O'Connor, 1961).

There are many natural ecosystems which approximate to chemostats, in that they are environmentally-controlled steady states, such as a lake, a forest floor, and many ocean waters. As noted earlier, such fluctuative ecosystems provide steady state conditions if the time constant of the system is considered. Even the laboratory chemostat fluctuates, since it is impossible to maintain an absolutely constant flow rate, although the time constant is much shorter than that in a natural ecosystem.

These considerations stress an important aspect of microbial ecology. Just what does control the population density of a system? In many natural ecosystems the controls are not immediately obvious and warrant study.

Many naturally occurring systems are heterogeneous but still exhibit steady state characteristics. For instance, downstream from the source of a sewage outfall, a polluted stream shows different characteristics at each milepost (see Figure 7-3), but at any one milepost conditions generally remain relatively constant from day to day. An animal intestinal tract and a soil profile are also examples of heterogeneous steady state ecosystems. Such systems are quite useful for analysis because they contain within themselves the history of their own evolution. A laboratory model of a heterogeneous open system was described by Reusser (1961) and Means et al. (1962). Dondero (1961) discusses the use of such systems in the study of stream infestations. An additional element of heterogeneity is seen in flowing systems in which organisms live attached to the bottom substratum. Such systems are heterogeneous both horizontally and vertically but may still be studied since the heterogeneity is not random.

Although ecosystems need not be in steady state conditions, it is useful in many cases to know whether or not they are, since analysis is much easier on steady state systems.

In complex systems with many kinds of organisms, our attention naturally focuses on how these organisms may interact. Information theory provides a basis for such an analysis, and the reviews of Yockey (1958), Elsasser (1958), Quastler (1953, 1958), and Wiener (1948) may be sought for details. To date little application of these ideas has been made to microbial ecosystems so we will restrict our discussion here to a few general remarks. Interaction between organisms requires communication, the transfer of information between the units. In biological systems, information can be conveyed by chemical substances, electrical impulses, mechanical forces, light rays, thermal movements, or a combination of these. Information may be contained in chemical substances in the unique spatial configuration of a molecule (e.g., hormone, antibiotic), or in a specified sequence of certain repeating elements (e.g., genetic information). The transfer of information may affect the unit in a positive or negative way; if the unit is not affected at all, then by definition information has not been transferred. Thus, information cannot be equated only with the element transferred but must refer to the response of the recipient as well. (For instance, the information content of a hormone is not conveyed by its chemical structure alone but by both its structure AND its target.) Two units may exchange information in a reciprocal fashion, or the transfer may be unidirectional. In a unidirectional transfer, the donor may benefit in some way by the transfer, or it may be unaffected. The coupling between two units may be tight, or it may be loose. "If two parts are coupled, in any fashion, then knowledge of the state of one must imply some information about the state of the other" (Quastler, 1958). In microbial ecosystems complete coupling among all units is extremely unlikely because of the enormous number of individuals and populations. As Quastler (1958) has said: "It is an empirical fact that when a system is complex enough to require many components, the phenomenon of *unitization* occurs. That is, some components get organized in such a way that they interact strongly among each other, and act as a unit with respect to the remainder of the system. . . . Unitization is always coupled with the phenomenon of limited span. Any real part has a limited information content. In any single act of communication, the capacity for non-redundant transmission of a part is limited by its own information content. This amount must somehow be partitioned into interaction with the external world, and interaction with the other members of the unit. If each of these interactions is to be of significant size, then only a limited number is possible. The interaction of a unit with the outside may be only a fraction of the information traffic within the unit. Hence, several units can be organized into a secondary structure of greater versatility, and this process can be repeated on successive levels of organization." Clearly unitization makes possible an enormous simplification of the analysis of the interaction of populations.

Any system which exhibits tight coupling possesses certain integrative properties which are useful in characterizing and analyzing the system. These are: homeostasis, evolution, defense, repair, and reproduction. Homeostasis is the ability of the system to maintain itself in the face of varying external influences. This does not mean that the system is not affected by external influences, but that it is able to maintain its integrative properties intact. Evolution is analogous to homeostasis but differs in that evolution occurs over a long period of time whereas homeostasis occurs over a short time. Defense is an aspect of homeostasis but is a response to more violent external influences, and repair results if a portion of the system is removed and the system is able to replace this. And finally, reproduction results in the complete replacement of the system by another one which is similar or identical. The above integrative properties are exhibited by cells, by organisms, and by ecosystems, although the coupling between the elements, and consequently the degree of development of the integrative properties, is much greater with the cell and organism than with the ecosystem. In a tightly coupled system, it is difficult to remove a portion of the system experimentally and maintain it in isolation in an unchanged state; this is clearly shown by attempts to maintain subcellular organelles or animal organs in the laboratory. The fact that coupling exists in microbial ecosystems is shown by the frequent difficulty in isolating pure cultures of organisms which reproduce readily in mixed culture.

We see that as we fit together the elements into an organized whole, we begin to lose sight of the elements. Even with unitization, the whole becomes so complex in terms of its elements that we can no longer talk about the whole in terms of the action of its elements. There are two ways of dealing with this difficulty. One is to continue to look at the individual elements but now to treat them statistically. This has been done for certain ecological problems by Bartlett (1960). The other approach is to ignore the individual elements and study the system as a whole. In the same way that we can study the behavior of an animal without reference to the firing of individual neurons, so can we study the behavior of an ecosystem without reference to the CO_2 fixation of a single plant. This is not to say that the latter is not important, but rather that the latter is not at a level at which we wish to work. At intermediate levels of complexity we may be able to bridge the gap between the deterministic and the stochastic views by the use of computers to analyze deterministically systems which are too difficult to handle with conventional techniques, but microbial systems are usually too complicated to handle even with computers.

The ecosystem must have some sort of phase boundary, separating it in some way from the outside world. The phase boundary may be sharply defined, as in the rumen, or it may be ill defined, as in the open ocean, but in all cases a phase boundary of some kind must exist and is the initial aspect of the definition of an ecosystem. The uniformity of a system is also an aspect of its characterization, and in a homogeneous system a small sample taken from any part of the system will be representative of the whole system. In natural systems we have all degrees of uniformity although rarely complete homogeneity. For experimental work a fairly homogeneous system (e.g., the rumen) is ideal because the microscopic behavior of the organisms is automatically amplified to the macro scale, making sampling as well as studies on ecosystem physiology more meaningful.

The Biology
of the Ecosystem

In characterizing the microorganisms found in an ecosystem, we may wish to study all of the organisms which are present. However, if we are not interested in the organisms as individuals but are using them merely to define the system, it is possible that certain organisms which possess distinctive characteristics, such as certain protozoa, fungi, or even metazoa, but which are present in small numbers, might provide more useful information for a biological characterization of an ecosystem than the large numbers of rather nondescript bacteria. This idea has long been recognized by pollution biologists who may characterize a polluted stream on the basis of certain distinctive organisms, even though these play a much smaller role in the metabolism of a stream than do the large numbers of sewage bacteria (Kolkwitz and Marsson, 1908; Fjerdingstad, 1964). But it should be clearly recognized that the use of such indicator organisms is merely a convenience, and that in terms of the overall functioning of the ecosystem it is not the kinds of organisms which are most relevant but their activities.

When ecosystems are characterized in terms of their biotic components, it is usually found that certain kinds of organisms frequently occur together in the same environment. If two or more organisms are found living together in the same ecosystem, this may be merely because they have similar environmental requirements, or they may benefit in some way by their association and thus survive better together than separately. Ecologists speak of communities or associations of organisms, and this same usage has been applied occasionally to microorganisms (Westerdijk, 1949; Mossel and Ingram, 1956). Although such an association or community may occur because of mutual benefit, without experimental studies in the laboratory it is usually not possible to distinguish an association from a mere collection of organisms with similar environmental requirements and tolerances.

SUCCESSION

Initially a fresh uncolonized substrate provides an excess of nutrients, and many organisms in the inoculum begin to grow. As time goes on the activities of these initial populations lead to changes in the environment such as decreases in nutrient supply, alterations in pH or redox potential, or the appearance of toxic metabolic products. These changes are most likely to be brought about by organisms which were most numerous at first, or by organisms in the inoculum which could grow most rapidly and were thus by definition the best adapted to the original environment. In the altered environment, however, these early organisms may be less well adapted than some other organisms which were perhaps only poorly adapted to the original environment. Now these latter organisms begin to increase rapidly until they become dominant, and the initial organisms are now replaced or become diminished in numbers. An example of this type studied by Barker (van Niel, 1955) involves phytoplankton succession in a marine bay after fertilization. At first a heavy diatom bloom occurred, followed later by a decline of the diatoms and an increase in dinoflagellates. The diatoms were favored as long as the nutrient concentration was high, but the growth of the diatoms reduced the nutrient concentration to the point where they could no longer multiply, although the dinoflagellates were able to grow in the more dilute medium and thus took over. Another example involves the initiation in wounds of the growth of *Clostridium tetani*. This organism is an obligate anaerobe and its spores will not germinate within the aerobic host tissues, but facultative bacteria inoculated into the wound along with the tetanus bacillus reduce through their activities the redox potential to the point where the pathogen can begin growth (Woods and Foster, 1964). The anaerobic conditions in the animal intestine are also maintained by facultative organisms, thereby enabling obligate anaerobes to grow. Occasionally it happens that the initially dominant organisms so alter the environment that no later organisms can become established, in which case the initial organisms remain dominant. Such phenomena occur, for instance, in the development of acid mine waters or acid bogs, the organisms which produce the acid being very acidophilic, thus insuring their own dominance.

An equilibrium position is usually reached which is a function both of the environment and of the dominant organisms. Table 7-1 provides data on the stages in the development of a rumen ecosystem. As this table shows, the bacterial count in the one-month-old calf had already reached its maximum, but cellulose digestibility was low, and protozoa were absent. Within the next month cellulose digestibility increased markedly even though there was no change in the bacterial numbers, protozoa appeared, and the relative proportions of the various organic acids had changed. By 12 months maximum digestibility had developed and after this time the fermentation balance remained essentially constant throughout the life of the animal. Thus, once the rumen microbial flora had developed and the environmental conditions were poised (the Eh and pH values being mainly controlled by the microbial population), the existing flora

TABLE 7-1. DEVELOPMENT OF RUMINAL FUNCTION IN THE CALF AS AN EXAMPLE OF A DEVELOPING ECOSYSTEM

Age of calf	Total bacterial count, direct microscopic ($10^9/g$)	Protozoa count ($10^3/ml$)	Gas production from cellulose (ml)	Succinic-Lactic	Average content of organic acids (m moles/liter)				
					Formic	Acetic	Propionic	Butyric	Total
1 month	46	0	0.8	56	5.5	48.8	25.2	16.2	152
2 months	28.5	137	4.2	6.6	1.5	69.7	32.4	18.6	129
3 months	38	659	3.8	6.1	1.5	75.0	26.8	17.9	127
6 months	44	738	5.4	13.5	2.5	73.3	18.7	22.4	130
12 months	53	843	7.3	6.8	1.2	67.7	16.3	18.0	110
Adult, over 2 years	66	477	9.4	5.2	1.3	63.0	18.1	14.5	102

Data of Lengemann and Allen (1955).

continued to insure its own continuance through its activities even though fresh nutrients (and fresh inoculum) were being added at every meal. But it does not necessarily follow that two similar mature ecosystems went through the same historical sequence, since the same final state could be obtained through different intermediate states.

In a heterogeneous continuous flow ecosystem the whole history of the succession can be seen at one time through observations at various points along the longitudinal axis of the system. Immediately below a sewage outfall (Hynes, 1960) (Figure 7-3) organic concentration is high, dissolved oxygen is low, NH_4^+ concentration is high, the bacterial and protozoal counts are high, and animals are absent except for Tubificid worms. Farther downstream the organic concentration has decreased, dissolved oxygen has increased, NH_4^+ has disappeared and has been replaced by NO_3^- (a result of nitrification), bacterial and protozoal counts have dropped, the Tubificid worms have been replaced by larvae of the genus *Chironomus,* and algae appear. Even farther downstream clean water fauna appear, and the water resembles that occurring above the outfall. The same sequence of events would probably be seen if a batch of the polluted water taken directly at the outfall were aerated and samples were taken at various time intervals. The polluted stream contains at one point in time all of the stages which the batch would exhibit throughout its lifetime. The animal intestinal tract also shows a sequence of events along its axis which reveal the nature of the developing system. A growing plant root also provides a continuously changing longitudinally oriented system upon which fungi and bacteria develop in characteristic ways (Parkinson et al., 1963).

Chance often determines which organism will colonize a new substrate, and if a pioneer obtains a considerable head start, it may be able to so adapt itself to the substrate or the substrate to it that the organism is able to maintain itself in the face of potentially stronger competitors which arrive later. Even when the first species is considerably weaker, it may remain for a long time in the face of competition simply because it was there first. Only rarely will a late arrival be able to become dominant (Gause, 1936).

In most ecosystems successional changes cannot be seen and one is presented with an already mature system. Succession can be studied in such a system in several ways. A fresh substrate can be placed in a chosen environment and population changes observed after various periods of time. Gause (1936) described experiments by Duplakov on the colonization by algae of glass slides immersed in lake water. The number of species increased for several days, but after about nine days there was little further increase and the species list remained essentially constant until the end of the experiment at 42 days. However, some of the species which appeared early on the slides disappeared later, suggesting that their initial

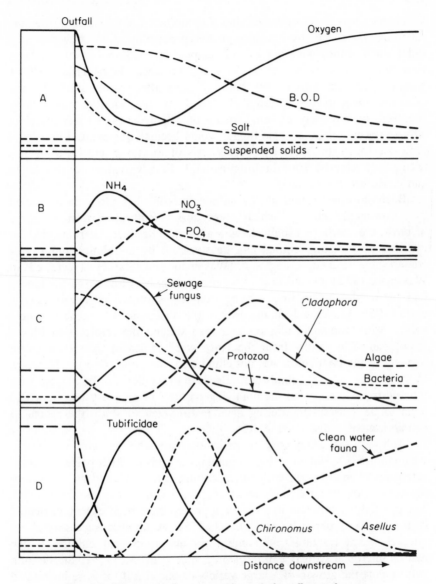

Fig. 7-3. Diagrammatic presentation of the effects of an organic effluent on a river and the changes as one passes downstream from the outfall (after Hynes, 1960). A AND B—physical and chemical changes; C—changes in microorganisms; and D—changes in larger animals. Sewage fungus is predominantly *Sphaerotilus natans*.

appearance was due to the fact that they occurred abundantly in the surrounding water, thereby having a greater probability of meeting the glass slide, but that they were not as well adapted to conditions on the slide as were the later arrivals which eventually replaced them. Tribe (1957) buried cellophane films in soil, removed them after various intervals, and examined them microscopically. He found that the cellulose was initially colonized by a variety of fungi, many of which developed side by side, although occasionally a single fungus would become dominant. Later, bacteria developed, probably by causing lysis of the fungi and by using nutrients they released from the fungi as food. Finally, nematodes developed and consumed the bacteria.

Bacterial colonization of the animal intestine has often been studied by following the changes which occur during maturation from the time of birth, the newborn usually having a sterile intestine. Alternatively, the intestine of a mature animal can be sterilized by antibiotics and its recolonization studied. Using soil, Waksman and Starkey (reviewed in Waksman, 1932) studied succession after partial heat treatment, the inoculum for recolonization thus coming from the surviving organisms. Davis et al. (1956) eliminated the majority of the organisms in a beech tree hole habitat with gamma irradiation and then studied the reformation of the population. The results from the latter work indicated that if an entire segment of the population was not eliminated, the population would return in time to the original equilibrium. Because irradiation can be applied with little destructive effect on the nonliving portions of an ecosystem, it would seem to be a useful interfering agent with which to study the return to equilibrium of a disturbed system.

Although the usual goal of an investigator who prepares an enrichment culture is to obtain a single dominant organism which possesses characteristics of interest, an enrichment culture can be viewed as a developing ecosystem, and the population changes which occur can be studied. The possibilities inherent in such an approach have been clearly presented in the excellent paper by van Niel (1955). A familiar successional sequence, which resembles in some ways an enrichment culture, is the natural microbial sequence in fermented milk (Elliker, 1949). Sterile milk will support the growth of a large variety of bacteria if they are inoculated into it in pure culture. Natural milk is always contaminated with a diversity of organisms derived mainly from the cow or barn, most of which never develop, since *Streptococcus lactis,* which arises first, forms lactic acid and lowers the pH to the point where most other organisms cannot grow, but to a point at which it also is inhibited from growing. *Lactobacillus casei* or *L. bulgaricus,* which are more acid tolerant, then develop and lower the pH further until they become inhibited. Yeasts and molds then develop, forming a film on the surface of the milk and oxidizing the lactic acid aerobically, thus raising the pH again. Since there is no more sugar left, the lactic acid bacteria are unable to take advantage of the raised pH to begin growth again, but the proteolytic bacteria are now able to grow by digesting the casein and other proteins. Eventually the milk will be completely cleared. Some of the interactions discussed in this sequence were also discussed in Chapter 6, pointing up the fact that microbial succession is another aspect of the interactions between species.

From the above analysis we see that it is impossible to state that a microbial ecosystem is determined solely by either environmental or biological factors. Organism and environment interact in an intricate manner, and the outcome is determined by both. In some systems it is the environment, in others it is the organism which is more important. Some systems will tolerate greater environmental disturbances than will others. No factor can be overlooked in attempting to understand how a system operates and is controlled.

Most microbial ecosystems lack the great stability which is possessed by many macroecosystems. Thus in terrestrial environments the stable climax sytem (e.g., forest, grassland) so modifies the environment that it is able to maintain itself in the face of considerable disturbance from the outside. In these systems the organisms are large and complex, and they have evolved to cope with the highly variable terrestrial environment (Odum, 1959). Microorganisms, on the other hand, are much simpler, with much less ability to create stable modifications in their environments. Thus a microbial ecosystem is less likely to resist an environmental change, but rather will adapt to it by changing its population structure (*see* page 160), essentially becoming a new ecosystem.

THE ORGANISMS OF AN ECOSYSTEM

It is possible to distinguish three main groups of organisms in an ecosystem: (1) dominants, those possessing the greatest activity in the system and thus having a controlling influence on the grouping of other organisms; (2) associates, those which are dependent for their development on the activities of group 1; and (3) incidentals, those which are more or less indifferent to the actions of groups 1 and 2 and which in turn have no influence on the others. In rather unselective environments, numerous species may grow, and if no one species is able to become dominant, then at equilibrium there will be a large number of species each with a small number of individuals. Interactions among species will occur, but these will be on a small scale, leading to the breakup of such an ecosystem into many small ecosystems. An analysis of the large system will be difficult and often baffling. In highly selective environments many species will not be able to grow and the few which do so will be competing more directly for the limited resources available. In the latter case, the successful competitor will most likely become dominant. Dominance will lead to interaction on a larger scale, and the analysis of the system will be simpler and more direct. However, in an unselective environment in which a given organism is able, because of some favorable opportunity, to modify the environment drastically so that other organisms can no longer grow, the favored organism can then become dominant even though the environment was initially unselective. Many polluted environments are characterized by a scarcity in number of species and by almost pure cultures with a high population density of one organism, e.g., *Sphaerotilus natans, Beggiatoa alba* (Fjerdingstad, 1964).

The manner in which various organisms and species are distributed within the ecosystem is also an important aspect of its biological characterization (Gause, 1936). Rarely are organisms randomly distributed in space. In soil, for instance, most bacteria exist in microcolonies (Jones and Griffiths, 1964), and these microcolonies also show patterns of distribution (*see* Figure 3-1). The study of these microdistributions is of great importance in autecological studies, since it provides an important element in the understanding of the interaction of an organism with its environment and with other organisms (*see* Chapter 3). Also, such distributional studies may aid in characterizing the ecosystem as a whole, since they provide an additional level of biological characterization.

ADAPTATION IN THE ECOSYSTEM

As noted earlier, a well-integrated system shows considerable ability to adapt itself to changing environments. Ecosystems can adapt in several ways. The individual members (cells) of the ecosystem may show physiological adaptation by synthesizing new enzymes in response to enzyme inducers added to the environment. Second, a change in the environment may allow for the selection of mutant types within the existing populations, leading to genetic adaptation. Third, a change in the environment may make conditions favorable for an organism which was initially present in small numbers because it could compete only poorly, but which in the new environment is able to compete well. This has been called sociological adaptation by Wuhrmann (1964b) and although unfamiliar to the physiologist or geneticist is probably the most important type of adaptation from the point of view of the microbial ecologist.

Adaptation in microbial ecosystems has been studied mostly by the sewage biologist who is concerned with the ability of treatment plants to adapt to the oxidation of new substrates. In the adaptation of sewage to the oxidation of pyridine (Ettinger et al., 1954) (Figure 7-4) there is initially a lag before the substance is oxidized, but then adaptation occurs and the material is destroyed. If now a second addition of the material is made, it is oxidized rapidly. Anaerobic sewage digesters, activated sludge

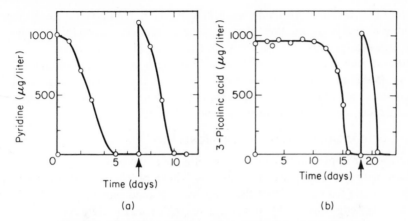

Fig. 7-4. Microbial oxidation of pyridine (*a*) and 3-picolinic acid (*b*) in river water 20°C (after Ettinger et al., 1954). At the arrow a second aliquot of the substrate was added. This figure illustrates the ability of the microbial ecosystem to adapt to new conditions. Oxidation of the first aliquot proceeds only after a considerable lag, but oxidation of the second aliquot begins immediately.

tanks, and trickling filters all show enormous powers of adaptation. Almost any organic substance added to the system is eventually oxidized.

Adaptation in the intestinal flora is often seen when an animal or human is given an antibiotic orally. The antibiotic-sensitive bacteria are prevented from growing, and yeasts, which normally occur in the intestine in only small numbers, now multiply rapidly. Such an observation shows that the intestinal environment is not inimical to yeasts, but rather that the yeasts are unable to compete with the better-adapted bacteria. Apparently the yeasts are able to multiply sufficiently in the untreated intestine to maintain themselves, thus providing a suitable inoculum when the antibiotic arrives.

Intuitively, it seems likely that since organisms do exist frequently in nature as aggregates of similar cells (*see* Chapter 5), and since this state can be maintained only by an expenditure of energy, then organisms derive benefit from associating which justifies their expenditure of energy. This raises the question of whether or not a mixed population derived from a fluctuating natural environment and placed under steady-state conditions would become simpler as time progressed. Luckey (1963) has discussed various observations related to germ-free animal research which suggests that when normal contaminated animals are placed in germ-free isolators, their bacterial flora becomes simpler with time. Although this could be due to changes in the physiology of the animal which would now make its environment inimical to the growth of some of its previously resident bacteria, it seems more likely that changes occur regularly in the normal animal microbial population, some organisms being eliminated while others are being added. In the isolators, if some organisms are eliminated, no source of new bacteria is available, so that the flora becomes simpler with time. If this interpretation is correct it suggests that in the normal animal there is a continuous tendency towards simplification of the flora which counteracts any tendency towards greater diversity.

INOCULATION OF NATURAL ENVIRONMENTS

Another approach to studying the biology of an ecosystem is to inoculate it with pure cultures of organisms which are marked genetically in some unique fashion, so that they can be reisolated unequivocally at later times. Although essentially autecological, such studies relate readily to the concepts of succession and dominance which we are discussing here. The difficulties of establishing a new organism in a functioning ecosystem are well known from studies with pathogenic and symbiotic organisms. For instance, although typhoid bacilli readily establish themselves in the intestines of many people, their introduction into the intestine of experimental animals is frequently difficult. The inoculation of legume seeds with *Rhizobium* cultures before sowing MAY result in better nodulation but often has no effect (*see* Table 8-5). Rarely does the inoculation of a cucumber or sauerkraut fermentation with special organisms provide any special advantage over allowing the natural organisms to develop. The introduction of an antibiotic-producing organism into a nonsterile soil rarely leads to its growth even though it is able to produce an antibiotic active against many of the resident organisms. Studies on the effect of environmental conditions on the rate of disappearance of introduced organisms might provide important clues to the nature of competitive interactions in natural ecosystems. Such studies have been done in model bacterial systems by Ozawa and Freter (1964), Tanami (1959) and Spaulding et al. (1964).

An experimental study with a genetically marked strain of *Paramecium aurelia* was performed by Holzman (1959). Approximately 5×10^6 animals containing equal numbers of both mating types were introduced into a small pond which already contained natural populations of two other species of paramecium but no detectable *P. aurelia*. The latter organism was readily recovered during the subsequent 3 months and seemed to be holding its own with respect to the two resident species. However, significant differences developed in the proportions of the marker genes, the frequency of one allele increasing while the other decreased, and other deviations occurred more frequently than was to be expected on the basis of random mating. Because of the length of the generation time in paramecium, three months is not a long time, and the fact that genetic changes took place suggests the rapidity with which the introduced strain began to adapt to the more selective natural conditions. The possibility for studies of this kind seems barely to have been touched.

Another use of inoculation studies could be in the analysis of food chains. Odum and Kuenzler (1963) used P^{32} to label plants in an old field ecosystem and followed the passage of label through the various members of the food chain. In principle, this procedure could be done with microorganisms, in which a pure culture could be labeled in the laboratory and introduced into the system, the label being followed through both the biotic and abiotic components of the system by microradioautography and chemical fractionation techniques.

Assessment of Microbial Substance in the Ecosystem

In assessing the activities of an ecosystem, we are mainly concerned with the various chemical transformations which are responsible for the conversions of matter and energy in the system. Since the chemical transformations in ecosystems are brought about mainly by the protoplasmic mass of living cells, we are thus concerned with the determination of the amount and activity of this protoplasmic mass. Since protoplasmic mass is often correlated with cell number, it is frequently assessed by counting the number of cells, but it should be clearly stated that CELL NUMBER ALONE IS USUALLY OF SECONDARY INTEREST and is only a way of approaching protoplasmic mass. Cell number is of primary significance only in studies on population genetics and microbial dispersal. Unfortunately, however, rarely or never can we measure directly in a complex microbial ecosystem the relative metabolic contributions of different organisms, so that to obtain some estimate of the relative contributions of various organisms, we are forced to evaluate cell numbers.

THE SIGNIFICANCE OF CELL NUMBERS

First, let us recall that many microorganisms do not exist as cells of finite and constant size. Most fungi, many algae, and some bacteria are filamentous, and in a single species filaments may vary as much as a thousand-fold in size and mass. Thus, when we consider numbers, we are usually limiting ourselves to those organisms which are unicellular and which vary in cell size within only narrow limits. Even if we limit ourselves to unicellular organisms, what do numbers really mean? Consider the data presented in Table 7-2. These data show that a single paramecium cell is equivalent in mass to 1,000,000 average bacterial cells, so that in terms

TABLE 7-2. WET WEIGHT OF SINGLE CELLS

Cell or organism	Wet weight (g)
Ostrich egg (without shell)	1.2×10^3
Valonia ventriculosa, the largest unicellular alga	6.8×10^1
Hen egg (without shell)	5.1×10^1
Typical paramecium	4.6×10^{-7}
Tetrahymena pyriformis	1.9×10^{-8}
Human erythrocyte	9.5×10^{-11}
Saccharomyces cerevisiae	7.1×10^{-11}
Chlorella vulgaris, a small alga	$\sim 3.4 \times 10^{-11}$
Typhoid bacillus	1.7×10^{-12}
Escherichia coli	9.6×10^{-13}
Influenza bacillus	2.4×10^{-14}
Pneumococcus bacterium	1.9×10^{-15}
T-even bacteriophage	3.3×10^{-16}

Data gathered from various sources.

of the amount of mass concentrated in it, a paramecium cell is a million times greater than a bacterial cell. If we assume 100% efficiency, then it would take 1×10^6 bacteria as food in order to make one new Paramecium cell. However, metabolic activity is not directly proportional to cell mass. As the mass and size of a cell increase, the metabolic activity per unit mass decreases. Representative values illustrating this point are given in Table 7-3. The reader may find a detailed compilation of respiration rates in Spector (1956).

If we assume that the QO_2 of a paramecium population is 1 and that the QO_2 of a bacterial population is 1000, 1000 bacteria are metabolically equivalent to 1 paramecium cell, and in terms of energy transformations, a paramecium cell is 1000 times as important as a bacterial cell. Thus 100 paramecium cells/ml of sample would be metabolically equivalent

TABLE 7-3. RESPIRATION RATES OF VARIOUS ORGANISMS[a]

Organism	Temperature	(QO_2)[b]
Bacillus mesentericus vulgatus	16 C	12.1
Azotobacter chroococcum	28 C	500-1000
Bacillus fluorescens non liquefaciens		4100
Neurospora crassa	26 C	6.4
Saccharomyces cereviseae	26 C	8-14.5
Paramecium	20 C	0.5

[a] From Giese (1962).
[b] QO_2 represents ml O_2 taken up per gram wet weight per hour.

to 10^5 bacterial cells/ml. Presumably metabolic reactions other than oxygen uptake would be similarly related in the two organisms.

When we consider the production of biologically active molecules, it is even more difficult to assess the activities of a cell. A bacterial cell, for instance, may produce an extremely potent toxin, so that only a few cells are needed to bring about a given effect, or it may produce a substance with low activity, so that many cells are required. The highly poisonous botulinum toxin will cause the death of a mouse when as little as 10^{-4} g is injected (Lamanna, 1959). How many cells are required to produce this much toxin? Bonventre and Kempe (1960) found that under presumably optimum conditions, 1 minimum lethal dose of toxin was produced per 100 cells; 100 cells in isolation, however, will produce no toxin, since toxin production is a population effect and at least 10^6 bacteria/ml were required before any toxin was produced. In this case, we have the additional problem of scale to consider; the mouse is so much larger than the bacterium that it would be unreasonable to expect a few bacteria to produce a significant effect. Rumen microbiologists (Annison and Lewis, 1959) consider that 10^6 bacteria/ml is the lower population limit at which a given bacterium can be expected to play any significant role in rumen activity. The sensitivity of the detection of bacteria with the microscope is such that between 10^6 and 10^7 bacteria/ml must be present before organisms can be easily seen; thus it can be suggested that if one cannot see any bacteria by microscopic examination of the habitat, then it is unlikely that bacteria are playing any particular role in this habitat. Production of substances like toxins, antibiotics, bacteriocines, enzymes and certain vitamins can thus be expected to be significant only when the population density in a given environment is fairly high, and for bacteria this critical density may be about 10^6/ml of a SINGLE SPECIES. In many cases the bacterial count is a composite of many species and consequently the significance of this count is less readily determined. Further, the production of substances which are less active per molecule would require comparatively more cells. For larger organisms such as protozoa, algae, and fungi, the number of cells needed may be considerably less, but it should also be remembered that these cells may produce less substance per unit mass, so that it is not possible to scale up the data directly from bacteria. A good rule of thumb might be that if no microorganisms are visible microscopically in a given habitat, then one should seriously question whether microorganisms are of any significance in that habitat.

Thus we must conclude that it is impossible to evaluate, from numbers alone, the ecological significance of an organism in a given habitat. One must have data on its mass, its metabolic activities, and its possible ability to produce and react to substances which have unique biological activities. Only then can cell numbers be meaningful.

However, given knowledge about an organism, one can use cell numbers in several ways. First, one can compare the numbers of an organism from two different habitats and thus evaluate the relative importance of the organism in these two habitats (Hungate, 1962). Second, since an organism, even if present in small numbers, may quickly respond to a change in environment by multiplying, it is useful to know the number of organisms which is present in order to predict whether or not there is sufficient inoculum in this environment to permit an increase if the environment changes. Third, numbers may reveal whether the habitat in question might contain a significant reservoir of an organism so as to insure its dispersal into other environments. Therefore, it is of some interest to consider ways in which cell numbers may be obtained.

METHODS FOR ENUMERATING MICROBES

The method of choice (and indeed essentially the only method) for counting protozoa and algae is by DIRECT MICROSCOPIC COUNT. These organisms are large enough to be seen easily under the microscope and they are structurally complex enough to classify microscopically. Among the algae, such methods work only for the unicellular species, the units of which are about equal in size and thus equatable with any other unit of the same species. It should be remembered, however, that two cells of the same size may differ significantly in mass, EVEN IF THEY ARE OF THE SAME SPECIES, since they may vary markedly in amount of storage products or protoplasmic content, without any difference in size (Fogg, 1965). Direct counting may be done for unicellular bacteria, and it has been done in aquatic (Collins and Kipling, 1957; Collins, 1963) and terrestrial (Allen, 1957) environments, but because of their lack of structure, it is difficult to classify bacteria in any ecologically useful way under the microscope. Further, it is difficult to distinguish a living from a dead bacterium under the microscope.

Direct microscopic observations can also be used in a qualitative manner to get some idea about the kinds of organisms present, and although this may be basically an autecological study, the information may prove useful in the overall characterization of an ecosystem. Many fungi (Menzies, 1963) can be identified microscopically or even macroscopically. Schramm (1966) has been able to identify by direct microscopy the rhizomorphs of several mycorrhizal fungi and thus has been able to relate them to both the fungus fruiting body and to the mycorrhizal root.

Using the radioautographic technique described earlier (*see* page 49) we have studied the incorporation of tritiated thymidine into *Leucothrix mucor* filaments directly in nature, as a means of determining which cells or filaments are growing. Results to date have shown gross heterogeneity; in a given area of an algal frond, most *L. mucor* filaments may be rapidly dividing, whereas a few filaments, apparently healthy, may be completely dormant. In other areas, most of the filaments may be inactive, but a single filament may be rapidly dividing. By combining radioautography with direct counting, one can obtain a considerably greater amount of information than by direct counting alone, and this technique seems to hold considerable promise for the future.

Since a single cell can give rise in culture to a single colony or clone, it is possible to get some idea of numbers by CULTURAL PROCEDURES. In liquid medium, this can be done only at limiting dilutions since, if more than one cell is inoculated into a single tube, all the progeny will mingle and cannot be separately counted. In or on semisolid media, the progeny of a single cell remain together, and eventually a macroscopic colony may be formed. Solidifying agents for culture media include agar, gelatin, and silica gel; one can also use porous supports such as membrane filters, cellophane, or papers made of glass fiber or cellulose. It is usually assumed that the solidifying agent or support is inert and does not affect the growth of the organisms, but this is rarely true. In addition to considering the effects of ingredients of the substratum, it should be remembered that the very fact that the progeny are kept together in one place opens up the possibility of growth-modifying interactions among the cells of a clone (*see* Chapter 5). Techniques for colony counting have been described for soil (Allen, 1957), fresh water (American Public Health Association, 1961), food and dairy products (American Public Health Association, 1953) and marine environments (ZoBell, 1946) and will not be elaborated here.

Provided that the semisolid medium really prevents organisms from moving around on its surface, the count obtained can never be higher than the true count; it is usually lower and frequently much lower. (Note that the words "true count" have no real meaning; any count is operationally defined and the true count cannot, by definition, be determined.) The cultural count is low because it is impossible to devise a universal medium in which all organisms are able to grow simultaneously, and it is also impossible to devise a medium which is completely selective for only one organism; if several media are used, in the hope of providing in one medium what is lacking in another, some organisms will grow on more than one medium and will thus be counted more than once, whereas some organisms will not grow on any medium and will never be counted. But the most serious difficulty of the cultural methods using semisolid media is that they are (1) selective for unicellular organisms or organisms which produce many propagules and (2) they are selective for organisms which spread rapidly on the surface of the medium, either because of motility or because of growth by extension of filaments. Alternatively, semisolid media are selective against organisms which cannot grow well against the resistance which is offered by the solid surface. Finally, an organism which was dormant in the ecosystem may still produce a colony. Thus, the organisms counted on the agar plate are not necessarily the ones which are functioning in the ecosystem.

MEASURING PROTOPLASMIC MASS

Protoplasmic mass can be used as a parameter for characterizing an ecosystem, but it is technically impossible to obtain a meaningful measure of the total biomass in most ecosystems, if by biomass we mean the living functional protoplasmic mass. Although dead organisms may carry out metabolic functions such as respiration for limited lengths of time, we look to the living organisms for the main contributions to the metabolism of the habitat, and there are unfortunately no methods for evaluating the amount of living mass, since cultural methods (*see* above) cannot be used.

The most characteristic materials of living organisms are the organic compounds. Chemical analyses for organic carbon (wet combustion) and organic nitrogen (Kjeldahl) are quite sensitive and have been widely used in limnology and soil science. As an estimate of the amount of plant material, chlorophyll content is often measured. Different groups of living organisms possess characteristic chemical substances which can be measured, such as cellulose (plants), chitin (certain animal groups and most fungi), keratin (animal hair and feathers), or diaminopimelic acid (bacteria). We have used protein and RNA analyses in the relatively simple hot spring ecosystem (*see* page 45), but in many environments even these macromolecules might upon release from dead organisms resist decomposition for considerable periods of time. In many environments such as the soil, it is usually impossible to distinguish total protoplasmic mass, living and dead, from organic debris and decomposing litter.

Measuring Microbiological Activity

Activity is a dynamic concept and expresses the ability of organisms to modify their environment. Activity can be expressed in terms of the transformations of either energy or matter, although these two factors are frequently related, since energy in living organisms is often derived from and stored as material substance. In a closed system neither energy nor matter is entering or leaving; the living organisms of the system will eventually die and the system will come to a standstill. In an open system energy is arriving and leaving. The simplest type of open system is that which is in steady state. Steady state systems can be of two types, depending on whether there is flow of energy only or of both energy and matter. A sealed microcosm (Beyers, 1963) is an example of a steady state with only energy flow. In such a system, high-grade energy enters as light, is absorbed by the system and is converted into low-grade energy as heat which then leaves. Since living organisms cannot utilize heat energy alone for metabolic functions, any energy which they convert to heat is lost as useful energy. If sufficient light energy is available to balance the energy lost, the system will be able to maintain itself. Living organisms will grow, reproduce, get old, and die, but the population density will remain generally constant. Matter will neither decrease nor increase but will cycle through the system. The earth as a whole is an open system of this type. Like the microcosm, the world is dependent on light energy and therefore on the activities of photosynthetic organisms. Although a microcosm may be a useful model, it should be realized that it lacks one of the important attributes of the world macrocosm—complexity. Random events or disease might lead to the death of the limited variety of organisms present, and the system would then be at a standstill, while complexity provides a buffer against catastrophic events which might destroy them. Lakes which acquire very little allochthonous material also approximate to microcosms (Forbes, 1887; Davis, 1958).

POPULATION TURNOVER

Although growth may be occurring at a reasonable rate, the population size and the amount of biomass in a steady state system remain essentially constant so that we cannot determine population turnover by assaying population size at different time intervals. With some microorganisms it is possible to distinguish dividing from nondividing cells microscopically. Thus we might be able to determine the percentage of cells which at any moment are in the process of mitosis or fission. If we then knew from experiments how long the fission process itself took, we might be able to estimate the turnover rate. For example, if fission took 1 hour to complete, and 1% of the cells were seen dividing at any one time, then the total population would turn over in (or the generation time would be) 100 hours. This is a procedure which is frequently used by animal embryologists and pathologists. Obviously, in a natural ecosystem with a variety of organisms present, this technique would present many difficulties, and it is also limited by the fact that one must first know the intrinsic growth rate of the organism. Cushing (1955) has measured the population turnover rate of certain diatom populations in the sea by measuring the sizes of the individual cells. He was able to do this because diatom frustules decrease in size through successive divisions, so that the number of divisions can be estimated approximately from the average size of the cells. Samples were taken from a certain station on two successive cruises, the decrease in size determined, and the division rate calculated. Then by determining the population density (the standing crop) the productivity (*see* page 179) of the system could be calculated. Cellular turnover in mammals has been estimated by the use of tritiated thymidine (Cronkite et al., 1959; Nossal and Mäkelä, 1962), based on the fact that DNA synthesis occurs only in dividing cells and occupies only a short part of the division cycle. By radioautography the portion of cells which have divided during any given time period can be determined, since only these cells will contain radioactivity derived from the labeled thymidine. We have adapted this technique to the study of the growth rates of microorganisms directly in nature (Brock and Brock, 1966a), and our preliminary results suggest that the growth rate of *Leucothrix mucor* in nature is of the same order of magnitude as it is in laboratory culture.

An interesting approach to the problem of population turnover in a bacterial system was made by Meynell and Subbaiah (1963). As noted by Woods and Foster (1964), the growth of pathogenic bacteria within an animal resembles a continuous culture more than a batch culture, since the activities of the host keep the environment constant and also limit through defense mechanisms the population density of the microorganism. Meynell and Subbaiah were interested in determining the rate of multiplication of the pathogen *Salmonella typhimurium* in the mouse, where they were faced with the problem that unknown numbers of bacteria were being eliminated by the defense systems of the animal. They made use of the fact that it was possible by abortive transduction to introduce into the organism a genetic marker which, upon division, was passed to only one of the offspring, the other daughter becoming genetically different. Thus, the proportion of cells carrying the specific marker was halved at each generation (assuming both types of cells were removed at equal rates) so that the number of divisions that had occurred at any instant could be calculated from a measure of the proportion of viable cells containing the genome as compared with the proportion in the original inoculum. Although such a technique has a restricted use, it does illustrate in principle a kind of approach that might be used.

In a system with a long time constant, such as a freshwater lake, most of the growth may occur at a particular time of the year, and if the rate of population increase is measured during this bloom, a fairly good estimate may be obtained of the yearly population turnover, although as Fogg (1965) points out: ". . . it is not strictly correct to speak of 'growth rate' in connection with natural populations of phytoplankton; 'rate of increase' is better, since the same population is not necessarily being sampled all the time, and since depletion by removal or death of cells is going on concurrently with multiplication."

In a system with continuous flow of matter, such as a chemostat or the rumen, it is possible to estimate the turnover rate directly if the flow rate and the volume are known, since the turnover rate must be just sufficient to maintain the population at a constant density. For instance, the rumen has about 10^{10} bacteria/ml of rumen contents. The rumen volume in a sheep is between 4 and 10 liters (Annison and Lewis, 1959), and the turnover rate is between 1 and 2 turnovers per day (El-Shazly and Hungate, 1965). If we assume a volume of 5 liters and a turnover time of 1.5, then using the formula of Novick (1955):

$$\alpha = \text{doubling (turnover) time} = \frac{w}{v} = \frac{\text{flow rate}}{\text{volume}} = \frac{x}{5 \text{ liters}} = 1.5/\text{day},$$

so that the flow rate is about 7.5 liters per day. With about 10^{10} bacteria/ml or 10^{13}/liter, about 7.5×10^{13} bacteria are produced in the sheep rumen ecosystem each day.

El-Shazly and Hungate (1965) have used an indirect fermentation method to measure net growth of rumen microorganisms. They assumed that if substrate is in excess, the rate of fermentation would be proportional to the total number of microbial cells. They thus determined fermentation rate as measured by gas production (volumetrically) of rumen samples to which a hay-grain mixture was added at a concentration sufficient to achieve maximum fermentation rate. By measuring maximum fermentation rate of samples immediately after removal from the rumen, and again one hour later on a parallel sample which had been incubated, they calculated the per cent net growth. This figure averaged about 8% per hour or 192% (1.92 turnovers) per day, in fairly good agreement with the estimated turnover time cited above.

Material Turnover

In terms of matter, we are interested in the rates at which specific elements and compounds are metabolized or are converted into cell material in the system. Since in the steady state the concentrations of all elements remain constant, the dynamics of the system can be measured only with isotopes. This can be illustrated by studies which have been made on the rumen fermentation. In this process, one of the main reactions is the conversion of cellulose from the feed into volatile fatty acids, of which acetic, propionic, and butyric acids are the most important. Steady state conditions are maintained, since these fatty acids are removed into the bloodstream as they are formed, so that the concentration of fatty acids varies little. In order to measure the rate of production of fatty acids in the normal rumen of the sheep, Gray et al. (1960) added known amounts (10-30 μC) of a C^{14} labeled fatty acid directly to the rumen through a fistula. Samples were taken at intervals and the fatty acids were separated by steam distillation and column chromatography; the amount and radioactivity of each acid was measured. From these values, the specific radioactivity could be calculated. Immediately after addition of the radioactive material, the specific radioactivity would be the highest, but as time went on, production of new fatty acid would lead to a decrease in specific radioactivity, the rate of which provides an estimate of the rate of synthesis. The rate of loss for each of the three acids is shown in Figure 7-5, and it can be seen that the rate is logarithmic. The rate of decrease of specific radioactivity can be expressed as $\dfrac{-dc}{dt} = kc$ where c is the concentration of C^{14} acid and k is the specific rate constant in terms of the fraction of the amount present that disappears in unit time. Upon integration we obtain $k = \dfrac{1}{t} [\log_e (\text{initial } C^{14} \text{ acid}) - \log_e (C^{14} \text{ acid at } t)]$. From the data of Figure 7-5 for acetic acid we can determine that (in 5 hours) $k = \dfrac{1}{5} [2.55 - 1.58] \times 2.3$ (converting from $\log_{10}$ to $\log_e$); $k = \dfrac{0.97}{5} \times 2.3 = 0.45/\text{hr}$. Since the concentration of acetic acid in the 5 ml sample taken was 220 mmoles, the rate of disappearance was therefore 0.45 × 220 or 99 mmoles/hr. Since the amount of acetic acid in the rumen remained approximately constant over the 5-hour period (as to be expected in a steady state), the rate of disappearance closely approximates the rate of production of the acid. In the same way the rates of produc-

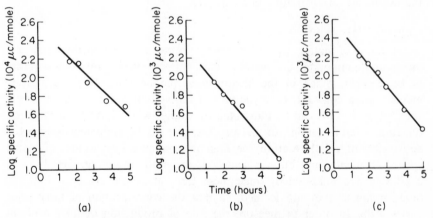

Fig. 7-5. Rate of loss of activity of labeled acids in the rumen, (*a*) acetate experiment; (*b*) propionate experiment; (*c*) butyrate experiment (after Gray et al., 1960). The loss of specific radioactivity is due to the further formation of that acid in the rumen. Since the absolute amount of each acid remained essentially constant, the rate of its formation can be calculated from the data given (*see* text).

tion of propionic and butyric acids were calculated to be 44 and 21 mmoles/hr, respectively. It is of some interest that the rates of production and the total concentrations of the three acids vary in the same way, so that a comparative measure of the total concentrations does give some idea of the relative rates of production, but of course gives no idea of the absolute rates. It is essential to know the total volume of the rumen and that this volume does not change during the time of study; the authors measure this by adding a nonmetabolizable insoluble substance (polyethylene glycol) and measuring the rate of change of its concentration with time. Also, there is some interconversion of one fatty acid to another, so that some of the radioactivity added as acetic acid ends up as propionic acid and butyric acid. If only one radioactive acid is added so as to study the rate of production of only one acid at a time, this does not present any serious difficulty, since the other acids can be isolated and their radioactivities determined. But to study the rate of production of all three acids in the same animal at the same time, all three must be added in radioactive form simultaneously, which means that the rates of interconversion cannot now be measured and must be ascertained in separate experiments. The authors have later used this technique to relate studies in an artificial rumen to in vivo studies (Gray et al., 1962, 1965).

The above analysis in a nearly ideal ecosystem indicates some of the possibilities and complications in studying ecosystem metabolism. Some of the restrictions on the method should be emphasized: (1) It is necessary to know the amount of nonradioactive material present at the time the radioactive material is added. If the nonradioactive concentration is not or cannot be measured, the radioactive technique can tell only the rate of utilization of the added compound but not the significance of this rate. Thus, one could say that the rate of utilization of a compound is 1% per hour, but without knowing the concentration of nonradioactive compound, one would not know whether this was 1% of 1 mg/ml or 1% of 1 μg/ml! Further, it would be impossible to compare two different ecosystems. (2) It must be assumed that there is no discrimination between radioactive and nonradioactive forms (which to a first approximation is a valid assumption). (3) It must be assumed or ascertained that there is complete mixing of the radioactive with the nonradioactive material. (4) It is imperative that the duration of the experiment be short as compared to the time constant of the process under study, so that only the steady state rate will be measured, for as time goes on the radioactivity initially absorbed will be released from its initial absorption sites and passed to other sites and will now be diluted with nonradioactive material derived from the initial site. Obviously, at final equilibrium the radioactivity will have been distributed exactly as the nonradioactive element, and a radioactivity measure will then give no more information about the system than would have been obtained from a chemical assay of non-radioactive material. A series of samples taken at various times should make it possible to extrapolate and determine either the initial rate or the rate of approach to equilibrium. Both of these rates may be useful on occasion.

This isotope method is an extremely useful way of studying ecosystem physiology, but in an open system with both material and energy flow (such as the rumen), the isotope technique can be used only if the flow rate is known, so that the rate of dilution of the radioactive material is known. Gray et al. (1960) measured this with polyethylene glycol, but if the flow rate is not known or is difficult to calculate, an alternative procedure is to create an artificial system without material flow within the bigger system. This is basically the procedure of the artificial rumen (Barnett and Reid, 1961; Gray et al., 1962; Walker and Forrest, 1964). The limnologist or oceanographer uses a sealed bottle of water to which the isotope has been added. With this method he knows that the concentration of isotope will not change during the duration of the experiment as a result of diffusion or convection. However, since adsorption to the bottle wall may lead to complications (*see* page 72), it would be desirable to devise a technique where the isotope could be added directly to the open water. It might be possible to follow the procedure of Gray et al. (1960) and add some nonmetabolizable substance and measure the change of its concentration with time to correct for dilution effects. The $C^{14}O_2$ technique for measuring the rate of photosynthesis in aquatic environments has been discussed in some detail by Steeman Nielsen (1963), and his review should be sought for details. Again it should be noted that the experiment must be kept short relative to the time constant of the system so that only the instantaneous rate of CO_2 fixation is measured.

Radioisotopes have also been used to measure the rate of transport of an element through an ecosystem or the transfer from mud to water (Hutchinson, 1957; F. R. Hayes, 1964; Pomeroy, 1963; Pomeroy et al., 1965). It should be clear that the isotope is then being used in a different manner from that discussed above, since in one case the interest is in the physical transport of the element and the other case, in its chemical transformations.

In ecosystems with clearly defined influx and efflux sites, it is possible to measure material transformations by measuring the chemical differences between the two kinds of sites. Clearly, the ELEMENT composition will be the same at both influx and efflux (since matter can neither be created nor destroyed) but the CHEMICAL composition can vary considerably. Such techniques have been extensively exploited in studies on the rumen and on sewage treatment plants, both of which are excellent steady state systems.

Frequently, a major element of the system is a gaseous product which is either taken up or released from the system (e.g., O_2, CO_2), providing a convenient product for measurement, since influx and efflux sites can be located at the air-water or air-land interface. If the major source of the element in the ecosystem is derived from the gas, then a measure of its flux can provide a convenient measure of the dynamic state of this element. In aerobic systems, the measurement of O_2 uptake also provides an overall indication of the energy relationships of the system, just as the measurement of O_2 production indicates photosynthetic rate. It is unfortunate that there is not a good radioisotope of oxygen, since this would make many studies easier. The chemical methods for measuring oxygen are not sufficiently sensitive to measure small changes during short periods of time, so that in oligotrophic ecosystems (e.g., lakes and oceans), determinations of O_2 flux have been mainly discarded for the more sensitive $C^{14}O_2$ methods. However, since O_2 is rarely assimilated into protoplasm to any extent, whereas CO_2 is both assimilated and converted into metabolic products, the measurement of O_2 exchange provides a more direct measure of the metabolic reactions coupled to ATP production than does CO_2 exchange. The assay of CO_2 uptake, on the other hand, provides a good indication of organic matter production (*see* page 179).

In systems in which light is the main source of energy, there is a diurnal cycle and a seasonal cycle of photosynthetic activity. Such systems lack short-term stability and are thus steady states only when viewed over a long period of time, so that diurnal variations in O_2 production or CO_2 uptake may be used to obtain a measure of the photosynthetic activity of the system. Alternatively, both day and night changes in O_2 concentration may be made at the same time by the use of paired bottles, one black and one clear. Because of seasonal variations in light intensity in the temperate climates, measurements must be made at different times of the year.

Because of the complications discussed above, each ecosystem must be considered as a separate case in any attempt to estimate material flow. The type of information that is desired must be kept clearly in mind, since each type of measurement reveals something different.

ENERGY TURNOVER

Heat energy is the basic form of energy to which all other forms are related by thermodynamic considerations, and the measurement of heat produced provides a direct estimate of the energy flow through an ecosystem. Heat production is measured by calorimetry, a technique used recently in the rumen ecosystem by Walker and Forrest (1964). Their technique makes use of a reaction vessel which holds 250 ml and is immersed in a constant temperature water bath at 39°C (the temperature of the rumen). A balance vessel identical to the reaction vessel contains water, and as heat is generated in the reaction vessel, the balance vessel is heated at the same rate by electrical energy which is measured by a strip-chart recorder. Figure 7-6 shows the rate of heat production and of gas (CO_2 plus CH_4) production for rumen contents removed from a sheep 24 hours after feeding, and it also shows the decrease in pH. Heat production increased exponentially with time after removal of the rumen contents from the sheep, and the heat production at the time of removal was determined by extrapolating to zero time. This then gave an estimate of the rate of heat production in vivo. The effect of feeding time and nature of feed on in vivo rumen function could thus be estimated, and the effect of various additives such as O_2, acid, lactate, or cellobiose on the metabolic properties of the system in vitro could be studied.

In most cases energy flow is measured indirectly by the measurement of changes in chemical substances whose potential energy is known. It has been clearly demonstrated that precisely as much heat is produced by the complete oxidation of a mole of glucose in a bomb calorimeter as in a living organism (Giese, 1962), so that unless there are indications

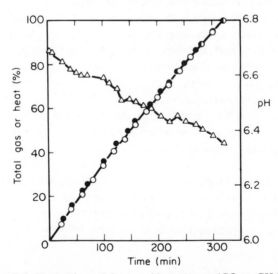

Fig. 7-6. Production of heat, acid, and gas ($CO_2 + CH_4$) in samples of rumen contents removed to a calorimeter (after Walker and Forrest, 1964). The close correspondence between the rates of production of heat and gas is noteworthy. OPEN CIRCLES, heat; CLOSED CIRCLES, gas; TRIANGLES, pH.

to the contrary it can be assumed that measurements on metabolic changes can be related to energy flow. In a steady state system (such as an adult animal) in which energy storage does not occur, the chemical energy consumed is partitioned into two parts, that excreted and that oxidized, of which the energy in the latter is released as heat. The energy content of a cell will vary with the proportions of carbohydrate, fat, and protein, but to a first approximation the cell can be considered to be at an oxidation level of carbohydrate, so that the energy content per cell can be determined from its dry weight. In aerobic microorganisms about 50% of the carbon supplied as glucose can be converted to cell substances under conditions where the glucose concentration is the limiting factor for growth, the other 50% of the carbon being converted to CO_2. The complete oxidation of glucose to CO_2 is accompanied by the release of 690 kcal/mole, and we can therefore calculate that the organism in question is liberating as heat one half of the energy supplied.

Anaerobically, the efficiency of glucose conversion to cell substances is much lower, so that considerably lower amounts of heat are released per mole of substrate metabolized and most of the energy remains in the fermentation products (e.g., lactic acid, alcohol). Forrest et al. (1961) have shown by direct calorimetry that *Streptococcus faecalis* releases about 30 kcal per mole of glucose converted to lactic acid, a value quite close to that calculated from the thermodynamic values of the glucose and lactic acid. Note that in anaerobic growth, little or none of the substrate is assimilated, the materials for cell building blocks coming from other constituents of the medium or from a small amount of the substrate which is not oxidized. The importance of this point in the energy relations of the rumen fermentation is discussed in Chapter 8 (*see* page 201).

Photoautotrophic systems present even greater difficulties to the direct measurement of energy flux. Although the energy content of incident light can be calculated precisely, it can rarely be determined how much of the light is absorbed in a photosynthetically active form. Most of the light is transmitted, reflected, or absorbed by nonphotosynthetic materials. Note that not even all of the light absorbed by a cell is photosynthetically active, since constituents other than the photosynthetic pigments are able to absorb light. Since the energy acquired from light is dissipated through respiration, energy flux could be measured calorimetrically by measuring the heat production in the system. This has apparently never been done, and energy flow is usually calculated indirectly through measurements of biomass turnover or photosynthetic rate. In the latter case, O_2 production or CO_2 consumption is measured, and it is assumed that photosynthesis leads to the production of carbohydrates by the stoichiometry: $6CO_2 + 6H_2O \rightarrow C_6H_{12}O_6 + 6O_2 + 690$ kcal. In such studies, losses due to respiratory activity of both the plants themselves and their predators should be deducted, although these losses are usually undefinable.

Note that unless calorimetry is used, the measurement of energy flux is being derived from data on material turnover, so that in principle no new information is obtained by converting the values from grams of carbon to kilocalories of energy. Although energy flux is a more fundamental measure of the function of an ecosystem than is material flux (Macfadyen, 1963), because of the impossibility of calorimetric studies in many ecosystems, energy flux is not readily measured. Parenthetically, it should be noted that microbial ecosystems are the most susceptible to calorimetric analysis. The value of calorimetry in the study of ecosystem metabolism was emphasized by Walker and Forrest (1964): ". . . heat production is a fundamental physical quantity directly related to the rate of metabolism, so that changes in a steady state of metabolism will be reflected by changes in the rate of heat production."

Energy flow and the food chain

In many ecosystems, essentially all of the incident energy is dissipated within the system. For example, in an activated-sludge sewage treatment plant (*see* page 149), up to 95% of the organic material is oxidized within the system to CO_2 and H_2O, with the production of heat. In such a process the primary energy converters are the zoogloeal bacteria which oxidize about half of the organic matter but convert the rest into cell substance. In the absense of predators some essential nutrient in the environment would probably become limiting and the organisms would stop growing. They would slowly decompose by autolysis, releasing more energy as heat, but retaining much of the energy in the autolytic products. If predators are present the situation is much different, since they consume the bacteria and release the bacterial energy as heat. Although flocs of a single kind of organism can accomplish much in the degradation of organic matter, the most efficient flocs are those with a population of animals which eat the bacteria and thus keep the floc in a dynamic state (Lackey and Smith, 1956). The protozoa may play a similar role in the rumen ecosystem (Coleman, 1963).

In an extended food chain, energy loss occurs at each step so that eventually all of the energy of the system is degraded to heat. If the efficiency of the conversion were, for example, 50% at each step in the chain, then for a food chain of three organisms the energy remaining would be $0.5 \times 0.5 \times 0.5 = 0.125$; i.e., 87.5% of the energy would be dissipated. Slobodkin (1962b) has provided a useful discussion of energy in animal ecology; the principles apply equally well to heterotrophic microorganisms. Unfortunately, microbial food chains are extremely difficult to analyze in quantitative or even qualitative terms because of the small size and enormous numbers of cells (*see* Chapter 9).

PRODUCTIVITY

The productivity of an ecosystem is usually defined as the total amount of organic matter fixed by the system. Primary productivity is that fixed photosynthetically, and secondary productivity is that fixed heterotrophically. The carbon of the organic substances fixed by primary producers is derived from CO_2. Productivity is easier to determine than either material turnover or energy flow in systems which have little importation or exportation of organic matter. Primary productivity can be divided into three components: cell substances synthesized, organic matter produced by the plant but consumed by plant respiration, and organic matter excreted into the environment. In the marine environment it is felt that excretion is insignificant (Steeman Nielsen, 1963) in terms of total energy content (although it may be significant in terms of the kinds of excreted molecules), but in the freshwater environment considerable primary production may occur in this form (Fogg, 1962) (*see* Figure 9-2). Excretion has not been measured quantitatively in the terrestrial environment, although it is known that the microorganisms in the rhizosphere of roots are living on excreted materials (Starkey, 1958). If we ignore excretory products, primary productivity may then be divided into gross productivity, which is the total amount of carbon fixed by the plants, including that eventually released in respiration, and net production, which is that carbon converted into plant tissues. The latter is of the most ecological interest, since it represents the material potentially available to heterotrophs.

In a steady state the total amount of organic matter should remain constant, so that production is balanced by consumption. Thus in a natural grassland or forest, without migrating animals, from one year to the next the standing crop may remain constant, but during the year a new crop is born and dies. In principle, since in terms of organic matter these are closed systems (there being neither importation nor exportation of organic material), it is possible to measure net productivity in two ways. One can measure the rate of CO_2 fixation and deduct an estimated value for plant respiration, which is difficult to do. Alternatively, one can measure the rate of decomposition of plant material by microbes; this has frequently been done in productivity studies with apparently valid results. Decomposition can be estimated by measuring the weight loss of a representative sample of plant material which has been laid on the ground in a more or less natural position (but with some device to prevent any of the material from blowing away). In this way the rate of decomposition over a yearly period can be estimated, and if the standing crop is known, the net productivity is calculable (Wiegert and Evans, 1964; Ovington, 1962). Net productivity could also be calculated by cropping, in which the plants would be cut, removed, and weighed. By cropping just sufficiently to maintain a constant amount of biomass, one could calculate the productivity rate, but essential soil minerals might be removed in cropping that would not be removed upon microbial decomposition; if the steady state were to be maintained, these minerals would have to be replaced.

In aquatic environments it is difficult to measure the decomposition rate or cropping rate, so productivity is usually measured by the fairly easy method based on CO_2 fixation. The role of microorganisms in overall productivity is discussed in Chapter 9.

CHAPTER 8

Interactions of Microorganisms with Macroorganisms

As noted in Chapter 6, it is convenient to distinguish between interactions of microorganisms with each other and their interactions with macroorganisms, since in the former case the interaction is between similarly scaled organisms, while in the latter case the macroorganism far exceeds in mass its associated microbes. For the microbe to have any noticeable effect on its macrohost will probably require the development of highly specific mechanisms on the part of the microbe. As also noted earlier, it is difficult to devise a clear-cut separation among neutral, beneficial, and antagonistic relationships, and relationships between the same two organisms can have elements of any of these categories, depending on environmental and other factors or on the interest of the investigator.

It is usual to distinguish obligate from facultative parasites and symbionts on the basis of whether or not the microorganism in question has
been cultivated in the laboratory, but this distinction has several difficulties. In addition to the fact that improved laboratory methods may convert
an erstwhile obligate parasite into a facultative one, the distinction ignores
the ecological relationship of parasite to host; the critical question is
whether or not the parasite can grow saprophytically in nature, i.e., in
competition with all other saprophytes. Many organisms (e.g., *Salmonella
typhosa*, *Ustilago zeae*) which can be cultured quite successfully in the
laboratory are most likely obligate parasites in nature and should be
treated as such in any attempt at an intelligent analysis of their relationship to the host, just as other organisms (e.g., *Clostridium botulinum*)
are quite successful saprophytes in nature but under certain conditions
may become converted into harmful BUT NOT PARASITIC organisms. Likewise, there are organisms such as many of the mycorrhizal fungi which
are obligate symbionts in nature, whereas there are organisms such as
the root-nodule rhizobia which are indubitably symbionts but also grow
quite successfully in nature as saprophytes.

Person (1966) has made a penetrating analysis of evolutionary and
genetic relationships between host and microbe and has emphasized the
requirement for complementarity between two organisms. Person develops
in particular the hypothesis of a gene-for-gene relationship between host
and parasite, stating that for each locus in the host which conditions
some aspect of invasion or virulence by the parasite, there is probably
a specific, related locus in the parasite which counteracts or comple-
ments the locus of the host. These complementary relationships evolve
because sensitive hosts will be eliminated if they become infected, and
any resistant mutants of the host will be favored, so that eventually the
population of sensitive hosts will decrease to the point where the parasite
is no longer able to maintain itself in the population. But as this point is
reached, selection will now be maximal with respect to the parasite which
can no longer find susceptible hosts, and mutants of the parasite which are
able to attack the resistant hosts will then be selected for and will increase in numbers, while the unsuccessful parasites will die. At this point,
the genes in the host which conferred resistance to the previous parasite
are superfluous and would be expected to disappear, so that when the
new parasite has risen again to a high density, selection in the host will
again be initiated against this new parasite. "These considerations lead
to the conclusion that systems involving parasitism are inherently un-
stable, with each microevolutionary step containing causal ingredients for
the step which follows . . . [and] the relevant factors function together
as a feed-back system, operating through the dynamics of density pres-

sure, selective pressure, and genetic changes within the interacting populations" (Person, 1966). Such gene-for-gene relationships have been demonstrated most clearly in the plant pathogenic fungi but have also been found in predator-prey relationships, virus-host interactions, the rhizobium-legume symbiosis, and in systems involving mimicry, where the genes for color and pattern that are to be of selective value to the mimic are predetermined by the relevant genes in the organism to be mimicked. As Person has noted, there is an element of circularity in the experimental demonstration of the complementarity of two genes, since a gene in one organism can be defined only in relationship to its complement in the other and vice versa. However, we may note that this same circularity exists in the definition of many other entities, e.g., antibody-antigen, enzyme-substrate, gene-enzyme.

Animals and plants live constantly in environments rich in microorganisms, and since the fluids and cellular substances of higher organisms are readily decomposable, it is obvious that barriers to the entrance and establishment of microorganisms must exist. In the living organism, microbes are usually only on surfaces which are exposed to the outside, but as soon as the organism dies, these barriers are breached and microbes spread quickly and colonize the whole creature. We will find that any mechanism of defense in a living host has its counterpart in a mechanism of invasion in a microbe.

Defense mechanisms can be grouped under three headings: (1) static defense structures existing prior to infection and acting mainly as barriers to penetration; (2) dynamic defense structures which appear after infection as a response to invasion and which prevent further spread; (3) physiological and biochemical mechanisms, such as are involved in the production of a toxic substance which affects the microbe, or which alter the nutritional and physiological aspects of the organism so that the microbe cannot grow and establish itself.

A microbe is able to grow on or in a higher organism if it: (1) is able to evade the defense mechanisms of the higher organism and (2) if it finds the nutritional and environmental conditions of the higher organism suitable for its needs. It should be remembered that even though plants and animals do contain rich stores of organic and inorganic nutrients, they still provide selective environments in which only certain microorganisms can grow. Indeed, each region of a plant or animal may provide a different selective environment in which will develop a different microbial flora (e.g., see Marples, 1965). In many cases, the macroorganism is essentially a magnified microenvironment in much the way that an enrichment culture is (see page 27) and thus offers us an ecological situation of relative simplicity, making analysis in both field and laboratory easier. It is mainly for this reason that we have here one of the most sophisticated areas of microbial ecology.

Growth of Microorganisms
on and in Plants

TERRESTRIAL PLANTS

Each plant cell possesses a cell wall which is a barrier to penetration. In addition, the waxy cuticle of the leaf surface not only offers resistance to penetration but also does not wet well, preventing the accumulation of any free liquid which could provide a means for initial multiplication. However, leaves have natural pores, the stomates, through which microorganisms can pass. Some plants deposit silicic acid on the surface of leaves which increases resistance to fungus penetration. Stems, especially of long-lived woody plants, often have effective barriers in the form of thickly suberized or lignified surfaces. Buds and flowers, however, are more vulnerable to invasion because their surface structures are less heavily suberized. Roots often have thick cortical areas of lignified tissue, especially in the older portions of the plant, but root hairs and unlignified root tips may be favorable portals of entry for many organisms (Akai, 1959). The lack of a continuous vascular system in plants, compared to animals, undoubtedly greatly restricts the ability of microorganisms to spread through the plant, which may partially explain the lack in plants of the more sophisticated defense mechanisms possessed by animals.

Many fungi can penetrate plant cell walls directly, usually by the production of cellulases and pectinases which cause local dissolution. Pectinolytic enzymes produced by soft-rotting bacteria and fungi cause dissociation of the middle lamellae of plant cells, thereby enabling the organism to spread through the plant tissue although still in an extracellular fashion (Wood, 1955, 1960). Plant cells have cytoplasmic connections called plasmodesmata through which some microorganisms and especially viruses can move. Root nodule rhizobia (Nutman, 1963) possess a specific mechanism for penetrating a sensitive host (*see* page 208). Many organisms enter plants through wounds and abrasions.

DEFENSE REACTIONS exhibited by plants against invading organisms include: (1) production of local regions of corky layers which wall off an infecting organism; (2) formation of gummy deposits (tyloses) in vascular bundles, preventing an organism from spreading through these vessels; (3) swelling and thickening of cell walls in the infected region; (4) necrosis of cells in the infected region, surrounding the microbe with dead tissues and interrupting its nutrient supply (Akai, 1959). No unequivocal evidence exists for the production by plants of specific antibodies.

Some plants produce DIFFUSIBLE SUBSTANCES which pass into the immediate environment and thereby prevent the establishment of microbes even in peripheral layers. Onions produce phenols, particularly protocatechuic acid, which are involved in their resistance to onion smudge. The HCN excreted by flax roots is involved in resistance to Fusarium wilt; sensitive flax varieties do not produce this substance (Allen, 1959). Some plants contain within their cells toxic substances which do not diffuse out but which an organism will encounter upon invasion. These include phenols like chlorogenic acid and alkaloids such as the fungitoxic substance tomatin produced by tomato plants. It is frequently difficult to obtain direct experimental proof that a substance found within a plant is responsible for resistance. It is essential to show that the substance is always present in resistant plants, is always absent in sensitive plants, and that the concentrations present within the plant are sufficiently high so that the invader would be expected to be inhibited.

One resistance mechanism which has been studied in some detail involves the fungus *Ophiobolus graminis* which causes take-all disease of oats, wheat, and barley. Oats are resistant to infection by this fungus because they produce a chemical substance, named avenacin, inhibitory to the growth of most varieties of the pathogen as well as other fungi. Avenacin is a complex glycoside containing a terpene, N-methylanthranilic acid, two glucose units and an unidentified sugar (Maizel et al., 1964; Burkhardt et al., 1964). Certain strains of the pathogen named *O. graminis* var. *avenae* produce an enzyme called avenacinase which removes the unidentified sugar, thus rendering avenacin nontoxic. This is an example of how a gene-for-gene relationship between host and parasite might be translated into molecular terms.

The reader is referred to the treatise by Horsfall and Dimond (1959) for details on the mechanisms by which microorganisms evade the chemical defenses of the host.

There is considerable unity in biochemistry, and the protoplasmic constituents in one organism usually resemble those in another, but it is still possible for one organism to lack a specific growth factor required by another, thus preventing the establishment of an invader. For instance, vitamin B_{12} is not produced by plants (Hutner et al., 1956), and an organism requiring this vitamin would not be expected to grow within plant cells. Further, even if a growth factor required by a parasite is present in the host, it is possible that the concentration of this factor may not be high enough to insure optimal growth of the parasite.

Orchid embryos produce inhibitory substances when they are confronted with their fungal symbionts, leading to a system of balanced infection in which the symbiont grows but is prevented from proliferating extensively and becoming a parasite (*see* page 219). In many cases of injury induced by microorganisms, the wounded tissue produces phenolic substances which probably aid in defense (Allen, 1959).

The most interesting and widely studied region of the terrestrial plant has been the rhizosphere, which is the region immediately outside the root (Starkey, 1958; Rovira, 1965). It has long been known that the numbers of microorganisms are much higher adjacent to the root surface than elsewhere in the soil. In addition, the microorganisms in this region differ qualitatively from organisms elsewhere in the soil; many of them require amino acids, vitamins and other growth factors (*see* page 39). However, it is difficult to determine if there is a specific rhizosphere flora, since many of the organisms found in the rhizosphere may occur elsewhere in the soil, but in smaller amounts. It is also known that some of the organisms isolated from the rhizosphere are able to synthesize vitamins and growth factors which other organisms may then use. Roots excrete organic substances of a wide variety including amino acids, vitamins, sugars, tannins, alkaloids, phosphatides, and unidentified substances (Starkey, 1958). Since most of these substances are readily decomposable by soil microorganisms, it is understandable that the rhizosphere would be the zone in the soil of most intense microbial activity. A direct visualization of bacterial microcolonies in the rhizosphere was obtained by Linford (1942) and is illustrated in Figure 8-1.

In addition to the plant affecting the microorganism, the inverse is also possible: the microbe may do things of benefit or harm to the plant.

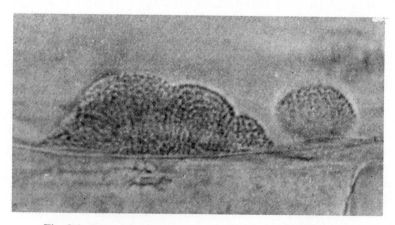

Fig. 8-1. Bacterial colonies on a root of a maize seedling (Linford, 1942) 1150X. Roots were carefully removed from soil, fixed in formalin–acetic acid–alcohol, cleared in lactophenol, and stained with acid fuchsin. The orderly arrangement of cells in the larger colony is noteworthy.

We are not concerned here with specific parasitic or symbiotic relationships but with more casual relationships. The microorganisms, through their metabolic activity, may alter the physical and chemical environment of the root, affecting the pH, oxygen tension, or CO_2 concentration. Further, microbes may produce specific organic substances which could enter plants and promote or retard their growth and activity. Unfortunately, there is little information on this point. As Starkey says: "Whereas there is considerable information about microorganisms in the rhizosphere, what is known is more general than absolute. The rhizosphere effect is definitely established but its significance is obscure." (Starkey, 1958)

The portions of plants which are above ground are less likely than the roots to contain large numbers of microorganisms. This is probably mainly a matter of moisture, since the air surrounding plants is rarely humid enough to support microbial growth, but it should also be noted in any case that a plant has much more root than shoot surface exposed to the outside world (Park, 1963). Further, there is less chance of excretion of organic materials through the waxy surfaces of leaves and the corky surfaces of stems. However, the phyllosphere is well developed in tropical plants, where high rainfall and humidity make the leaf surface more suitable for microbial colonization (Ruinen, 1961; Last and Deighton, 1965). As soon as the plant topples and comes in contact with the soil, the stems and leaves are rapidly colonized by microorganisms. Thus, the ability to remain rigid will promote long plant life, and it is no accident that the oldest plants are woody trees.

The flowers of plants do furnish transitory environments in which microbes can grow, especially in the nectaries. Fruits contain large concentrations of sugars and other organic storage products, and as soon as the waxy coating of the fruit is broken, microbes begin to grow. The universal presence of yeasts on apple fruits (Bowen and Beech, 1964) is due to the fact that the apple while still on the tree provides a large number of sites where yeast growth can be initiated. Later, when the apple is squeezed for cider, these yeasts are mixed with the sugary apple juice and develop rapidly, thus explaining why it is possible to produce hard cider (and many other types of wine) without intentionally inoculating the juice. Tree exudates (Phaff and Knapp, 1956) and insect tunnels in trees (Baker, 1963) also are favorable habitats for the growth of yeasts and fungi, the organisms presumably living on the soluble compounds exuded by the tree. The microcolonies which grow in these habitats become the food of the boring insects. An illustration of the extensive fungal growth in one of these insect tunnels is shown in Figure 8-2.

Unfortunately, little has been done on the growth of microorganisms on plant parts except in relation to plant disease or such practical problems

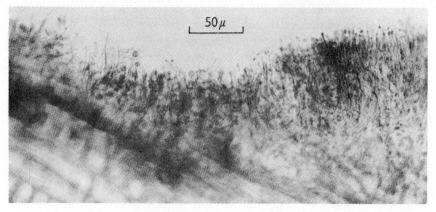

Fig. 8-2. Transverse section of tunnel of the oak pinhole borer, *Platypus cylindrus,* showing hyphae, conidia, and chlamydospores of the fungus *Sporothrix* (Baker, 1963).

as the origin of fecal microorganisms in foods (Mundt et al., 1962; Frazier, 1958).

AQUATIC PLANTS

Aquatic plants are almost always colonized with epiphytes which presumably live on nutrients diffusing more or less passively out of the plant parts. According to Gessner (1955) algae excrete primarily amino acids, whereas higher aquatic plants excrete carbohydrates. Up to 10% of the total photosynthate of higher plants may be excreted; this excretion shows a diurnal rhythm, occurring only in the daytime (Gessner, 1955). Thus we can view the microflora on the surface of aquatic plants as analogous to the rhizosphere flora, but it seems likely that the aquatic microflora should show a richer development, since conditions of moisture and nutrition are probably more uniformly favorable. I have estimated by direct microscopy that bacterial development on marine red algae is often greater than 10^8 cells/ml. Because aquatic plants are rarely of economic importance, there has been little done on their relationships to microorganisms. Presumably some of the same mechanisms discussed for terrestrial plants would be involved in defense. It has been reported (Conover and Sieburth, 1964) that the seaweed Sargassum produces antibiotics active against aquatic bacteria. The extensive colonization of the surface of most healthy aquatic plants with epiphytic bacteria, fungi, and algae suggests that these surfaces are not inimical to microorganisms, and that the main defense in these plants is the mechanical barrier of the plant cell wall. Although a dead terrestrial plant stem may resist decay for many years if it remains erect, a dead aquatic plant stem can resist decay only if it becomes buried in anaerobic sediment (Vallentyne, 1962; Francis, 1954). At least one factor which affects the susceptibility of aquatic plants to colonization by epiphytic microorganisms is the nature of the plant surface. For instance, I have observed that brown algae exude copious amounts of mucilaginous material and rarely contain permanently attached epiphytes, whereas red algae do not produce much surface mucilage and are frequently extensively colonized with epiphytes.

Growth of Microorganisms
on and in Animals

Knowledge of defense mechanisms in animals is restricted to two groups: insects (Benz, 1963) and vertebrates (Wilson and Miles, 1957). Invasion of the INSECT may be through the integument, tracheal system, gut, rectum, or by transovarian transmission. The chitinous epidermis is an effective barrier against penetration by protozoa, bacteria, and viruses, although some fungi produce chitinases which enable them to invade. The tracheal system, although chitinous, is more easily invaded, especially in the finer terminations where chitin is thin or absent. As in all animals, the intestinal tract of insects is easily accessible to microorganisms, and bacteria and protozoa are especially abundant, but these organisms are ordinarily unable to penetrate the gut lining.

Many microorganisms may induce fatal infections in insects once they break the exterior barriers. Phagocytosis may occur (Stephens, 1963), but it is not certain if this is important in immunity. Although acquired immunity can occur, the specificity and mechanism of such immunity is unknown, but it is fairly certain that typical mammalian-type antibodies are not involved.

Work on defense mechanisms against microorganisms by VERTEBRATES, especially mammals, is well covered in the literature on medical microbiology and will not be considered in detail here. The skin is an efficient barrier against microbial invasion, both in a mechanical way through the development of keratinized, hairy, and feathery layers, and through the secretion of specific antimicrobial substances, although the skin itself provides a variety of microenvironments in which microorganisms develop (Marples, 1965). Most organisms invade the skin through pores or wounds, but some dermatophytic fungi produce keratinases which probably promote invasion. The mucous membranes provide a mechanical barrier in the gastrointestinal, respiratory, genital, and urinary tracts. Antibacterial products such as lysozyme probably play an important role in defense against invasion, especially in the eye, although many bacteria are lysozyme resistant. However, such organisms may be converted to lysozyme sensitivity by the action of specific antibodies.

A variety of mechanisms exist in vertebrates which aid in defense against injurious agents. These include: inflammatory responses, phagocytosis, action of the reticulo-endothelial system, fibrin clotting, and immunological responses (e.g., specific antibody formation). It should be noted that nothing like specific antibody formation is found in higher plants or lower animals (The orchid defense reaction described on pages 185 and 219 lacks specificity.), and it might be inquired as to why higher animals have evolved a defense mechanism which discriminates among invaders. It should be noted also that if a higher animal encounters a foreign antigen in embryonic or early infant life, it usually becomes tolerant to this antigen and will not form antibodies against it. The fact that ruminants and many other mammals are dependent on microorganisms for their livelihood (see page 198) suggests that they have evolved mechanisms for discriminating between beneficial microorganisms, those it encounters early and to which it becomes tolerant, and harmful microorganisms, those it encounters later in life. The mammal is the most complicated of animals and has the most complicated array of defense mechanisms. It is regrettable that from a comparative point of view simpler animals have not been studied more, since it might be possible to sort out the importance of various mechanisms more readily in these lower creatures. Metschnikoff discovered phagocytosis while studying a disease of Daphnia! (Brock, 1961).

A phagocytic cell ingests microorganisms and thus the cell participates actively in the process of microbial penetration. Many bacteria are able to resist digestion within phagocytic cells, and some may even grow there. Viruses also enter cells passively, mainly by phagocytosis or pinocytosis, although the myxoviruses possess a specific enzyme, N-acetyl neuraminidase, which is probably involved in the invasion of mucous membrane cells.

The circulatory system of the higher animal provides a ready transportation route for a microbe which has breached the external barriers, but the lymph nodes, liver, and spleen straddle the circulatory system and function in the removal and destruction of microbes and foreign particulate matter. It should also be noted that areas such as the gastrointestinal, respiratory, genital, and urinary systems, are exposed to the outside world and in these areas microorganisms can and do flourish.

Although the interior of an animal body provides an ideal site for microorganisms to grow, even here a selective environment exists, since the high temperature and aerobic condition would select against many microbes. Even nutritionally the animal may be deficient, as shown by the decreased virulence of mutants of *Salmonella typhosa* requiring various growth factors (e.g., purines, aspartic acid, p-amino benzoic acid) and by the restoration of virulence by injecting into the animal the factor required by the mutant (Stocker, 1959).

The nature of the microbial flora indigenous to man and other mammals has been reviewed by Rosebury (1962). This work shows that a given animal provides a wide variety of selective environments, since even those areas of the body which are universally infected do not always contain the same kinds of microbes. The skin, upper respiratory tract, mouth, and intestinal tract all have their own unique microbial floras. Only in rare instances, such as in the Antarctic penguin (Sieburth, 1959), are animals found which lack an intestinal flora.

An interesting example of adaptation of parasites to their vertebrate hosts involves a mechanism called molecular mimicry (Damian, 1964). A number of bacterial, viral, and animal parasites produce antigens which are identical with or cross-react with host antigens. Since an animal does not form antibodies against its own tissue substances, this means that the animal does not produce antibodies against these antigens of the parasite, thus presumably giving the parasite an advantage in invasion. Conceivably, if the parasite were a highly virulent one, hosts which produced the antigen in question would be eliminated, and resistant hosts would arise which could not produce the antigen, resulting in a parasite-induced molecular evolution in the host. This would lead to the type of gene-for-gene correspondence between host and parasite described above (page 182), but with both organisms producing the same substance rather than complementary substances.

Effects of Microorganisms on Higher Organisms

First, it should be remembered that the use of words like "benefit" and "harm" represent value judgments on the part of the scientist and are not relevant to an evaluation of the interrelationship between a host and a microbe. What is required is a precise statement of the changes which are induced in a host upon interaction with the microbe, as influenced by environmental factors and by the genomes of host and microbe. It should be remembered that probably no organism does something merely for the benefit or harm of another; it must derive benefit itself or else it would be wasting energy which could go into more productive directions, although the benefit it derives may be indirect through the promotion of the survival of its required host.

A study of host-microbe interactions, whether related to pathogenesis, symbiosis, or neutrality, requires the use of the concepts embodied in

Koch's postulates. Both host and microbe must be experimentally available separately from the other, so that the properties of each can be examined and compared with the properties of the two in concert. Microorganisms usually present no unsurmountable problems as far as pure culture techniques are concerned, but the isolation of the host in pure culture (e.g., in the "germ-free" condition) is another matter. It is perhaps unfortunate that so much can be done with conventionally grown plants and animals, as this has tended to inhibit the development of germ-free techniques. In studying the more dramatic forms of pathogenesis, one does not need germ-free organisms because most creatures are already free from the microbe in question, otherwise they would not be alive. This explains the early success of Koch's school in isolating the causes of various diseases even without the availability of germ-free animals. With regard to the study of subclinical, latent, and beneficial infections, germ-free hosts are acutely necessary, as is now being more widely recognized (Luckey, 1963).

The culture of germ-free animals was once a technical tour de force, but with modern technology it is no longer a difficult matter. Recent reviews by Lev (1963) and Luckey (1963) should be consulted for current studies and for references to the earlier work. The establishment of a germ-free animal colony hinges on the fact that unborn animals are frequently sterile until birth, so that if Caesarian section is performed just before the time of expected birth, the germ-free infants can be placed in isolators and fed aseptically by hand. Once a germ-free colony is established, the second and subsequent generations can be derived by appropriate matings from the first generation. In birds the situation is easier, since the egg is usually sterile and the newborn chick is able to feed itself.

The problem of germ-free maintenance of lower animals is not great, although frequently difficulties are found in obtaining an initially germ-free stock. It may be possible to disinfect the surface of eggs by the use of merthiolate (Provasoli and Shiraishi, 1959) or other disinfecting agents. The eggs or animals may also be treated with antibiotics to eliminate bacterial contamination, but there are no nontoxic antibiotics which are really effective against all fungi and protozoa. Viruses and other intracellular organisms will probably not be eliminated in all cases. Since these organisms may remain latent for a long time, it is difficult even to know that they exist. The success of the operations depends on the ability to recognize all foreigners which may be present (*see* page 25). Even the most general sterility test medium will not allow certain organisms to grow, especially protozoa and viruses.

The mature seed of an angiosperm plant is usually surrounded by a tough seed coat, and the seed within is usually sterile. It is thus easy to disinfect the surface and then allow the seed to germinate in a sterile environment. Germ-free plants can be easily raised to maturity, although with large plants there are technical problems involving space. Lower plants and algae also present no problems, although some seaweeds in germ-free culture do not exhibit normal structure (Provasoli, 1958b). Considering how easy it is to raise germ-free vascular plants, it is surprising that more work has not been done with them.

ALGAE AND AQUATIC INVERTEBRATES

A wide variety of aquatic invertebrates harbor intracellular algae (Droop, 1963); such associations are found in both marine and freshwater forms. The algae are always coccoid and are mainly from three classes: blue-greens, greens, and Dinophyceae. The green algae, which occur exclusively in freshwater animals, are usually called zoochlorellae and can be assigned to the genus *Chlorella*. In the marine environment, the Dinophyceae predominate, and they are usually called zooxanthellae. Initial infection of an animal undoubtedly occurs by ingestion of free-living algae, but to persist the alga must be able to resist digestion and to grow. Once an animal is infected, the algal cells are distributed more or less equally between the daughter cells at division. Droop speculates that only a few species of algae have been able to survive intracellular ingestion, and that this is why the range of intracellular algal species is so limited. Presumably the cellulose cell wall confers some protection on the algae, but there must be additional factors, since Siegel (1960) has shown that various strains of Chlorella differ in their ability to infect various strains of *Paramecium bursaria,* and the genetics of host and symbiont must be matched. This suggests that zoochlorellae have evolved specific mechanisms to cope with the intracellular environment. Corals can be depleted of their zooxanthellae symbionts by placing the animals in continuous darkness, the animals extruding the algae under these conditions. Presumably the coccoid forms have some selective intracellular advantage over filamentous algae, explaining the restriction of the symbionts to only one morphological type.

In discussing the integrative properties of the alga-invertebrate association it should be remembered that just because the two organisms of a pair can be cultured separately in the laboratory, they are not necessarily able to lead independent existences in more competitive natural environments. The example of the lichen relationship (*see* Chapter 6) should be recalled. Further, even if the organisms were found to be able to live apart in nature, it can still not be denied that they do benefit by living together in nature, since they are found more often together than separately. *Paramecium bursaria,* for instance, is always found in nature with its algal symbiont, and coral reefs also show this obligate natural association (Yonge, 1963). As Droop has stated: ". . . this does not preclude an association, however casual, from having great ecological value, for an advantage, seemingly of marginal physiological consequence when viewed in isolation, may assume an overriding significance in the face of nature."

The photosynthetic algae synthesize O_2 in the light, and the positive phototaxis exhibited by animals with algal associates is almost surely due to an indirect aerotaxis, since the phototactic response ceases when the symbiont is eliminated (Droop, 1963). Under favorable conditions in corals, the amount of O_2 synthesized by the alga may greatly exceed that consumed by alga plus animal in the daylight, but over a 24-hour period consumption probably exceeds production, since the animals have no way of storing oxygen. However, since corals live in warm tropical waters where the solubility of oxygen gas might be limiting (*see* Table 2-3), it seems reasonable that the surplus oxygen synthesized by the alga might be just sufficient to convert a partially anoxic environment into an aerobic one, especially within the deeper portions of the coral where gaseous diffusion might be restricted.

During photosynthesis CO_2 is taken up, and Goreau (1961) has shown the probable relationship of this to the process of calcification and skeleton formation in corals. The tropical marine environment is saturated with calcium ions, held in solution as calcium bicarbonate. With the removal of bicarbonate during photosynthesis, the environment becomes supersaturated with respect to calcium which precipitates as calcium carbonate.

Muscatine and Lenhoff (1963) measured the rate of uptake of $C^{14}O_2$ by green or albino *Chlorohydra viridissima*. After the hydra were incubated, the algal-containing gastroderm was separated from the algal-free ectoderm and the relative rates of incorporation into these two fractions was measured. Figure 8-3 shows that most of the radioactivity was incorporated into the gastroderm, but that there was some incorporation into the ectoderm (about 12% of the total). Since the albino animals incorporated very little radioactivity, the authors assume that the incorporation into the ectoderm of the green animals is due to transfer from the gastroderm. By biochemical fractionation techniques they obtained further evidence to substantiate this point and conclude that at least some of the assimilation products of the alga can pass into the animal tissue. Whether or not ALL of the nutrition of the invertebrate could be obtained by way of algal photosynthesis has not been shown conclusively, although in view of the small biomass of the alga in relation to the animal (around 5% in coral), complete dependence on the alga would not seem likely. It is conceivable that the main contribution of the alga to the animal is in the form of vitamins, growth factors, or various other products which have a high biologi-

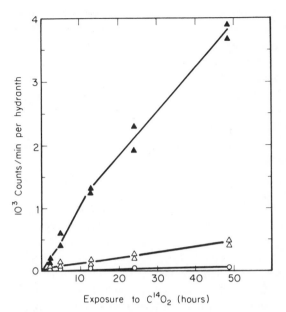

Fig. 8-3. Incorporation of radioactivity from C^{14}-bicarbonate into hydra tissues (after Muscatine and Lenhoff, 1963). SOLID TRIANGLES, algal-containing gastroderm; OPEN TRIANGLES, algal-free ectoderm; CIRCLES, whole albino animals (algal-free).

cal activity per molecule (Droop, 1963; Muscatine and Lenhoff, 1963). Such products would not have to be supplied in massive amounts to make a significant contribution to the metabolism of the animal. Algae may also contribute to the animal by aiding in the removal of waste products. Since even in complex organic media the animal with symbionts will grow faster than the alga-free animal, as long as it is maintained in the light, it can be assumed that micronutrient products of the alga are of some significance. In the nutritionally very poor tropical waters where corals live, the algal contribution may be relatively quite important.

It is also likely that the alga benefits from associating with the animal, although this would be more difficult to demonstrate experimentally. Since all of the algal nutrients must pass through animal tissues, the animal functions as an absorptive organ for the plant, concentrating the inorganic nutrients from the surrounding waters. Tropical waters are very deficient in nitrogen and phosphorus, and hence there are very low free phytoplankton populations in these waters (Yonge, 1963), so that intracellular algae could obtain nutrients without having to expend energy to concentrate them, a not inconsiderable advantage. Also in coral reefs, the algae are held in shallow waters where light intensities are very high, whereas as free-living forms they would have to expend energy maintaining themselves in the surface waters or would have to make up the loss, through division, of cells which settled.

In summary, there seems to be sufficient evidence to postulate that both alga and animal benefit by being together and no reason to postulate that they do not. Only laboratory research on defined cultures will provide conclusive answers to the questions raised.

One sees frequent references (Lederberg, 1952; Siegel, 1960) to the possibility that plant chloroplasts may have arisen from intracellular algal symbionts which had become obligately adapted to their intracellular environment. Although this question is unresolved, the existence of maternal inheritance of the chloroplast structure and the probable existence of chloroplast genes (Sager and Ryan, 1961) are both consistent with this idea.

LUMINESCENT BACTERIA

Luminous bacteria may be saprophytic, parasitic, or symbiotic (McElroy, 1961; Chase, 1964). Although the ecological advantage of luminescence is not known in most cases, some luminous bacteria inhabit special glands of certain deep sea fish, where they presumably live in symbiotic association with the fish, the bacteria deriving their nutrition from the animal, while the latter benefits by having a built-in light source which may be of some survival value in the continuous darkness of abyssal waters. Little is known about this relationship, but since the bacteria are concentrated in a special gland, it would seem likely that this organ is a selective habitat. Unfortunately, more is known about the biochemistry than the ecology of luminescence (McElroy, 1961).

MICROORGANISMS AND INSECTS

Many specific relationships exist between insects and fungi (Buchner, 1953; Baker, 1963; Brooks, 1963a; Koch, 1963). The fungi live either externally to the insect and are eaten by it or within the insect (usually in the lumen of the intestine) and perform a metabolic function. The former situation is exemplified by the ambrosia beetles and their fungi (Baker, 1963). These wood-boring insects create deep tunnels and introduce specific "ambrosia fungi" which grow on the tunnel walls (see Figure 8-2) and utilize the plant materials as nutrients, and the fungi are then in turn eaten by the insects. The ambrosia fungi occur in constant association with the insect and the adult frequently has special organs for fungus transmission. The eggs are laid in the tunnels, the larvae developing on the diet of fungus filaments present around them. In an analogous relationship, leaf-cutting ants and termites develop so-called fungus gardens and thus play a more active role in the fungus culture than do ambrosia beetles. It is likely that marine boring animals, e.g., *Limnoria,* also obtain at least some of their nutrients from marine fungi which grow in the tunnels created by the animals (Becker, 1959). Note, however, that *Limnoria* is able to digest and utilize wood cellulose, so that it is not restricted to a diet of fungi, although the fungi may well provide growth factors or other specific substances.

Many insects harbor within their intestine yeasts and fungi which, although probably not serving a metabolic function, may synthesize certain vitamins and growth factors which are required by the insect but which are ordinarily absent from their foods (Koch, 1963). Many insects have intracellular bacteria which live in cells of the intestine, and in certain groups of arthropods such as cockroaches, termites, lice, and ticks, all species possess them (Brooks, 1963*b*). From the limited amount of work done on insects experimentally freed of bacteria by the use of antibiotics, it would seem that these bacteria are true symbionts, since the cured insects grow and metamorphose very poorly. In many cases the symbionts are passed from one generation to the next through the egg.

Some microorganisms act as digestive agents for their hosts. Since the intestine is usually anaerobic, the main products of digestion are not incorporated into microbial cells, but are microbial fermentation products. In the case of the digestion of cellulose by flagellates in the termite, the main product is acetic acid which the insect then uses as its source of energy (Brooks, 1963*b*). As far as the insect is concerned, anaerobic digestion should be much more beneficial than aerobic digestion, since, as discussed in Chapter 3, considerably less energy is wasted as heat in anaerobic as opposed to aerobic digestion. Some species of termites have bacteria rather than protozoa as digestive agents.

In addition to direct nutritional effects, microorganisms can affect the sexual fertility of insects and may also play a role in sex determination. Buchner has shown that the symbionts of two scale insects are not uniformly distributed among the eggs, and that those eggs which possess symbionts develop into females whereas those lacking symbionts become males (Brooks, 1963*b*). A male develops if the egg lacks a sex chromosome, and it is felt that the symbiont somehow prevents the loss of a sex chromosome in the female, although this direct causal relationship has not been proved. Metabolic differences between normal and aposymbiotic insects have also been described by Brooks (1963*b*).

The insect may also regulate the activities of the symbiont. For instance, the hormones of the wood-eating roach *Cryptocercus punctulatus* control the sexual cycle of the associated protozoan, the protozoan reproducing asexually in the nymph and sexually when the insect molts. Molting is controlled by a hormone, ecdysone, which is produced in certain neurosecretory cells of the brain, and if pure ecdysone is injected into nonmolting nymphs or adults, gametogenesis in the protozoan is induced. Interestingly, the protozoa are even more sensitive to ecdysone than is the insect, responding to doses of the hormone which do not affect the latter.

The insects would seem to be well suited for detailed studies on the biochemistry of microbial symbiosis, since they should be more easily kept in germ-free conditions than larger animals, and the culture of the microbial symbionts should be possible.

MICROORGANISMS AND RUMINANTS

The bulk of the organic material produced in terrestrial environments by plants is tied up in insoluble substances such as cellulose, pectin, lignin, callose, and cork, which are unavailable to animals without the intermediate action by microorganisms. Cellulose is probably the most common single substance on the face of the earth, and its production and utilization are thus of great significance for both ecology and human affairs.

Mammals lack the enzymes necessary to digest cellulose, and all mammals which subsist predominantly on grasses and leafy plants make use of microorganisms as digestive agents. In nonruminants, such as the horse, pig, porcupine, and rabbit, cellulose digestion occurs in an enlarged cecum and is relatively inefficient, but ruminants have evolved a specific fermentation vessel, the rumen, in which the process of digestion predominantly occurs (Vonk, 1964). Ruminants include such animals of the forest as deer, moose, and elk, grassland animals such as the bison, antelope, and giraffe, desert animals such as the camel, and animals of the tundra and alpine regions such as the caribou, musk ox, mountain goat, and mountain sheep. Some of the most important domestic animals, the cow, sheep, and goat, are also ruminants. Thus, to a great extent the whole of the human economy is built on a food chain in which microorganisms play an early and crucial role.

First, it should be noted that ruminants are not obligately dependent on microorganisms. Germ-free lambs have been reared (Luckey, 1963), and as long as they are fed on a diet of which cellulose is not a constituent, they are able to thrive; microorganisms are required only for the cellulose digestive process. It should be noted also that even ruminants possessing a normal microbial flora cannot digest lignin, and indeed, the presence of lignin in a plant material inhibits the digestion of the associated cellulose (Barnett and Reid, 1961).

The rumen can be considered first as a self-contained ecosystem in the manner discussed in Chapter 7. The substances undergoing decomposition in the rumen are similar in composition to the organic residues decomposing in the soil (Hungate, 1960), yet the microbial populations and the end products of decomposition are entirely different. The high constant temperature (39°C) and the anaerobic nature of the rumen are probably the most important factors in its unique activities. Natural food contains a variety of individual substances, and the digestibility of these in the rumen varies, as is shown in Table 8-1. Not only are some materials more com-

TABLE 8-1. APPARENT DIGESTIBILITIES OF DIFFERENT COMPONENTS OF THE CARBOHYDRATE FRACTION OF ORCHARD GRASS HAY

| | | | Apparent digestion coefficients of plant fractions | | | | | |
Growth stage	Crude cellulose	Cellulose	Holo-cellulose	Pento-sans	Starch	Sugar	Organic acids	Undetermined
1	82	81	83	79	96	96	53	96
2	78	78	79	74	96	98	57	88
3	72	69	74	66	96	98	50	87
4	69	72	69	63	96	94	45	74

From Ely et al. (1953). Values are per cent of fraction digestible. The age of the plant increases with the growth stage number.

pletely digested than others, but younger plants are more digestible than older ones. Since cellulose is quantitatively the most important substance in feed, attention is naturally directed to its fate. Digestion proceeds to the sugars cellobiose and glucose, which then undergo anaerobic fermentation. A fermentation balance is given in Table 8-2. It can be seen that the main products are CO_2, CH_4, and volatile fatty acids. The bacteria responsible for the various reactions have been in general identified, and this work is summarized in Table 8-3. Hungate (1960) feels that a large proportion of the significant rumen bacteria have been identified, because: "(a) Many distinctive morphological types identifiable in the rumen contents by direct microscopic examination have been grown in axenic culture.

TABLE 8-2. FERMENTATION PRODUCTS DERIVED FROM 1 KG OF FEED IN THE SHEEP RUMEN

| Weight feed digested | CH_4 | CO_2 | Chemical component | | | Unaccounted for |
			Acetic acid	Propionic acid	Butyric acid	
			2.88 moles	1.11 moles	1.06 moles	
	1.69 moles	3.3 moles				
1 kg	27 g	145 g	173 g	82 g	93 g	45%

Theoretical stoichiometric relationships derived from the above data (assume breakdown of feed to triose level):

$$57 \text{ Triose} + 57 \text{ H}_2\text{O} \rightarrow 57 \text{ Acetic} + 57 \text{ CO}_2 + 114 \text{ H}_2$$
$$22 \text{ Triose} + 22 \text{ H}_2 \rightarrow 22 \text{ Propionic} + 22 \text{ H}_2\text{O}$$
$$42 \text{ Triose} \rightarrow 21 \text{ Butyric} + 42 \text{ CO}_2 + 42 \text{ H}_2$$
$$33.5 \text{ CO}_2 + 134 \text{ H}_2 \rightarrow 33.5 \text{ CH}_4 + 67 \text{ H}_2\text{O}$$

$$121 \text{ Triose} \rightarrow 57 \text{ Acetic} + 22 \text{ Propionic} + 21 \text{ Butyric} + 65.5 \text{ CO}_2 + 33.5 \text{ CH}_4 + 32 \text{ H}_2\text{O}$$

Data of Hungate (1960).

TABLE 8-3. A FEW CHARACTERISTICS OF SOME IMPORTANT RUMEN BACTERIA

Organisms	Growth factors required	Fermentation products										
		CO_2	H_2	For-mate	Ace-tate	Propio-nate	Butyr-ate	Valer-ate	Lac-tate	Succi-nate	Etha-nol	CH_4
Cellulose decomposers:												
Bacteroides succino-genes	rumen fluid, butyric, isovaleric, biotin, para-aminobenzoic acid, CO_2	+	+	+	+					+		
Butyrivibrio fibrisolvens	feed constituents (including starch)	+	+	+	+		+		+		+	
Ruminococcus	rumen fluid, volatile and higher acids; sugars	±	+	+	+				+	+	+	
Clostridium lochheadii	feed constituents (including starch)	+	+	+	+		+		+	+	+	
Starch decomposers:												
Bacteroides amylo-philus	peptones			+	+					+		
Bacteroides ruminicola	rumen fluid, xylan, CO_2	+		+	+					+		
Selenomonas rumi-nantium	rumen fluid, lactate	+		+	+	+			+	+		
Succinimonas amylo-lytica	peptones, CO_2				+	+				+		
Streptococcus bovis	biotin							+	+			
Using other substrates:												
Bacteroides amylogenes	peptones, sugars	++			++	+	+					
Lachnospira multiparus	peptones, pectin	++	++	+	++	+			++			
Veillonella gazogenes	peptones, lactate, succinate					+						
Peptostreptococcus elsdenii	peptones, lactate	+			+	+	+		+			
Borrelia	rumen fluid, sugars, CO_2	+		+	+				+	+	+	
Methanobacterium ruminantium	rumen fluid, CO_2, H_2											+

From Hungate (1960).

(b) The prevalent gram-negative reaction and the morphology of the predominant organisms in stained smears of rumen contents are consistent with the morphology of the pure cultures and with the gram-negative nature of the majority of them. (c) Culture conditions simulate the rumen so closely that most rumen types should find them suitable for growth. (d) All colonies which appear in initial dilution series grow in agar subcultures and can be maintained in pure culture. (e) Metabolic processes such as fiber digestion, hydrolysis of urea; production of acetic, propionic, butyric, lactic, formic, and succinic acids, methane, hydrogen, and carbon dioxide; and conversion of formate, lactate, succinate, carbon dioxide and hydrogen, all known to occur in the rumen, have been demonstrated in at least one of the pure bacterial cultures."

Because of the highly anaerobic environment in the rumen, only a small amount of the energy in the ingested foodstuff will be wasted as heat (*see* page 54); Marston (1948) showed that in the rumen, of the energy in the cellulose which was consumed, only 6% was dissipated as heat, 10% was locked up in the protoplasmic mass of the microorganisms, and 84% was present in the fermentation products such as volatile fatty acids and CH_4. Even the heat released is not completely wasted, as it helps maintain the body temperature of the animal. The inefficiency of the rumen fermentation is, of course, the reason why ruminants are able to benefit so effectively from their microbial symbionts, the preponderance of the energy of the cellulose feed still being available for the animal to use.

The volatile fatty acids, acetic, propionic, butyric, and valeric, are rapidly absorbed into the bloodstream and are oxidized by the animal as its main source of energy. Even nonruminant cellulose-utilizing animals such as the horse derive most of their energy from the oxidation of volatile fatty acids. Oxidation of volatile fatty acids is more inefficient than the oxidation of sugars, so that cattle and sheep produce much more heat per unit of food than do monogastric animals (Annison and Lewis, 1959), which may be one reason why ruminants are well adapted to cold climates but poorly adapted to hot climates. About 10% of the carbon of cellulose is converted to methane during the rumen fermentation and the loss of this gas represents a considerable wastage of energy.

The other main product of the rumen fermentation is microbial cells which are digested by the ruminant in its intestine and become the main source of amino acids for the animal. Nutrients required in the rumen for microbial growth besides carbon are various minerals, nitrogen, and phosphorus, all of which are ultimately derived from the feed. As is shown in Table 8-4, a considerable amount of phosphorus recycles through the animal, being secreted into the rumen in large amounts in the saliva, converted into microbial protoplasm, and then returned to the animal when the microbial cells are digested. Nitrogen may come from the plant proteins, but the microbes are also able to synthesize their own pro-

TABLE 8-4. Rumen Mineral Intake (g/day) Contributed by Saliva and Foodstuffs in a Sheep (weight, 40 kg) on Spring Grass

Source of intake	Sodium	Potassium	Calcium	Magnesium	Chloride	Inorganic P
Saliva	32	3.4	0.06	0.06	4.8	6.4
Foodstuffs	2.9	35	7.6	2.2	16	4.7

From Annison and Lewis (1959). These data show that the bulk of the sodium and phosphorus in the rumen recycle through the animal.

teins from ammonia or urea, the urea often being supplied in animal feeds in order to promote microbial growth, thus leading ultimately to more animal protein. However, microbial growth is ultimately limited by the restriction of energy available anaerobically, so that the growth of the animal will be limited by an anaerobic process even though the animal itself is aerobic (Hungate, 1963); this explains why ruminants convert a smaller amount of their digested food into protoplasm than do monogastric animals. A ruminant is nutritionally superior to another animal only when it is subsisting on foods that are nutritionally poor and can benefit from the synthetic activities of its microorganisms. As Hungate has noted, the ruminant cultures its own food, and one advantage of culturing as opposed to hunting is that in the former the animal need not expend energy searching for food; in this way the inefficiency of the culture process may be compensated for. The microorganisms also synthesize the vitamins required by the ruminant. Thus, in addition to their role in digestive processes, the microorganisms play an important nutritional role, and it is likely that one reason ruminants can live so efficiently on fibrous foods is that they are essentially independent in their diet of amino acids and vitamins.

When cereal grains are fed, the animal receives large amounts of starch, a polysaccharide which can be degraded both by enzymes produced by the animal in its small intestine and by certain microorganisms in the rumen (*see* Table 8-3). On starch feed, the proportion of starch-digesting bacteria rises considerably. As pointed out by Annison and Lewis (1959), since starch fermentation in the rumen represents a considerable wastage of energy as compared to hydrolysis by the animal itself, it might seem more efficient for the animal to dispose of its rumen microflora if it is to be fed starch. However, ruminants did not evolve to handle a starchy diet, and starch is fed merely for agricultural convenience, although its utilization in the rumen stimulates microbial growth and helps to maintain a flourishing microflora (Annison and Lewis, 1959). Other polysaccharides which occur as components of grass, such as xylan, pectin, and fructosan, are also readily fermented. Details of various fermentations and their role in the domestic ruminant are given by Annison and Lewis (1959) and

Barnett and Reid (1961). A detailed analysis of energy metabolism in the whole animal is given by Blaxter (1962). See Chapter 9 (page 243) for a brief discussion of the relationships of cobalt and microorganisms in the synthesis of vitamin B_{12} in the rumen.

Hungate et al. (1959) have presented fermentation data from a variety of African animals and have shown that fermentation in the cecum and large intestine of these animals is quantitatively negligible as compared with that in the rumen of other animals, although it is biochemically similar. The smaller ruminants, which have greater energy requirements per unit weight than the larger ones, showed a faster fermentation rate due to a faster turnover rate (i.e., the rumen emptied and filled faster). In spite of the technical difficulties of work on wild animals, more work is needed on their metabolism as an aid to understanding their role in the energy economy of ecosystems.

MICROORGANISMS AND NONRUMINANTS

The possible roles of microorganisms in man and in nonruminants such as the mouse and chicken have been discussed for many years, and it is just now, with the elaboration of germ-free animal techniques, that these roles are being examined experimentally (Luckey, 1963). Pasteur, for instance, believed that mammalian life without bacteria would be impossible, and much of the early work on germ-free animals was designed to test this hypothesis. Once it had been shown that animals could live without bacteria, it was logical to inquire whether mammals might not still derive some additional benefit from their presence. Microorganisms have been shown to have beneficial effects on an animal in four ways. (1) Specific microorganisms synthesize specific vitamins and growth factors needed by the animal. For example, if germ-free rats were kept on a diet deficient in vitamin K, they showed deficiency symptoms rather quickly, but conventional rats or germ-free rats monocontaminated with pure cultures of certain normal intestinal bacteria (e.g., *Escherichia coli*) did not show deficiency symptoms on the same diet. Further, it could be shown that the bacteria which alleviated the deficiency were able to synthesize vitamin K, whereas intestinal bacteria which could not alter the deficiency symptoms could not synthesize vitamin K (Lev, 1963). (2) The metabolic activities of the whole microbial population may affect the animal. The redox potential of the cecum of the normal guinea pig is much lower than that of the germ-free guinea pig (Lev, 1963). The microbial flora through its activities prevents the establishment of certain pathogenic microorganisms in the intestine, indirectly benefiting the host (Lev, 1963; Ozawa and Freter, 1964). (3) The microorganisms by their bulk may bring about beneficial changes in the host. Intestinal microorganisms challenge the host defense mechanisms and effect relatively nonspecific increases in resistance to disease (Luckey, 1963; Dubos and Schaedler, 1962). The lymphatic system of germ-free animals is usually quite underdeveloped, presumably due to this lack of immunologic challenge. Further, germ-free mammals frequently show grossly distorted ceca, the size of which can be reduced either by restoring the bacteria or by including sterile fiber in the diet (Luckey, 1963). According to Lev (1963) cecum distortion may have a nutritional or biochemical basis, but it may also result from the lack of bulk occasioned by the absence of microorganisms, so that the cecum is not stimulated to evacuate until it has filled with fluid. (4) The function of microorganisms in the digestive process of nonruminants is discussed in detail by Vonk (1964). Unfortunately, most work on the role of microorganisms in digestion has been done without adequate attention to the microbiological details, so that few firm conclusions can be drawn. Almost all vertebrates and invertebrates possess intestinal microbic floras, and workers tend to attribute any unusual function of an animal to microorganisms. It is clear that at least one invertebrate, the marine boring isopod *Limnoria*, produces its own cellulase and does not contain an intestinal flora to perform this function (Ray, 1959). Conflicting reports exist on the source of the multitude of digestive enzymes in the land snail *Helix pomatia*, but the current feeling is that microorganisms are probably not involved (Strasdine and Whitaker, 1963). It is possible that many invertebrates can digest cellulose without the intervention of microorganisms, and much more work needs to be done in this area.

Although germ-free animals can live if they are given a proper diet, the question is still not answered if animals under competitive natural conditions might have an absolute requirement for a microbial flora. Unfortunately this question cannot be tested experimentally for the reason that the microbial flora of the normal animal cannot be controlled.

Symbiotic Nitrogen Fixation

The conversion of atmospheric nitrogen into fixed forms is carried out by a variety of microorganisms associated in various degrees with plants. Some blue-green algae, mainly of the order Nostocales (Wilson, 1958) and some photosynthetic bacteria are able to fix nitrogen completely autotrophically and thus can carry out the process completely divorced from any associants. Some free-living heterotrophic bacteria can fix nitrogen but require organic compounds as energy sources and consequently in nature will fix nitrogen only when associated, at least loosely, with higher plants. In this category are several species of the anaerobic genus *Clostridium*, aerobes of the genus *Azotobacter*, and such other bacteria as *Klebsiella* (Silver et al., 1963) and Methanobacterium (Wilson, 1958).

Nitrogen fixation may also occur in certain fungi and yeasts, but this point needs confirmation. The association of nitrogen-fixing Azotobacter with the sand dune plant *Ammophila arenaria* was noted by Hassouna and Wareing (1964) who provided some evidence that root excretions may permit these organisms to proliferate in the rhizosphere with a concomitant fixation of nitrogen. It should be noted that sand dunes are notoriously deficient in combined nitrogen, yet *Ammophila* grows luxuriantly.

Symbiotic associations of a more specific kind exist between some nitrogen-fixing organisms and higher plants. Nitrogen-fixing blue-green algae, for instance, form symbioses with fungi, liverworts, ferns, cycads, and flowering plants (McKee, 1962). In these cases the alga is capable of fixing nitrogen by itself and does not acquire any new property upon association with the plant, although in several cases studied the alga could not grow or fix nitrogen photosynthetically and hence required a carbohydrate as a nutrient. Presumably this explains the necessity in some cases for the alga to live in association with the plant. A number of NONLEGUMINOUS PLANTS contain root or leaf nodules in which are found microorganisms, and nitrogen fixation has been demonstrated in at least some of these plants (McKee, 1962). Silver et al. (1963) have studied nitrogen fixation by the leaf-nodule endophyte of the nonlegume *Psychotria bacteriophila*. Using N^{15}_2, they demonstrated fixation by both the leaf nodule and the isolated bacterium. The bacterium was assigned to the genus *Klebsiella*, a close relative of *Aerobacter aerogenes*. Silver et al. (1963) believe that the bacterial endophyte also plays a role in controlling the morphology of the plant, since plants which have been experimentally freed of their symbionts grow as dwarfs, even in the presence of combined nitrogen sources, suggesting that the endophyte produces a plant growth factor. Some but not all of the dwarfing effects can be overcome by gibberellic acid. The importance of nitrogen-fixing symbioses in the ability of such pioneer plants as *Alnus* (alder) and *Myrica* to colonize new substrates was discussed by Bond (1958, 1963), and many other plants which fix nitrogen symbiotically are found growing in highly leached tropical soils. Schramm (1966) has found that the herbaceous plants which are able to colonize barren anthracite mine wastes are usually nodulated. The study of pioneer plants in such extreme environments may provide new insights into the importance of nitrogen fixation in nature. Unfortunately, little work has been done on nonagricultural crops.

The most interesting and widely studied nitrogen-fixing association is the LEGUME-RHIZOBIUM SYMBIOSIS. In this case neither the plant nor the bacterium can fix nitrogen when grown separately, but upon interaction between the two this new property is acquired. Interestingly, both legume and bacterium can proliferate readily in the absence of the other, either in nature or in the laboratory, so that the association between the two is in no way obligate. In fact, if it were not known that the legume root nodules fixed nitrogen, it would be concluded that rhizobium is a pathogen which induces harmful tumorous structures on susceptible legumes. Indeed, if a legume is infected with the wrong strain of rhizobium, or under conditions of boron deficiency (Manil, 1958), abortive nodules may be formed which do not fix nitrogen and which can thus be viewed as pathological structures. Workers speak of INFECTIVE bacterial strains, those able to enter root tissue and bring about nodule formation, and EFFECTIVE strains, those able to induce nitrogen fixation and enhance plant growth (Allen and Allen, 1958). An infective strain may be ineffective. An early illustration of root nodules on a legume is shown in Figure 8-4.

It seems to be the opinion of most workers that symbiotic rhizobia probably evolved from free-living forms, and even today most rhizobia grow more frequently nonsymbiotically under natural conditions. The Leguminosae is a family which evolved in the tropics and is represented even today by predominantly tropical species, most of them woody (Norris, 1958). The predominant rhizobium associated symbiotically with these

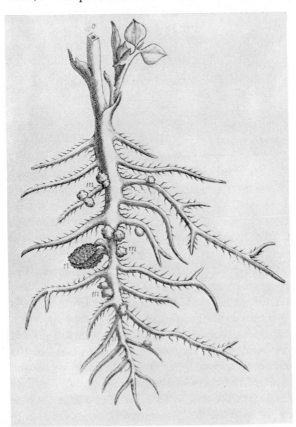

Fig. 8-4. Root nodules of broad bean, *Vicia faba,* as shown by Malpighi, 1679 (Fred et al., 1932).

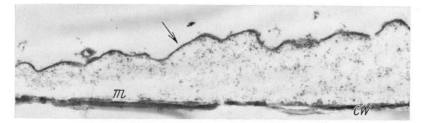

Fig. 8-5. Electron micrograph of thin section of barrel medic, *Medicago tribuloides,* root grown in vermiculite, showing portion of the granular matrix (*m*) and membrane (ARROW) outside the epidermal cell wall (*cw*) (Dart and Mercer, 1964*a*) 20,000X. Within the membrane, the root excretions and rhizobia are held together, and the bacteria can attain very high cell densities.

tropical plants is a relatively nonspecific kind called the "cowpea type" which shows little restriction to the plant species which it can infect. Certain legumes have become adapted to temperate soils and conditions, and it is from these plants that the agriculturally important species have developed. Here it is found that there is considerable specificity between rhizobium and plant, leading to the creation of the so-called "cross-inoculation groups" (Allen and Allen, 1958). This phenomenon is expressed more specifically in the genetic relationships which must exist between plant and bacterium. It is known, for instance, that there are host plant genes which will prevent the formation of effective nodules (or even the formation of any nodules), and there are probably genes in the bacterium which are necessary for infectiveness or effectiveness, and which can be lost by mutation or through bacteriophage action (Jensen, 1958), another example of a gene-for-gene relationship as discussed earlier in this chapter (*see* page 182).

The details of the infection process are now fairly well understood and present an interesting example of the various levels at which two organisms can interact. If legume plants are grown in nonsterile soil, secretions from the roots stimulate the growth of bacteria in the adjacent soil, leading to the creation of a rhizosphere flora. This stimulation is quite general and is not restricted to nodule bacteria. Legumes as a group seem to stimulate the rhizosphere population to a greater degree than nonlegumes (Nutman, 1958). Dart and Mercer (1964*a*) have recently shown by thin-section electron microscopy that there is an extensive granular matrix outside the epidermis which seems to be enclosed by a thin membrane and in which the rhizosphere bacteria proliferate most extensively. One of their pictures is shown in Figure 8-5. These latter workers believe that this matrix provides a protective niche within which the bacteria can multiply rapidly and build up high population densities. Since it is known (*see* below) that the later steps in infection require the elaboration by the bacteria of metabolic products, it seems reasonable that the attainment of these high population densities is an essential part of the infection process and is another example of the type of cooperative interaction between cells discussed in Chapter 5.

Infection of the root occurs by way of root hairs. One of the products released by the root is tryptophan which is converted into the plant hormone indoleacetic acid by the rhizobia. This hormone induces curling of some of the root hairs, a process which is often a prelude to infection (Nutman, 1963). The bacteria induce the plant in some manner to form polygalacturonase, an enzyme which probably alters the structure of the root hair cell wall. Dart and Mercer (1964*a*) feel that the root hairs which become infected are probably those which do not pass all the way through the matrix layer but remain confined within it, and they suggest that this serves to concentrate the polygalacturonase where it will do the most good. Dart and Mercer believe that certain heavily flagellated swarmer cells are the actual infecting agents, and that they pass directly through a microfibrillar cell wall network which has been loosened and spread by the action of the chemical agents mentioned above. "The active movement of the swarmers would enable them to slip between the open fibrillar network more easily than the relatively slow moving rod forms." An electron micrograph of a carbon replica of a root hair, showing the rhizobia swarmers in contact with the cellulose microfibrils is shown in Figure 8-6. After entry, the swarmer cells proliferate and form a hypha-like mass of cells which becomes surrounded by cellulose except at the tip, the so-called infection thread, which spreads down the root hair (Nutman, 1958). The host cell nucleus always seems to be present and active at the time and point of infection and remains close to the growing tip of the infection thread during its passage into the root cortex (Nutman, 1958).

The infected cells of mature nodules of many legumes are tetraploid. According to Allen and Allen (1958), it is likely that in the uninfected root there are always a small number of tetraploid cells of spontaneous origin, and the hypha-like infection thread passes through the cortex until it reaches one of these cells. Many diploid cells surrounding the infection thread usually show necrosis and degeneration, whereas the tetraploid cells are stimulated to divide and are invaded by the rhizobia. These cells and the nearby diploid cells thus constitute the nodule primordium. Certain factors controlling the number and distribution of nodules along a root are discussed by Nutman (1958) and will not be covered here. The production of auxins by the bacteria is probably at least one factor involved in the formation of the mature nodule, although attempts to induce nodules

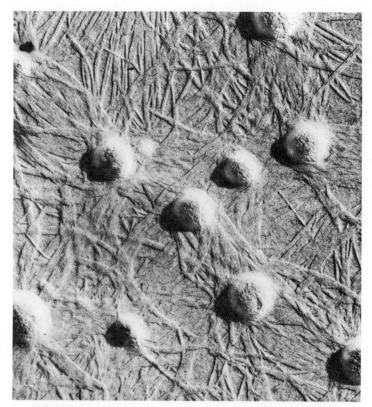

Fig. 8-6. Carbon replica of the surface of a root hair of barrel medic, *Medicago tribuloides*, showing the prominent network of root hair microfibrils with Rhizobium swarmer cells seated on the fibrils (Dart and Mercer, 1964*a*) 25,000X. It is thought that the highly motile swarmer cells are able to push through the microfibrillar network which has been previously loosened by partial dissolution of the cell wall matrix.

by the experimental injection into roots of growth-regulating substances have been unsuccessful (Allen and Allen, 1958).

Once the bacteria have invaded tetraploid cells, they multiply rapidly and become surrounded singly or in small groups by portions of the host cell membrane. The bacteria then are transformed into swollen, misshapen, and sometimes branched forms called bacteroids, the end result being a series of host cell membranes, each one surrounding a group of bacteroids. An electron micrograph of a thin section of a bacteroid-filled nodule is shown in Figure 8-7. During the time that the bacteroids are forming, hemoglobin appears in the nodule. Nitrogen fixation occurs only in nodules which contain both bacteroids and hemoglobin. Eventually,

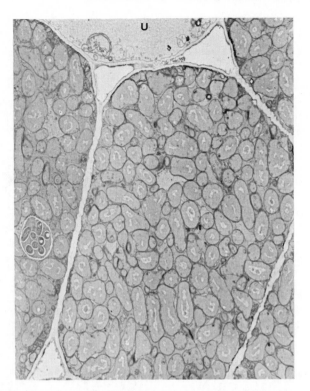

Fig. 8-7. Electron micrograph of a thin section of a subterranean clover, *Trifolium subterraneum,* nodule showing the large numbers of Rhizobium bacteroids, *u*—uninvaded cell with disorganized cytoplasm (Dart and Mercer, 1964*b*) 3600X. Very small amounts of cytoplasm and very few organelles are present in the cell. In the cell to the left, a residual infection thread containing rod-shaped rhizobia can be seen. The profound change in morphology of the bacteria from the swarmer cells shown in Figure 8-6 is noteworthy.

the nodule deteriorates and some of the cells which had lain dormant in the infection thread and had not been converted into bacteroids now proliferate and escape into the soil. The bacteroids probably never grow and thus represent terminal stages in the life of individual rhizobial cells.

The presence of hemoglobin in nodules provides an interesting example of a symbiotic interaction at the biochemical level; neither plant nor microbe alone makes this substance. First, it should be noted that this is not a typical mammalian hemoglobin, since it has a molecular weight of 17,000 and contains only one polypeptide chain (Allen and Allen, 1958). Although it was at one time thought that hemoglobin was found in the plant kingdom uniquely in legume root nodules, it has now been found in yeast,

Neurospora, and *Penicillium.* A functional hemoglobin requires the combination of the porphyrin hematin with an appropriate apoprotein. In view of current concepts in genetic coding, it would be of interest to know in what manner the amino acid sequence of the protein moiety of the root nodule hemoglobin is controlled. There is no evidence which would rule out either organism as providing the appropriate template, and conceivably one of the organisms synthesizes the protein and the other the hematin.

Hemoglobin may play a direct role in nitrogen fixation (evidence reviewed by Allen and Allen, 1958), and spectroscopic evidence shows that nitrogen gas can combine with hemoglobin and oxidize it to HEMIGLOBIN which is in turn reduced through the action of the bacteroids (Nutman, 1963). In this process nitrogen is probably reduced directly to ammonia (Wilson, 1958) which would then be assimilated by the plant. Since the hemoglobin has been located in the space between the bacteroids and the membrane, it is likely that NH_3 is formed here. The biochemical mechanism of nonsymbiotic nitrogen fixation is different in that hemoglobin is not involved (Allen and Allen, 1958), and its role is probably replaced by the nonheme iron protein ferredoxin or another electron carrier of low potential. In the soybean-rhizobium symbiosis (Shaukat-Ahmed and Evans, 1961), cobalt is required, although in a nitrogen-sufficient environment neither organism of the symbiotic pair shows such a requirement. Thus the symbiotic association, while making fixed nitrogen unnecessary, has introduced an additional mineral requirement.

Allen and Allen (1958) have also reviewed some of the practical aspects of the legume-rhizobium symbiosis. When a crop is planted in an area where it has not been previously grown or where it has not been grown for some time, artificial inoculation of the seed with an appropriate strain of rhizobium may be necessary, since the soil will probably lack an effective strain for this crop. An early example of the benefits of inoculation is shown in Figure 8-8. In this case, inoculation was achieved merely by transferring soil from one location to another. The potential benefits of the inoculation of seed with pure cultures depends on the soil and the length of time since the crop was last planted, as shown by Table 8-5. Clover was not indigenous to Australia, so that when it was first introduced, inoculation was necessary (Vincent, 1958), whereas rhizobia which infect native legumes were widely distributed. There seems to be little spread of rhizobia from a place where they are established to nearby fields (Vincent, 1958). Unfortunately, little has been done on the natural distribution of specific rhizobia, probably because of the difficulty of performing quantitative counts for a strain of interest. Brockwell (1963), using aseptically grown plants, has described a plant-infection assay which, although laborious, is accurate and which he and coworkers have used to study the ecology of rhizobium in Australia (Hely and Brockwell, 1962).

About 90% of the more than one thousand species of legumes which have been examined are nodulated (Allen and Allen, 1958), but some species are noteworthy in consistently lacking nodules. It has been demonstrated experimentally many times that, especially in nitrogen-deficient soils, legumes benefit markedly from being nodulated. Even in relatively rich soils, some benefit is probably obtained, although the effects may not be very dramatic. Conceivably, in competitive natural situations, any ability to dispense with fixed nitrogen may be beneficial, although this is more likely to be important in the tropics than in temperate climates (Norris, 1958). One is impressed by the fact that in temperate environments it is the grasses rather than the legumes which are the successful herbaceous plants in most environments. Further, it is a common agricultural experience that a legume pasture left unused for a few years slowly reverts

Fig. 8-8. The effect of transferred soil (inoculation) on the growth of clover (redrawn from Fred et al., 1932). First demonstration by Salfeld in 1887 of the benefits of inoculation; LEFT, uninoculated; RIGHT, inoculated.

TABLE 8-5. Effect of Inoculation on the Yield of Alaska Peas

Soil Class	Acidity	Years since last pea crop	Gain due to inoculation
Clay loam	very slight	10	no gain
Fine sandy loam	slight	4	4%
Fine sandy loam	strong	3	10%
Fine sandy loam	strong	5	34%
Fine sandy loam	strong	8	51%

From Fred et al. (1932). In this experiment, the seeds were inoculated with the appropriate rhizobium culture and planted in various soils. In the strongly acidic soil, inoculation produced considerable benefit, especially if the soil had not been cropped to peas for a number of years. In the other soils the benefit from inoculation was negligible, and it can be presumed that the appropriate rhizobium survived in these.

to predominantly grassland. In agriculture, however, one is concerned mainly with dollars and cents, rather than with the survival value of a given plant; Ellison (1958) has discussed the relative merits of planting legumes to increase the nitrogen content of soils versus adding nitrogen in the form of synthetic fertilizers. He concludes that in Holland, ". . . where population and land-use pressure are high a more intensive form of land use is demanded. . . . Under such conditions, almost complete reliance is placed on the 'bag' to provide the nitrogen required to obtain a high level of output. . . ." whereas in New Zealand in ". . . a relatively extensive and low cost system of grassland production in which great emphasis is placed on output per man. . . . the farmer relies entirely on white clover . . . to supply the major part of the nitrogen requirements." Calculations of the amount of nitrogen fixed annually by living organisms are in the order of 10^8 tons for the whole world, most of which is from symbiotic sources (Nutman, 1963). On acreage sown to legumes, about 10 times as much nitrogen fixation is derived from symbiotic as from nonsymbiotic sources (Allen and Allen, 1958).

The rhizobium-legume interaction is one of the most interesting problems in biology and can be studied from such viewpoints as agriculture, plant physiology, cytology, biochemistry, genetics, microbiology, ecology, biogeochemistry, and evolution. Clearly much work remains to be done, and it can be safely predicted that new concepts will still be forthcoming from this work.

Mycorrhiza

Mycorrhiza literally means root fungus. Probably the roots of the majority of terrestrial plants exist in association with fungi. Although the existence of such mycorrhizae have been known since the last century, it has only been in recent years that the symbiotic nature of the fungus-root association has been clearly demonstrated. Although the mycorrhizal fungus always remains the minor member of the pair, it is highly important, since it is through the fungus tissue that most of the nutrients of the plant must pass. Mycorrhizae can be divided into two general classes, ectotrophs and endotrophs, depending on the manner in which the fungus is disposed with respect to the root, although there are many gradations between these two extremes.

ECTOTROPHIC MYCORRHIZAE

In ectotrophic forms the fungus hyphae form an extensive sheath around the outside of the root, with some hyphae penetrating into the outer cortex by way of intercellular spaces, but there is no intracellular infection (Harley, 1959). The root systems of ectotrophically mycorrhizal plants are composed of both long and short roots. The short roots, which are characteristically dichotomously branched, show the typical hyphal sheath, while the long roots are either uninfected or less extensively infected. A comparison of mycorrhizal and normal roots from pure cultures is shown in Figure 8-9 (Hatch and Doak, 1933). The mycorrhizal roots are probably induced to form their characteristic short branched forms as a result of the infection process (*see* below).

Ectotrophic mycorrhizae are found mainly in forest trees, especially conifers, beeches, and oaks and are most highly developed in temperate forests growing on brown earth and podsolized soils (Harley, 1959). Almost every root of every tree in a forest is probably infected, but infection is less common in isolated trees growing on prairie or agricultural soils. The importance of inoculation in prairie soil is shown by the work of Hatch (1936) and is illustrated in Figure 8-10.

Although speculation on the nature and significance of ectotrophic mycorrhizae has been widespread, it was not until the critical culture work and laboratory synthesis with aseptic seedlings (reviewed in Melin, 1963, 1959) that the true nature of the association was clearly revealed. The fungi that participate are all Basidiomycetes, mainly Hymenomycetes (Melin, 1959), and most of them form typical mushroom fruiting bodies. Melin showed, however, that the mycorrhizal fungi were not typical wood rotters or cellulose decomposers and that they lacked any significant ability to grow on the nutrients available in leaf litter. Rather, the isolates utilized simple carbohydrates as carbon and energy sources, and they characteristically required one or several vitamins as growth factors. Since these mycorrhizal fungi are never found in nature except in association with tree roots, Melin considers these organisms to be true root-inhabiting fungi which in nature obtain the nutrients they need for growth only from tree

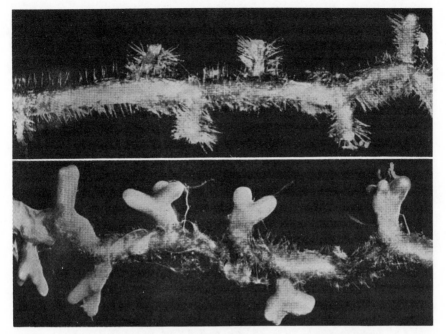

Fig. 8-9. Normal (TOP, 12X) and mycorrhizal (BOTTOM, 10X) roots of white pine, *Pinus strobus* (Hatch and Doak, 1933). Pine seedlings grown in aseptic culture. In the lower figure, the seedlings were inoculated with a pure culture of the mycorrhizal fungus *Lactarius deliciosus*.

roots. These fungi require or are stimulated by another root product of unknown nature, which Melin calls the *M*-factor, and are also inhibited by another substance produced by the roots. Further, the fungus produces a plant growth substance which induces various morphogenetic effects in the root, and this substance is probably responsible for the typical appearance of the short dichotomously branched mycorrhizal root. Thus it appears that root exudates allow the fungus to grow and surround the root, but the inhibitor prevents the fungus from initiating a pathological state. The fungus on its part produces substances which modify the shape of the root, so that the ultimate typical aspect of the ectotrophically mycorrhizal root is the outcome of a series of interactions between the two organisms. There seems, however, to be little species specificity in the interactions; a single species of pine can form mycorrhizae with over 40 species of fungi.

Mycorrhizal formation occurs best in nutrient-deficient soils and may be inhibited in rich soils, especially those high in nitrogen and phosphorus

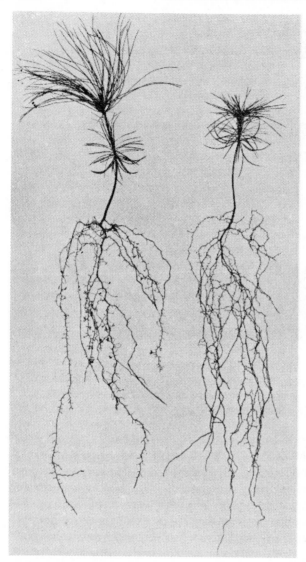

Fig. 8-10. Mycorrhizal (LEFT) and nonmycorrhizal (RIGHT) seedlings of *Pinus strobus* grown in inoculated and uninoculated prairie soil, respectively (Hatch, 1936). Inoculum was *Boletus luteus*. The seedlings were about three months old when inoculated and nine months old when photographed.

(Björkman, 1949). In the discussion of lichens (*see* page 125) it was shown that conditions of low nutrition were necessary for lichen formation or else the relationship would break down, and it seems that a similar phenomenon obtains here with respect to mycorrhizal formation. Further, mycorrhizae develop best when the plants are placed in fairly strong light, under conditions where photosynthesis would be expected to be high and photosynthetic products would be transferred most effectively to the roots where they could promote mycorrhizal growth. By using radioactive CO_2,

Melin (1963) has shown that radioactive products assimilated by the plant are transferred to the fungus. Thus we see that a complex series of interactions, modified by environment, are involved in mycorrhizal formation.

The beneficial effect on the plant of the mycorrhizal symbiosis has been inferred frequently on the basis of many field observations by ecologists and foresters. On poor soils only trees which become mycorrhizal thrive (Melin, 1959). If trees are planted in soils which lack a suitable fungal inoculum (e.g., prairie soils), trees which are artificially inoculated at the time of planting grow much more rapidly than uninoculated trees (*see* Figure 8-10). Studying the colonization of nutrient-poor coal mine wastes, Schramm (1966) has shown that only trees which are mycorrhizal are successful. Laboratory studies with aseptic seedlings also show that the mycorrhizal plant grows better than an uninfected plant in nutrient-poor conditions. Alternatively, in nutrient-rich conditions, the mycorrhizal plant does not grow any better than the control or may even be slightly retarded (Harley, 1963).

Since in the mycorrhizal tree, the fungal sheath lies between the root and the soil, it is reasonable to postulate that the beneficial effect of the fungus arises from its function as an absorptive agent. There is no evidence that nitrogen fixation occurs in mycorrhizal plants. It has been shown that mycorrhizal plants have a much higher accumulation rate of radioactive phosphate than nonmycorrhizal ones and that the radioactivity appears first in the fungus and later in the plant (Harley, 1963). Unfortunately, the lack of a suitable radioactive isotope of nitrogen has prevented similar studies with this element; it might be expected that, because of the higher demand for nitrogen than phosphorus by the plant, the strong ability to accumulate nitrogen might be of even more physiological and ecological significance. Schramm (1966) has shown that nonmycorrhizal plants growing on anthracite waste respond dramatically to fertilization with nitrogen but not with phosphorus. Whether the improved uptake in mycorrhizal roots is due to the increased absorptive surface available as a result of the presence of the hyphae, or is due to an active metabolic participation by the fungus, is not known.

The fungus as well as the plant benefits from the symbiosis. Hyphae growing out from the roots frequently form multistranded structures called rhizomorphs, which eventually approach the surface and, under favorable conditions, differentiate and form fruiting body initials which expand and push above ground. By microscopic examination, Schramm (1966) has been able to discover distinctive morphological characteristics of the hyphae of several mycorrhizal fungi and has been able to locate the same type of hypha attached to fruiting bodies, within rhizomorphs, and attached to mycorrhizal roots. Because he was dealing with isolated trees growing on mine wastes, there was no danger of confusing the fruiting body derived from one fungus with the mycorrhizal root of another tree. Experiments reviewed by Björkman (1949) showed that fruiting bodies were never formed when the tree roots were isolated from the fruiting body region by metal plates sunk into the ground, confirming that fruiting bodies form only when there is a direct hyphal connection to the tree.

It is therefore clear that the ectotrophic mycorrhiza is a true symbiosis, since both partners benefit, the fungus by obtaining a permanent home and energy supply, the plant by obtaining an efficient absorptive organ. It is noteworthy that, compared to the legume-rhizobium symbiosis, there is a marked lack of specificity between fungus and tree. However, this may mean only that the fungi, although morphologically different, are identical in the ecological characteristics which are of relevance to the association. Specificity does occur in certain combinations, *Boletus Grevillei,* for instance, infecting larch and no other tree (Melin, 1959). It should be emphasized that because a fungus rhizomorph is found attached to mycorrhizal roots in the field, this does not mean that it is the relevant organism. Many kinds of hyphae look alike, and hyphal morphology is greatly affected by environment, so that there may be two (or more) fungi associated with a root, of which only one is the true mycorrhizal form. It is essential, therefore, to isolate the fungus in pure culture and demonstrate with aseptic seedlings that this isolate is able to produce the mycorrhiza. It should also be noted that the same tree, or even the same root, may be infected with more than one mycorrhizal fungus (Melin, 1963).

ENDOTROPHIC MYCORRHIZAE

In endotrophic mycorrhizae the fungus is generally confined to the root itself and does not form a sheath or spread into the surrounding soil. Endotrophic mycorrhizae occur in a much greater variety of plants than do ectotrophic mycorrhizae, but except in the orchids experimental difficulties have delayed an understanding of their essential nature. It is probable that endotrophic mycorrhizae are of diverse origin and function (Harley, 1963), so that it cannot be assumed that what holds true for one holds for another. By far the commonest type of endotrophic mycorrhiza is that called vesicular-arbuscular (reviewed critically by Mosse, 1963), but cultural difficulties have prevented any real understanding. Mycorrhizae in the heath family have been studied by Burgeff (1961) by cultural and other means, but the results obtained on the physiology of absorption do not permit firm conclusions.

Because of their economic importance and intrinsic interest, the orchids have been studied for a long time, and here the picture is clearer. The seeds produced by an orchid flower contain only partially differentiated embryos, which usually grow saprophytically for several years and then produce chlorophyll and begin to grow autotrophically. (Some, however, remain saprophytic throughout life.) Although the grower of orchids usually cultures the embryos on organic media in a germ-free state, in nature the orchid must develop on natural substrates. Those seeds which in nature do not become infected usually die, but those which become infected with fungi either become parasitized by the fungus and are killed, or they achieve a state of equilibrium with the fungus and develop. In this latter case the fungi do not colonize the apical meristem but penetrate the mature cortical tissue and eventually become restricted to those regions in contact with the soil. In some of the infected cells of the orchid the fungus is healthy, whereas in other cells the hyphae are disintegrating and are being digested. The equilibrium between fungus and orchid is maintained because the orchid produces the antifungal substances orchinol and hircinol in response to infection (Nüesch, 1963). Since uninfected cells lack these substances, the fungus can begin to grow, but the substances are then produced and further growth is prevented. This is an example of what might be called balanced parasitism and also reveals an interesting biochemical mechanism for a microorganism-induced defense reaction.

The fungus is able to utilize complex carbohydrates in the soil such as cellulose and lignin (Harley, 1963) and indirectly provides the nutrients which the immature orchid embryo requires. The fungi in question are all Basidiomycetes, and most of them are able to live free apart from their hosts, in contrast to those of the ectotrophic mycorrhizae. Thus the fungi may not themselves benefit from their growth in the orchid, and it would almost seem as if the orchid has evolved a means of using the fungus to its own end, suggesting that this is not really a symbiotic interaction.

The slow-growing nature of the mycorrhizal plants has undoubtedly inhibited extensive work on many aspects of these interesting associations. Surprisingly, even mycologists have to a great extent ignored the mycorrhizal fungi (in the index to Bessey, 1950, the word mycorrhiza does not even appear), so that our ignorance of all phases of this work is great. Especially the endotrophic forms are poorly known, and because of their widespread distribution, these are the ones which require the most urgent work.

CHAPTER 9

Microbes in
Macroecology

In this chapter we consider the relationships of microorganisms to the world at large. It is rare that any study in nature can be strictly microbial, since for all their interesting activities, microorganisms represent only a small part of the total biomass of the world, and our attention must naturally be directed to the higher organisms which in most places form the dominant creatures of the earth. But although microorganisms do not sequester within themselves large amounts of energy and chemical elements, their high metabolic activities enable them to participate importantly in the turnover and transport of the elements. Further, microorganisms often break "bottlenecks" which exist in food chains and biogeochemical cycles of macroecosystems. Thus microorganisms can never be ignored if we wish to understand the ecology of macroorganisms. Unfortunately, because microbes are usually invisible to the naked eye, it is possible to move through a forest or grassland, lake or marsh, without ever having our attention directed to them, and many aspects of ecology may have suffered because of this.

As discussed in Chapter 7, it is useful to study ecosystems which are steady states, in which the rate of production of any element equals its rate of consumption when averaged over a sufficient length of time. Given a steady state, one can characterize the ecosystem functionally in terms of energy flow and biogeochemical cycle (Odum, 1959). A typical energy flow diagram is shown in Figure 9-1. Energy arrives mainly in the form of sunlight and is converted into organic matter by the photosynthetic organisms (the so-called primary producers); some of this energy is consumed by the primary producers themselves during the process of respiration, and the rest is passed on to other components of the system. In the figure there are two main channels of energy flow, one to the herbivores and the other to the decomposers. From the herbivores, energy flows through several levels of carnivores and is either eventually all dissipated within the system or there is export of some energy to other systems. Because each trophic level represents the food supply of the next level, such a system is often called a food chain, although a simple food chain diagram usually does not provide the quantitative information which is expressed by the energy flow diagram. As will become clear shortly, this energy flow diagram probably underemphasizes greatly the role of microorganisms.

To a considerable extent the chemical elements of many ecosystems remain within them, so that the substances from the environment which are converted into protoplasm by the primary producers are eventually returned to the environment after passing through the various trophic levels. Thus it is said that energy flows THROUGH the system, but chemical elements cycle WITHIN the system. However, different habitats may reveal quite different kinds of biogeochemical cycles. In the following discussion we will attempt to examine the role of microorganisms in the energy flow and biogeochemical cycles of several representative types of ecosystems in order to emphasize both the similarities and differences which are found.

It should be emphasized that there are many processes of a nonbiological nature which are occurring in the world. Although living organisms can do many things, there are many things which occur in their absence. Photochemical reactions occur in the atmosphere, in aquatic environments, and on the surface of the earth; various materials can oxidize spontaneously, and certain oxidation reactions are efficiently catalyzed by metal ions. Surfaces provide the opportunity for catalyses of various sorts. Especially in biogeochemistry such considerations are important, and it is frequently difficult to sort out the biological from the nonbiological fac-

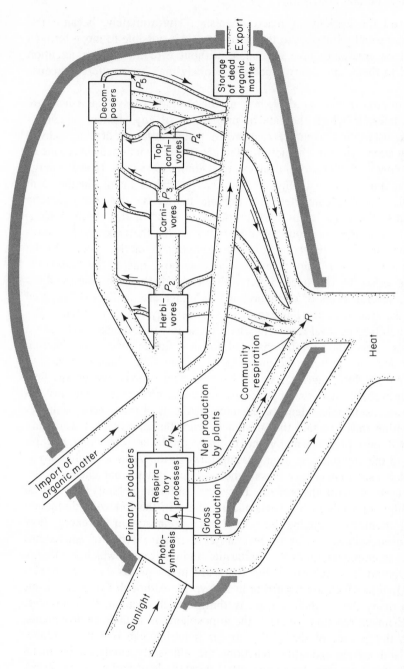

Fig. 9-1. Energy flow diagram of a community; P—gross primary production; P_N—net primary production, and P_2, P_3, P_4, and P_5—secondary production at the indicated levels (after Odum, 1959). Sizes of boxes and channels indicate the approximate relationships among the various levels. For certain modifications regarding the role of microorganisms, *see* text.

tors in a process. For instance, Kuznetsov et al. (1963) have shown that oxidation of H_2S in a sulfur spring is about 15-20% abiogenic and the rest biogenic, but in many cases the tools are not available to make such estimates.

Aquatic Environments

ENERGY FLOW

Except in shallow marshes, the primary producers in aquatic environments are predominantly photosynthetic microorganisms. Much is known about primary productivity in aquatic environments, and Table 9-1 surveys some of these data. Note that in all these cases, only energy derived from sunlight is being considered. Only in very polluted or very restricted environments would there be sufficient organic matter added from external sources to alter the energy balance. The factors which control primary

TABLE 9-1. GROSS PRIMARY PRODUCTIVITY OF VARIOUS AQUATIC ECOSYSTEMS AS DETERMINED BY GAS EXCHANGE

Ecosystem	Rate of production (g dry organic matter/m^2/day)
Averages for long periods—6 months to 1 year	
Infertile open ocean, Sargasso Sea	0.5
Infertile open ocean, Pacific	0.2
Shallow, inshore waters, Long Island Sound	3.2
Texas estuaries, Laguna Madre	4.4
Clear, deep (oligotrophic) lake, Wisconsin	0.7
Shallow (eutrophic) lake, Japan	2.1
Bog lake, Minnesota (phytoplankton only)	0.3
Lake Erie, Winter	1.0
Lake Erie, Summer	9.0
Silver Springs, Florida	17.5
Coral reefs, average three Pacific reefs	18.2
Values obtained for short favorable periods	
Fertilized pond, N. C.	5.0
Pond with treated sewage wastes, Denmark	9.0
Pond with untreated wastes, South Dakota	27
Silver Springs, Florida	35
Turbid river, N. C.	1.7
Polluted stream, Indiana	57
Estuaries, Texas	23
Marine turtle-grass flats, Florida	34
Mass algae culture, extra CO_2 added	43

See Odum (1959) for original references. The data may not be strictly comparable, as they were obtained by various workers with various methods.

productivity are discussed in general by Odum (1959) and for aquatic environments by Harvey (1957), Steeman Nielsen (1963), Ryther (1963), Raymont (1963), Strickland (1965), and Fogg (1965). The most important factors limiting production are inorganic nutrients, especially nitrogen and phosphorus, although vitamin deficiencies may limit production under certain conditions (Provasoli, 1963), and silicate may limit production for diatoms (*see* page 98). Marine environments always have high concentrations of bicarbonate and sulfate, so that the quantitatively important elements carbon and sulfur are never limiting, although carbon can be limiting in soft fresh waters. The vastly greater productivity of inshore waters in comparison with the open ocean is probably due to the much greater quantities of nutrients available from land drainage. As Ryther (1963) has stated: "The richest ocean water, exclusive of local polluted areas, contains about 60 μg atoms/l or 0.00005% nitrogen, four orders of magnitude less than fertile land. A cubic meter of this sea-water could support a crop of no more than about 5 g of dry organic matter. . . . the maximum depth of the euphotic zone is about 100 m. This surface layer is normally poor in nutrients relative to the deeper waters and seldom contains more than 10-20 μg atoms/l of available nitrogen." Once phytoplankton begin to grow, they not only consume the nutrients, but they absorb light and thus shorten the depth of the euphotic zone. Only at the very surface of the water can dense populations develop, but of course sinking depletes the water of some of the organisms. Although high productivity can occur for brief periods of time in the sea, these high rates can be maintained only ". . . by the constant replacement of the water . . . with a new supply of nutrient-rich water. . . . Upwelling of rich water from intermediate depths to the surface does occur more or less continuously in certain restricted areas. Over most of the ocean, however, no mechanism exists for such regular and persistent vertical transport . . . the sea is a desert compared to moderately productive land." Coral reefs present an interesting exception to this situation, being highly productive formations surrounded by quite sterile tropical seas. The possible reasons for the high productivity of reefs have been discussed by Yonge (1963), but as yet no definitive answer is forthcoming. The symbiosis of coral with algae has been discussed in Chapter 8, but this is clearly only part of the story. One point to remember is that productivity as measured by CO_2 fixation does not really indicate the rate of accumulation of new organic matter, and much of the organic matter produced may be converted back into CO_2 by the action of organisms later in the food chain. Thus the gross productivity measurements reveal the energy captured by the system but not necessarily that energy stored. Energy cannot be stored in living organisms without the concomitant storage of the chemical elements of which photoplasm is constructed (C, N,

P, S, etc.). If an ecosystem has an efficient food chain, with organic substances passing quickly from one link to the next and also has an efficient method of retaining within it the various nutrients, then this system may show a rapid turnover of material and a high rate of production, even though it may be surrounded by a nutrient-poor environment. This is precisely the situation in shallow lagoons of coral atolls and explains at least in part how these ecosystems are able to exhibit such high production rates. Thus in any analysis of the efficiency of energy capture by an ecosystem, it is clearly important to consider the various steps in the food chain.

It is generally considered that the phytoplankton which represent the primary producers are consumed mainly by small crustaceans (zooplankton), and that the bulk of the primary productivity flows from the algae directly through these animals. However, recent work reveals that much of the organic matter in aqueous environments exists in soluble form and in nonliving particles, the latter probably being formed spontaneously from organic matter which has been excreted by phytoplankton (Parsons, 1963; Riley, 1963; *see* page 21) or derived from dead organisms by fragmentation (Odum and Cruz, 1963). The relative distribution of organic matter in various forms for sea water is shown in Table 9-2. Parsons found it impossible to assess the bacterial content of sea water from available data, but it is known that bacteria are usually found in association with particles and probably modify them extensively. However, much of the dissolved organic carbon in deeper waters may be resistant to bacterial attack, and most of the bacterial action may occur in the surface waters (Menzel, 1964). A comparison of the production by algae of particulate and soluble organic matter in Windermere Lake, using the $C^{14}O_2$ method, is presented in Figure 9-2. It can be seen that the proportion of soluble organic matter produced varies with the depth and is highest in surface waters, being almost 80% of the total at this point. Fogg (1963) believes that the soluble material represents substances liberated from intact cells rather than from cells disintegrating during incubation or filtration.

TABLE 9-2. RELATIVE PROPORTIONS OF
ORGANIC MATTER IN VARIOUS
FORMS IN SEA WATER

Soluble organic	100
Particulate organic	10
Phytoplankton	2
Zooplankton	0.2
Fish	0.002

Data of Parsons (1963).

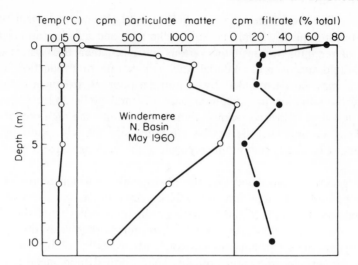

Fig. 9-2. In situ radiocarbon experiment carried out in the North Basin of Windermere on 17 May 1960, showing liberation of extracellular products of photosynthesis (Fogg, 1963). Bottles were exposed at different depths from 12:30 p.m. to 3:45 p.m. Conditions were mainly overcast with occasional bright intervals, and the most abundant species in the phytoplankton were *Cyclotella glomerata, Asterionella formosa, Chlorella pyrenoidosa,* and *Chrysochromulina parva.*

Newell (1963) has shown that fine particles (< 0.1 mm) acquire organic matter when suspended in filtered sea water but not if bacteria are prevented from growing by periodic boiling; most of the organic matter is probably bacterial cells. This fine silt containing organic matter can then serve as food for the prosobranch snail *Hydrobia ulvae* and the clam *Macoma balthica,* both of which grow best in natural environments containing fine silt high in organic matter. On the basis of carbon and nitrogen analyses of silt and fecal pellets, Newell concludes that the animals obtain their nutrition by digesting the bacteria which adhere to the particles. Newell (1963) also reviews other work which suggests that filter-feeding animals may obtain their food from bacteria. He points out the vagueness of the term "detritus" and suggests that it is essential to define the exact nature of the material which is serving as a food source.

In fresh waters much of the organic matter is allochthonous (Hutchinson, 1957; Hynes, 1963), being derived from the surrounding land in the form of humic substances, dead leaves, and other detrital materials. It is likely that these materials are acted upon by bacteria and converted at least partially into microbial protein. Recent data by Minshall (1965) suggest that this detritus can be an important food source for aquatic invertebrates.

A clear relationship between bacterial growth and productivity of trout was found in the experimental studies of Warren et al. (1964) in an Oregon stream. These workers arranged in a controlled section of this stream to add sucrose to the water at a slow constant rate of 1-4 $\mu g/ml$, and the trout production in this section was compared with a control section which was just upstream from the source of sucrose. The addition of sucrose stimulated the growth of the bacterium *Sphaerotilus natans* which provided food and habitat for tendipedid (Chironomid) larvae, as shown by the fact that *Sphaerotilus* filaments could be seen microscopically in the intestinal contents of the larvae, and that the biomass of larvae was over 50 times higher in the experimental than in the control sections. These larvae were an important source of food organisms for the trout, as shown by microscopic examination of the fish intestinal contents. The production rate of trout in the experimental section was as much as ten-fold greater than in the control section. These experiments directly demonstrate the potential significance of bacteria in the food chain. They also raise an interesting question on the concept of pollution, since high organic matter concentrations which lead to massive growth of *S. natans* are usually associated with pollution, but yet in the present experiments, the increase in concentration of a single organic substance, sucrose, led to an apparently polluted stream and at the same time to a greatly increased fish production. The present experimental approach would seem to have far-reaching implications.

Thus it is likely that bacteria in aquatic environments function not only as decomposers and mineralizers, but that they also exist at early places in the food chain. It is also possible that the bacteria which adhere to the phytoplankton modify these cells, either by partially digesting them or by producing vitamins, so that they are more palatable to zooplankton (Parsons, 1963). According to Golueke and Oswald (1964), algae are fairly indigestible for mammals, but if the algae are passed through anaerobic bacterial digesters (such as are used in sewage treatment plants), they are made digestible. At the same time, the bacteria probably make up by synthesis nutritional inadequacies of the algae. To examine adequately the role of bacteria in the aquatic food chain will require the development of germ-free cultures of both phytoplankton and zooplankton. Although the former are now readily available (Hutner and Provasoli, 1964), germ-free zooplankton cultures are still a rarity, although it seems only a matter of time before they will be available routinely (Zillioux and Wilson, 1964; Taub and Dollar, 1964).

In terms of the energy efficiency in food chains, a knowledge of the

role of bacteria is of great importance. For instance, the relatively sophisticated thermodynamic considerations derived by Slobodkin (1962b) are
based on experiments with *Chlamydomonas-Daphnia* populations which
are not bacteria-free. The 10% efficiency in the conversion of algal calories
to animal calories found by Slobodkin may be low because bacteria are
consuming large and unknown amounts of the available energy. Only
pure cultures will provide a meaningful answer.

Even if bacteria do not enter early into the food chain, they may
still provide considerable food for later trophic levels. Figure 9-1 suggests that all the energy flowing into the decomposers is lost from the
system, yet a consideration of the energetics of bacterial growth (*see*
Chapter 7) reveals that this is hardly likely. Under aerobic conditions
most bacteria are close to 50% efficient in converting carbon into cell
substance, and even under anaerobic conditions 5-10% efficiency is the
rule. Thus much of the energy which flows to the bacteria remains there.
It is possible, of course, that these cells die, lyse, and release nutrients
which are then consumed by other bacterial cells, so that eventually all
energy is destroyed within this one trophic level. But it is more likely
that the bacteria are consumed by organisms such as protozoa, crustaceans,
and molluscs, so that the energy is eventually dissipated through other
members of the food chain. Although all such organisms might be lumped
together as decomposers, this would be essentially ignoring potentially
important aspects of the energy flow system. If we really wish to know
how energy flows through the food chain, then we should attempt to
discover all links in the chain.

Although we can see how the role of heterotrophic microorganisms
in the food chain could be studied in the laboratory, how is it possible to
perform effective field studies? By using radioactive phosphorus Odum
and Kuenzler (1963) have been able to identify and isolate individual
members of a food chain consisting of macroorganisms. Radioactive phosphorus has been used with microorganisms by McMahon and Rigler
(1965) who studied the feeding rate of *Daphnia magna* (although not
in germ-free culture) by adding to the cladoceran culture microorganisms
labeled with P^{32} and measuring the decrease in radioactivity in the suspension. The feeding rate increased with increasing concentration of microorganisms supplied, until a plateau value was reached which was characteristic for each organism. The maximum feeding rates for the four different
organisms are given in Table 9-3, where it is shown that in terms of the
number of cells removed per hour, the rates for the different microorganisms differed markedly, but in terms of the volumes of microbial cells
consumed, the rates were more similar. Extending this technique to the
field will not be easy, however, since if a pure culture of labeled microorganisms were added to a natural environment, the specific radioactivity

TABLE 9-3. MAXIMUM AND OPTIMUM FEEDING RATES OF *Daphnia magna* (2.8–3.3 MM) ON P^{32} LABELED MICROORGANISMS OF DIFFERENT SIZE

Food organism	Cell volume (μ^3)	Maximum feeding rate $(\times 10^6 \text{ cells}/hr)$	Volume of food consumed per animal (mm^3/hr)
Escherichia coli (bacteria)	0.9	5.6	0.005
Chlorella vulgaris (alga)	34	0.50	0.017
Saccharomyces cerevisiae (yeast)	66	0.25	0.016
Tetrahymena pyriformis (protozoa)	1.8×10^4	0.0028	0.051

Data of McMahon and Rigler (1965).

of the added organisms would be diluted by whatever natural organisms the zooplankton were already eating.

BIOGEOCHEMICAL CYCLES

Our knowledge of biogeochemical cycles in aquatic environments is more advanced than our knowledge of energy flow. Extensive work has been done in both freshwater lakes (Hutchinson, 1957; Kuznetsov, 1959) and marine environments (Hill, 1963; Harvey, 1957; Sorokin, 1964b; Oppenheimer, 1963). By the use of radioactive and stable isotopes, studies on the transformation and transport of elements can be done in the field, and by correlating such studies with laboratory work on pure cultures, one can obtain a reasonably clear picture. In the biogeochemical cycles the dominant role of microorganisms, especially bacteria, should be noted. In anaerobic areas of a body of water, such as the sediments and hypolimnion, bacteria are practically the exclusive forms found, but even in aerobic environments they play a large role, especially in the decomposition of plant and animal remains.

A simple OXYGEN cycle is described in the following equations:

$$H_2O \xrightarrow{\text{light}} O_2 \qquad \text{Photosynthesis. Oxygen production.}$$

$$O_2 \xrightarrow[\text{dark}]{\text{light and}} H_2O \qquad \text{Respiration. Oxygen utilization.}$$

$$O_2 \xrightarrow[\text{dark}]{\text{light and}} \text{Organic oxygen} \qquad \text{Oxygen assimilation.}$$

$$\text{Organic oxygen} \xrightarrow[\text{dark}]{\text{light and}} H_2O \qquad \text{Decomposition processes.}$$

Many organisms require O_2 as a building block of protoplasm, in the synthesis of steroids, unsaturated fatty acids, certain amino acids, etc., and even some microorganisms which are able to dispense with O_2 as an electron acceptor still require O_2 for assimilatory processes, if the biochemicals which ordinarily require O_2 for their synthesis are absent from the environment (Goldfine and Bloch, 1963). But much larger amounts of O_2 are required in respiratory than in biosynthetic processes, so that a deficiency of O_2 is likely to be felt here first. Although O_2 is one of the most plentiful gases in the atmosphere, its restricted solubility in water and the slow rate of diffusion through large water masses make it likely that O_2 will often become limiting in nature (*see* Chapter 2), and because larger plants and animals are strict aerobes, the distribution of O_2 is probably more likely to be crucial in controlling the distribution of these organisms than is any other element. Since the solubility of O_2 in water is markedly affected by temperature and pressure, and because convection and turbulence may modify the restrictions imposed by diffusion, complex interactions are possible. A detailed analysis of these interactions is provided by Hutchinson (1957), and the discussion here will be restricted to the role of microorganisms in controlling O_2 concentrations.

The photosynthetic production of O_2 occurs only in regions which receive light and is thus restricted in a lake to surface layers. Organic matter which is not consumed in these surface layers sinks to the depths and serves as nutrients for microorganisms. The O_2 which reaches these deeper waters is consumed by facultatively aerobic microorganisms which, because they are able to use O_2 as an electron acceptor, can utilize organic nutrients more efficiently than can anaerobes and are thus able to reduce the O_2 content to a low level. Without the action of these microorganisms, there would be no significant alteration of the oxygen content in deeper waters, so that O_2 depletion requires the presence of both facultative microorganisms and oxidizable, usually organic, substrates. (In theory, O_2 depletion could result from the action of chemosynthetic organisms utilizing substrates such as H_2S and NH_3, but the concentration of these inorganic oxidizable nutrients derived from nonbiological sources is rarely high enough to be significant.) In summer, when a lake becomes thermally stratified, the deeper layers are often very anaerobic, and it is only when the water mass turns over in the fall of the year that the oxygen deficit is replenished. Since some of the organic matter which settles through the water is deposited on the bottom, the sediments also become anaerobic, and even in highly aerated water the aerobic zone may extend only a few millimeters into the sediment because of the greatly reduced convection currents in the sediment (Oppenheimer, 1960). Mud at a lake bottom probably always has reducing properties except occasionally at the mud-water interface (Hutchinson, 1957). Since

O_2 will become analytically undetectable before any detectable drop in redox potential has occurred (Hutchinson, 1957), it is evident that O_2 will be generally absent from any sediment, although if the mud is in contact with oxygenated water an oxidized microzone several millimeters thick will develop at the surface. This oxidized zone will act as a barrier to the diffusion of nutrients from the mud, so that if the water above the mud becomes anaerobic and the zone disappears, this diffusion barrier is eliminated, and extensive amounts of nutrients may pass into the water. Thus the development of reducing conditions in deep waters will be responsible for profound changes in the chemistry of the hypolimnetic water and indirectly of the whole lake. Similar nutrient enrichment also occurs during flooding of rice paddy soils (Grist, 1959).

The O_2 is less likely to become deficient in the deeper waters of marine than freshwater environments, due to the extensive mixing action of ocean currents. In certain bays, fjords, and inland seas, however, mixing of deep waters is prevented by the presence of a shallow sill at the entrance to the bay (Redfield et al., 1963). Under these conditions, anaerobic conditions do develop in the deep waters, H_2S is produced, and metallic sulfides are precipitated. Such a condition exists in the Black Sea, Baltic Sea, and certain Norway (Dietrich, 1963) and British Columbia fjords (Gucluer and Gross, 1964).

Although the action of microorganisms is crucial to the whole process of oxygen depletion, the organisms themselves may often be ignored and the process studied in a strictly geochemical fashion. But since temperature, pH, and other environmental factors can often greatly modify or restrict the actions of microorganisms, it would seem wise to study oxidation-reduction processes from a microbiological point of view.

The biogeochemical cycle of CARBON in a freshwater lake is shown in Figure 9-3. The carbon entering a lake comes from several sources: (1) bicarbonate in rain water; (2) bicarbonate leaching out of the rocks and soil of the lake basin; (3) CO_2 diffusing from the air into the lake; and (4) organic carbon compounds originating in the terrestrial plants surrounding the basin (e.g., leaves, root excretions). Carbon 14 is being created continuously in the atmosphere from N^{14}, and since C^{14} has a half-life of only 5600 years, the carbonate in limestone rocks is devoid of radioactivity, whereas modern-day plants and animals have a C^{14} content which is identical to that of the atmosphere. In certain hard water lakes the C^{14} content is lower than that of the atmosphere (Hutchinson, 1957), suggesting that some of the carbon is derived from the limestone of the basin, but the carbon of most lakes is clearly derived from modern sources. The proportion of organic matter which enters a lake from outside, as opposed to that produced within the lake, is determined greatly by the nature of the lake basin and the surrounding environment.

Hutchinson (1957) lists values from 30% to 75% for the amount of organic carbon of external origin for a series of Wisconsin lakes. Sea water generally derives less carbon from exogenous organic matter than lake water (Harvey, 1957), unless influenced by land drainage, and more carbon from carbon dioxide. The complexities regarding the solubility of CO_2 and its relation to pH and $CaCO_3$ concentration have been discussed in Chapter 2 (page 10).

The fate of carbon compounds in aquatic environments is of considerable interest to the geologist, geochemist, and paleobiochemist, since our great stores of the fossil fuels, coal and oil, derive from these sources. Organic geochemistry has been recently summarized in the excellent volume edited by Breger (1963) which should be consulted for details of many aspects of microbial interest. A surprisingly large variety of organic biochemicals escape decomposition and appear in sediments, although Vallentyne (1962) has emphasized the much greater stability of insoluble compounds like cellulose and lignin as opposed to soluble organic substances. An important factor in the stability of insoluble compounds is that they sink into and become buried in anaerobic sediments where they escape decay. Although cellulose can be decomposed anaerobically by certain bacteria (for example, it disappears very rapidly in anaerobic sewage digesters [McCabe and Eckenfelder, 1958] and in the anaerobic rumen [see page 199]), in anaerobic aquatic sediments acidic fermentation products rapidly accumulate and lower the pH sufficiently so that the bacteria can no longer function. Acidic fermentation is probably of considerable importance in the formation and preservation of peat in bogs (Burgeff, 1961; Francis, 1954) and also in the preservation of lake sediments, although the low temperature of these environments is also a major factor in preservation (Francis, 1954). Lignin is even more resistant to decay than cellulose, especially anaerobically. Ultimately, the resistant lignin and cellulose are converted into humic acids and ulmins which are eventually converted into coal (Francis, 1954). Because of the greater importance of woody plants in fresh water as opposed to marine environments, coal is considered to be mainly a product of the great freshwater forest swamps of Carboniferous and Miocene times (van Krevelen, 1963). Wood is derived mainly from land sources and is relatively unimportant in the sea, and in marine environments oil is the predominant fossil fuel which is formed, probably being derived from the anaerobic alteration of marine algae (Whitehead and Breger, 1963).

It is possible to obtain a general idea of the source of organic matter by measuring the carbon:nitrogen ratio of a sediment. Gucluer and Gross (1964) give the average C:N value for plankton as 5.7, and for wood as 54.0. The coalification process itself can be followed by measuring the H:C and O:C ratios at various depths (van Krevelen, 1963). It should

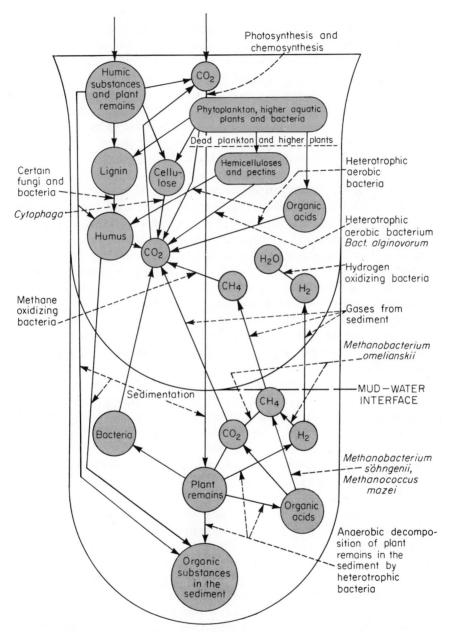

Fig. 9-3. Carbon cycle in a freshwater lake (after Kuznetsov, 1959)

be noted that once organic matter is preserved in sediments, most of the transformations which occur during coalification are probably geochemical rather than microbial (van Krevelen, 1963). Marine environments usually have considerably less organic matter in sediments than do eutrophic lakes (Swain, 1963) because of the low productivity of oceans and because the relatively favorable aerobic conditions on the ocean floor promote more extensive decomposition of organic matter. Marine sediments formed in anaerobic environments are much higher in organic matter (Gucluer and Gross, 1964).

It would be of great interest to know the rates of the various transformations listed in Figure 9-3. Deevey et al. (1963) and Deevey and Stuiver (1964) have begun to approach this problem by measuring the relative contents of C^{12} and C^{13} in various carbon components of a lake. The basic principle of the technique is that reactions in living organisms discriminate against C^{13}. Although strictly chemical reactions may also show isotope discrimination at low temperatures, chemical reactions proceed so slowly at these temperatures that they are much less important than biological reactions. Thus carbon compounds of biological origin will be low in C^{13} with respect to the carbon source from which they are derived. The results of Deevey and co-workers show that the carbon of the mud has the same isotope ratio as does the plankton and is thus derived from the plankton by sedimentation. However, the methane in the mud is lighter than that of the plankton, whereas the CO_2 in the mud is heavier. The authors believe that this indicates that the CO_2 derived from the oxidation of organic remains is discriminated against by the methane bacteria, so that these bacteria convert more of the light $C^{12}O_2$ molecules to methane than they do those of the heavier $C^{13}O_2$ molecules; the heavier molecules then rise and mix with the CO_2 of the hypolimnion which has been derived from other sources. The carbon of the CO_2 of the hypolimnion is therefore lighter than the carbon of the plankton but heavier than that of the air. These results, although preliminary, suggest the experimental possibilities available for determining the rates of the various reactions in Figure 9-3, especially if such observations were coupled with the use of C^{14} as a tracer.

Although an enormous amount of the carbon at the earth's surface is present in the form of coal and oil (*see* Figure 2-1), relatively little is known about the decomposition of these products by microorganisms. Petroleum products are destroyed aerobically by many microorganisms (Beerstecher, 1954), but apparently little is known about the rates at which this occurs in nature. Coal is basically aromatic in character (Francis, 1954) and thus in theory could be decomposed by organisms which could attack the benzene ring. Amorphous carbon, such as occurs in charcoal and lampblack, might also be oxidized by microorganisms

(Potter, 1908) although no modern work on this problem has come to my attention. It would be quite interesting to know how a bacterium can attack amorphous carbon, especially in comparison to the mode of attack of free sulfur by thiobacilli (Schaeffer et al., 1963).

The NITROGEN transformations in a freshwater lake are shown in Figure 9-4. Some nitrogen gas of the atmosphere is converted photo-

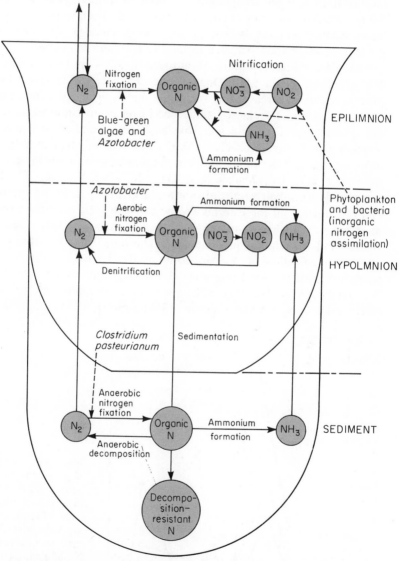

Fig. 9-4. Microbiological processes in the nitrogen cycle in a freshwater lake (after Kuznetsov, 1959).

chemically into nitrate and ammonia which are brought to the lake in rain water (*see* Table 2-2), and some nitrogen compounds are introduced by land drainage; these sources probably account for the bulk of the combined nitrogen of lakes. The nitrogen transformations of most microbiological interest in aquatic environments are nitrogen fixation and denitrification, since these two processes oppose each other in affecting the total level of fixed nitrogen compounds in a body of water. Symbiotic nitrogen-fixing organisms are not common in aquatic environments, and the only well-substantiated case is that of the blue-green alga *Anabaena azolae* growing in association with the aquatic fern *Azolla folliculoides* (McKee, 1962). Direct measurements of nitrogen fixation in lake waters using $N_2{}^{15}$ (Dugdale et al., 1959; Dugdale and Dugdale, 1962) reveal that this process occurs at a reasonably rapid rate and is light dependent; the free-living organisms of greatest significance in nitrogen fixation are probably blue-green algae (Dugdale and Dugdale, 1962), and *Azotobacter* plays a rather minor role (Kuznetsov, 1959). The assimilation of three forms of nitrogen, N_2, $NO_3{}^-$, and $NH_4{}^+$, was followed over a whole season in a freshwater lake by Dugdale and Dugdale (1965) using N^{15} labeled compounds, and their results are shown in Figure 9-5. In the spring, high uptake rates for all three forms are noted, with $NH_4{}^+$ assimilation being most extensive, whereas in the fall bloom, uptake of $NH_4{}^+$ and $NO_3{}^-$ is low, and N_2 fixation predominates. The data from the spring bloom suggest that fixation of N_2 can occur at the same time that combined sources of nitrogen are being utilized, showing that one process does not completely inhibit the other, although in other situations the presence of $NH_4{}^+$ inhibits N_2 fixation (Wilson, 1958; Stewart, 1964). Dugdale et al.

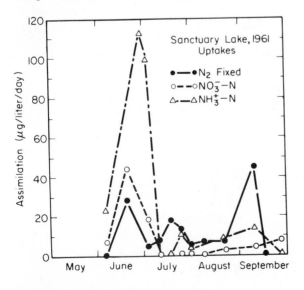

Fig. 9-5. Assimilation rates of the three inorganic nitrogen sources into the particulate organic nitrogen in Sanctuary Lake water, as measured by incorporation of N^{15}-labeled compounds (after Dugdale and Dugdale, 1965).

(1961) have shown that nitrogen fixation also occurs in the Sargasso Sea during blooms of the blue-green alga *Trichodesmium thiebautii*. Odum and Odum (1955) suggested the possibility of nitrogen fixation by the blue-green algae associated with coral reefs. Blue-green algae are more common in tropical than in temperate seas. Anaerobic nitrogen-fixing bacteria referable to *Clostridium pasteurianum* can be isolated from lake waters (Kuznetsov, 1959) but apparently no direct measurements of anaerobic nitrogen fixation using N_2^{15} have been performed. Likewise, direct measurements of the rate of denitrification have not been made, although Kuznetsov (1959) has presented data which suggest that about ⅓ of the nitrogen acquired by the lake from various sources is lost through denitrification. It should be noted that the detection by cultural means of either nitrogen-fixing or denitrifying bacteria does not indicate that the organisms are actually performing these processes in nature. Nitrogen fixation is inhibited by combined nitrogen compounds (Wilson, 1958), and denitrification is inhibited by oxygen (Jannasch, 1960). It is thus essential to measure these processes directly with the use of isotopes. Unfortunately, the lack of a radioactive isotope of nitrogen has probably delayed efforts in this area. The ultimate goal should be to attach numerical values to all of the transformations described in Figure 9-4.

SULFUR can exist in a number of oxidation states: $-II$ (H_2S, sulfur amino acids), 0 (elemental sulfur), $+II$ (thiocyanate), $+IV$ (sulfite), and $+VI$ (sulfate). In nature, only three oxidation states occur in any significance, $-II$, 0, and $+VI$ (Hutchinson, 1957), so that the discussion to follow will involve only these forms.

The sulfur cycle in a freshwater lake is shown in Figure 9-6. The concentration of sulfate is much higher in sea water than in fresh water, although acid lakes and mineralized lakes in closed basins may also contain large amounts of sulfate. Some sulfate enters lakes by solution from rocks of the lake basin, but most of the sulfate is derived from rain water. Sulfate is the second most common anion in rain water (after bicarbonate) (Hutchinson, 1957) and is probably derived from sulfur dioxide in the air. The SO_2 arises from two sources, industrial gases and biologically and geologically produced H_2S, which is spontaneously auto-oxidized. Primary producers can use sulfate as a sulfur source, reducing it to the $-II$ oxidation level. Many decomposing bacteria can liberate H_2S from sulfur-containing amino acids, and in aerobic environments this is a major source of H_2S. Sulfate-reducing bacteria are mainly responsible for H_2S production under anaerobic conditions. Kaplan and Rafter (1958) and Deevey et al. (1963) have used $S^{32}:S^{34}$ ratios to sort out the biological and nonbiological components in certain sulfur transformations, using the principle of biological discrimination against a heavy isotope as discussed earlier for carbon. The use of this method is especially pertinent

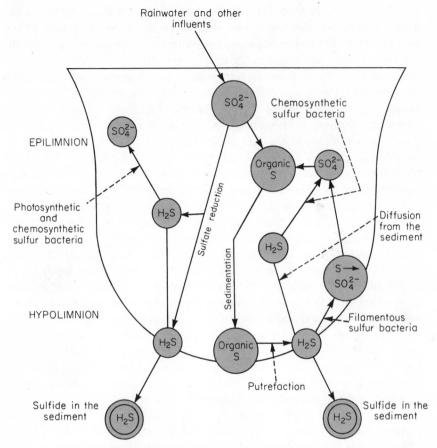

Fig. 9-6. Microbiological processes in the sulfur cycle in a freshwater lake (after Kuznetsov, 1959).

for sulfur, since many sulfur compounds undergo spontaneous nonbiological transformations (Kuznetsov et al., 1963). Sulfate which sinks into the mud and hypolimnion is reduced by sulfate-reducing bacteria which use it as an electron acceptor for the oxidation of organic materials, and H_2S is produced which is enriched in S^{32} with respect to S^{34}. Ferrous ions present in the mud then react with the H_2S, producing FeS which is highly insoluble and escapes further biological action. If there is a deficiency of iron in the mud, or if amounts of H_2S are produced in excess of the amount necessary to precipitate all of the iron, then this H_2S can be oxidized by bacteria. In anaerobic regions of the lake where radiant energy penetrates, photosynthetic sulfur bacteria can develop which use H_2S as an electron donor and produce sulfur granules. Kuznetsov (1959) has studied the vertical distribution of such an organism, Chromatium, in Lake Belovod and showed that the organism existed in a layer at a depth of around 15 meters, being absent in shallower and deeper areas, suggesting that at this depth the H_2S concentration and the light intensity are optimal (see Figure 3-5). Hutchinson (1957) has described a number of other cases in which photosynthetic sulfur bacteria occurred in strata; in some of these cases the water from the bacterial layer was opalescent due to the presence of elemental sulfur. If H_2S reaches areas which are aerobic, it can then be oxidized by chemoautotrophic sulfur bacteria which also deposit sulfur.

Sorokin (1964b) has used radioisotopes of carbon and sulfur to study the activities of sulfate-reducing and chemosynthetic sulfur bacteria in the Black Sea. Because of the stagnation which occurs in this body of water, the lower layers are continuously anaerobic, and sulfate reduction leads to the production of large amounts of H_2S. Although H_2S is found throughout the deeper waters, Sorokin found by the use of $S^{35}O_4$ that sulfate reduction occurred only in two areas, at the bottom (around 1600 meters) and in a layer at a depth of 200–300 meters (Figure 9-7). Presumably, these two sulfate-reducing regions develop because the organic matter which is formed in the eutrophic zones may occur in two components, one of which may be more oxidizable than the other. The readily oxidizable material may be initially attacked in the aerobic zone, but that which escapes oxidation here may then be attacked at the top of the anaerobic zone (200–300 meters) where sulfate could serve as the electron acceptor. The less readily oxidizable material then would settle to the bottom where it would accumulate and serve as an energy source for further sulfate reduction. Measuring $C^{14}O_2$ fixation in the dark in the presence of added Na_2S, Sorokin studied primary production due to the chemosynthetic sulfur bacteria. He found that CO_2 fixation occurred only in a sharp layer at a depth of 200 meters, with no fixation occurring either above or below this (Figure 9-8). Colony counts revealed that it was in this same layer that colorless sulfur bacteria could be found. The formation of this layer presumably reflects the requirement of these bacteria for both H_2S and O_2, so that they develop only where the gradients of these two substances meet (see page 41). Aerobic heterotrophic bacteria were found only in association with algae in the photosynthetic zone at the surface and with the chemosynthetic bacteria.

Kuznetsov et al. (1963) describe experiments using S^{35} labeled sulfide to study the biological and nonbiological components in the oxidation of H_2S in a lake fed by a sulfur spring. About 55% of the H_2S was oxidized, of which about 50% was oxidized by chemoautotrophs, 15% by photosynthetic bacteria, and the rest was oxidized nonbiologically. Most of the sulfide was oxidized only as far as free sulfur, but some was oxidized all the way to sulfate. Kaplan and Rafter (1958) have shown

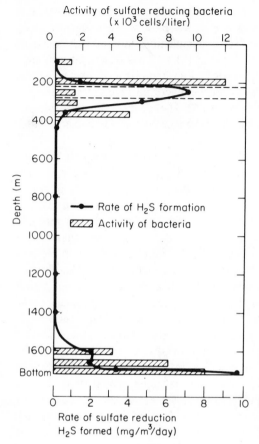

Fig. 9-7. The rate of sulfate reduction in the water column of the Black Sea (Station 4745) (Sorokin, 1964b). Rates measured by use of S[35]-labeled sulfate. Radioactivity of H₂S produced in the experiments with the addition of Ca-lactate.

that chemoautotrophic bacteria discriminate against S[34] when oxidizing H₂S, and by comparing the relative enrichment of S[32] brought about by pure cultures of thiobacilli with that existing in natural sulfur deposits in Australia, they have shown that the natural deposits are of biological rather than nonbiological origin. Similar conclusions have been made concerning the extensive sulfur deposits along the coast of the Gulf of Mexico (Kuznetsov et al., 1963).

Elemental sulfur and metallic sulfides in nature are rapidly oxidized aerobically to sulfuric acid. Kaplan and Rafter (1958) have shown that thiobacilli do not show the discrimination against S[34] when oxidizing sulfur that they do when oxidizing H₂S (the reason for this difference is unexplained) so that isotope ratios cannot be used to distinguish the biological from the nonbiological components in this oxidation. Although it is likely that thiobacilli are involved in the oxidation of elemental sulfur (Kuznetsov et al., 1963), their exact contribution is unknown.

Metallic sulfides, mainly FeS, are often exposed to the air in mining operations, and a rapid oxidation of the sulfur to sulfuric acid leads to the creation of highly acidic waters (values as low as pH 1.0 are reported) which drain these areas. The oxidation of these sulfide ores by thiobacilli (mainly *Thiobacillus ferroxidans*) under aseptic conditions in the laboratory is readily demonstrated and these bacteria are known to be extremely

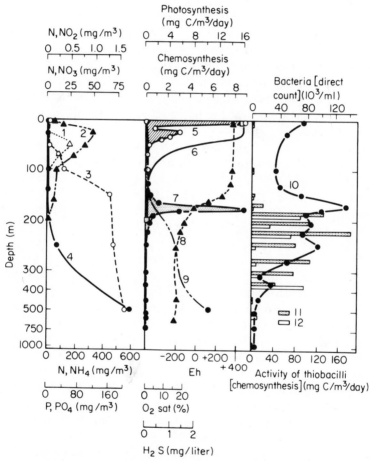

Fig. 9-8. Daily chemosynthetic production and some factors influencing it (Sorokin, 1964b). Central Black Sea, October; 1) NO₂⁻; 2) NO₃⁻; 3) PO₄; 4) NH₄⁺; 5) photosynthesis; 6) O₂; 7) chemosynthesis; 8) Eh; 9) H₂S; 10) bacteria (direct count); 11) aerobic thiobacilli; 12) anaerobic (denitrifying) thiobacilli. Photosynthesis measured by C¹⁴O₂ fixation in the light. Chemosynthesis measured by dark fixation of C¹⁴-labeled bicarbonate in presence of added Na₂S.

tolerant to the acid conditions which they produce. Approximately four-fifths of the sulfuric acid produced is probably of biological origin, the rest resulting from strictly chemical reactions (Kuznetsov et al., 1963).

Only rarely (Fish, 1955) does sulfur function as an element limiting productivity or biological development under natural conditions (Wiame, 1958), but the toxicity of H_2S and H_2SO_4 to many organisms, the economic importance of sulfur deposits, and the wide variety of oxidation states of this element make the sulfur cycle of considerable ecological importance. In the Black Sea, for instance, the concentration of H_2S below 150 meters is so great as to exclude all forms except microorganisms (Wiame, 1958). H_2S and sulfuric acid, mainly of microbial origin, are involved in the corrosion of iron pipes (Beerstecher, 1954). The dominant role of bacteria in sulfur transformations is evident; because of the availability of a good radioisotope of sulfur, we should see considerable extension in our knowledge of the sulfur cycle in various aquatic habitats in the near future.

IRON exists in two readily convertible oxidation states, ferrous (+II) and ferric (+III), both of which form insoluble hydroxides. The form in which iron will be found in nature will be greatly influenced by pH and redox potential (*see* page 13). At neutral pH, ferrous iron is oxidized spontaneously so readily to the ferric form that it is extremely difficult to determine whether the same oxidation can be carried out by living organisms. At acid pH values and under reducing conditions, ferrous iron is formed spontaneously. Microorganisms participate in the conversion of ferric into ferrous ions in two ways, by altering the redox potential and pH through their metabolic activities, or by using the ferric ion directly as an electron acceptor (Alexander, 1961). The ferrous ions in anaerobic sediments react with H_2S, and the FeS formed is responsible for the typical black color of most muds. Iron exists partly in the form of soluble or colloidal iron organic chelates and if it were not for these chelates, iron would probably be completely unavailable in many waters, especially in the alkaline marine environment. Many bacteria precipitate iron by oxidizing the organic compounds to which it is chelated (Alexander, 1961), and this phenomenon has occasionally been confused with an action of the bacteria on the iron itself. Under the acid conditions found in mine water drainages, ferrous ions are not autooxidized even in the presence of air, and here it is possible to demonstrate the biological oxidation by the bacterium *Thiobacillus ferroxidans* (*Ferrobacillus ferroxidans*). This organism is a true autotroph, using CO_2 as its sole source of carbon and ferrous ions as its energy source (Kuznetsov et al., 1963; Alexander, 1961). For details of this and other aspects of the iron cycle in nature, the reader is referred to Hutchinson (1957), Kuznetsov (1959) and Kuznetsov et al. (1963).

"Of all the elements present in living organisms, *phosphorus* is likely to be the most important ecologically, because the ratio of phosphorus to other elements in organisms tends to be considerably greater than the ratio in the primary sources of the biological elements. A deficiency of phosphorus is therefore more likely to limit the productivity of any region of the earth's surface than is a deficiency of any other material except water" (Hutchinson, 1957). Although reduced forms of phosphorus are known to occur both in meteorites (Goldschmidt, 1954) and to be produced biologically (*see* Hutchinson, 1952, for a brief discussion of the will-o'-the-wisp), phosphorus occurs in the biosphere almost exclusively in the fully oxidized state as phosphate. Phosphate exists as soluble inorganic phosphate, insoluble ferric and calcium phosphates, soluble and colloidal organic phosphate, and particulate organic phosphate. The soluble inorganic phosphate in lakes is usually around 10% of the total, about half of the total is organic phosphorus, and the rest is particulate inorganic phosphate. The concentration of phosphorus in a lake will be determined mainly by the nature of the surrounding rock and other geochemical factors. Often there is an increase in soluble phosphate in the anaerobic portions of a lake due partly to the microbial decomposition of sinking plankton, but due mainly to the removal of iron from ferrous phosphate by the formation of the more insoluble ferrous sulfide, thus releasing phosphate. Many microorganisms can solubilize phosphate in rocks by producing organic acids (Alexander, 1961), and this may be an important source of phosphate in environments where there is much organic matter. Pomeroy (1963) studied the effect of antibiotics on the release of phosphate-P^{32} from an insoluble form in a marine environment and obtained data which suggested that bacteria play only a small role in this process, and these experiments were extended by Pomeroy et al. (1965). On the other hand, Phillips (1964) believed bacteria play an extensive role in phosphate turnover in both fresh and sea water, based on P^{32} studies with the antibiotic tetracycline. P^{32} has also been used as a tracer to study the circulation of phosphorus in lakes (Hutchinson, 1957).

The biogeochemistry of other elements is discussed briefly by Hutchinson (1957), Goldschmidt (1945), and Day (1963), and the reader is referred to these sources for information.

Of the trace elements which are involved in the nutrition of living organisms, COBALT is of particular interest because of its presence in the vitamin B_{12} molecule. (There are a number of chemical forms which have B_{12} activity, and not all organisms respond equally to all forms [Hutner et al., 1961]. This complication is not taken into consideration in the present brief discussion.) Both the requirement for vitamin B_{12} and the ability to synthesize it are irregularly distributed among living organisms. Higher plants, for instance, neither synthesize nor require B_{12}, their metabolic machinery being so arranged that they can completely dispense with it. Animals and many microorganisms require vitamin B_{12} and cannot synthesize it. It is probable that B_{12} is synthesized in nature only by bacteria (Hutner et al., 1961). A surprisingly large number of marine algae require B_{12}. Coastal waters are richest in B_{12}, but some waters in the open sea have low or undetectable amounts (Provasoli, 1958a); it is not clear if this is due to a deficiency of cobalt in the surrounding water or to a deficiency in another element which would prevent the growth of B_{12}-synthesizing organisms. The B_{12} assay is many times more sensitive than is any assay for cobalt itself (Hutner et al., 1961). In fresh waters, both bacteria and blue-green algae have been identified as B_{12} synthesizers, and in one lake as much as 13% of the total cobalt was tied up as B_{12} (Provasoli, 1958a). Although much of the vitamin B_{12} found in sea water is probably autochthonous, significant quantities may be washed into the sea with freshwater drainage (Hutner et al., 1956; Lochhead, 1958) and be responsible in part for the development of dinoflagellate blooms. Cobalt deficiency in many soils limits the development of ruminants which obtain their B_{12} from bacteria which synthesize it in the rumen (Hutner et al., 1961). Man obtains B_{12} from his diet, and if only plant materials are eaten, a vitamin deficiency may develop; since man obtains his B_{12} from animal food sources, the synthesis of this vitamin is ultimately traceable to the rumen microflora. The activities of B_{12}-synthesizing microorganisms might thus provide a basic control of the activities of a whole ecosystem in which B_{12}-requiring organisms, such as the dinoflagellates, are the primary producers.

Terrestrial
Environments

There is no clear demarcation between aquatic and terrestrial environments, but rather there is a continuum of habitats from lake through marsh and swamp to grassland and forest. At the borderlines, certain habitats can be studied sometimes from the point of view of the limnologist, other times from the point of view of the soil scientist, as illustrated by the work of Burgeff (1961) on the microbiology of sphagnum bogs. Even in typically terrestrial environments a continuum can be described from those sites which are poorly drained through those which are well drained (Curtis, 1959). Terrestrial environments show much greater variability and complexity than aquatic environments (Odum, 1959), and consequently generalizations are more difficult to make. To keep the present discussion within bounds, we will have to ignore these complexities and discuss only a few key situations. Terrestrial environments are dominated by vascular plants which have clearly evolved to cope with the problems of this environment. The value to a plant of being able to stand erect should not be underestimated; while upright a plant is easily able to resist microbial attack and decay, whereas as soon as a plant topples, it is quickly colonized by countless numbers and kinds of microorganisms. The roots, which must of necessity remain underground, provide a continual battleground where microbial activity is high. It is not by chance that most plant symbioses with microorganisms have developed through the roots (*see* Chapter 8), although in tropical areas with high rainfall, leaf symbioses also occur (Silver et al., 1963).

In terrestrial environments our attention is inevitably turned to the SOIL, as it is here that most of the key processes occur which influence the development of the ecosystem. The process of soil development involves extremely complex interactions with the parent material, topography, climate, and living organisms (Barshad, 1964; Russell and Russell, 1950; Burges, 1958). Soils can be divided into two broad groups, mineral soils and organic soils, depending on whether they derive initially from the weathering of rocks or have been laid down in bogs and marshes. Because organic soils have received little study (Alexander, 1961), the following discussion is restricted to mineral soils. The initial weathering of rock is a result of physical, chemical, and biological processes. Although little is known about the role of microorganisms in weathering, it is likely that they play a central role and that chemical and physical processes mainly modify microbial activities. A careful examination of almost any exposed rock will reveal the presence of algae, lichens, or mosses. These organisms are able to withstand the intense heat and desiccation in the absence of rain and to grow when moisture is present. At Ind'ana University, for instance, limestone walls which are constructed of newly mined and consequently alga-free material develop within only a few years a fairly extensive covering of algae.

Webley et al. (1963) have shown by the use of plate counts that the numbers of bacterial and fungal colonies developing from rock material increase directly with an increase in the degree of lichen or plant cover of the rocks. In rock crevasses formed by physical action, a raw soil developed which they found to be high in organic matter and also high in bacteria and fungi. The interior of porous weathered stones also contained bacteria and fungi, but the interior of unweathered stones lacked these organisms. A high proportion of the bacteria and fungi they isolated could solubilize silicate minerals. Henderson and Duff (1963) showed that rock-associated fungal isolates decomposed natural silicates by producing citric or oxalic acid or both, and the bacteria which could decompose these silicates produced 2-ketogluconic acid. These organic chelating agents probably react with and solubilize metal ions which are an integral part of the mineral structure. The possible role of bacteria in the weathering of stone monuments was studied by Krumbein and Pochon (1964), and Winkler (1965) has discussed the value of studying the process of weathering on such objects of known age. Because microorganisms are able to bring about complex chemical changes at low temperatures, microbial processes are likely to play a greater role in weathering than chemical processes do. Further, as microorganisms grow the amount of catalyst should increase with time, and thus the rate of weathering should increase with time, whereas with purely chemical processes the rate should be constant.

As soon as a raw soil is formed, pioneer plants can develop, and the biomass then increases markedly. The plant roots affect the soil structure physically, and their excretions provide substrates for the rapid growth of microorganisms. When the plant tops die, these remains are added to the soil, and microbial activity progresses even further. Minerals are further solubilized, and as water percolates down it carries some of these chemical substances deeper, and as weathering proceeds the soil increases in depth, although soil genesis is counteracted to some extent by the processes of erosion. Larger plants develop and modify the processes even further. If rainfall is high enough, a forest can develop, while grasslands are restricted to regions of lower rainfall. The kinds of plants which develop greatly modify the nature of the soil, although vegetation and climate are so intimately interwoven in pedogenesis that it is difficult to separate the contribution of one from that of the other. Soil animals develop and play an important role in keeping the upper layers of the soil mixed and aerated. Eventually, the movements of materials downward results in the formation of layers, and a typical soil profile is born, consisting of: (1) the surface litter, (2) the *A* horizon, from which minerals have been removed by downward leaching, (3) the *B* horizon, a deeper layer in which the materials leached from the *A* horizon usually accumulate, and (4) the *C* horizon which consists mainly of unaltered rock fragments and parent material.

ENERGY FLOW

Except in extreme habitats restricted to algae, lichens, and mosses, the primary producers in terrestrial environments are higher plants. PRODUCTIVITY in terrestrial environments is usually measured by harvest rather than by gas exchange and consequently usually ignores root growth which may be 25% to 30% of the total productivity (Wiegert and Evans, 1964). A collection of representative values for net productivity are given by Odum (1959) and vary from values as low as 0.11 g/m^2 per day for Nevada desert to 18 g/m^2 per day for sugar cane under intensive cultivation. Most values in both cultivated and noncultivated systems range from 1 to 6 g/m² per day but are markedly influenced by local conditions. Ovington (1962) has compared woodland and grassland productivity and has concluded that woodlands are more efficient collectors of solar energy than grasslands. In a natural meadow (Wiegert and Evans, 1964) or forest (Ovington, 1962) essentially all of the productivity remains within the system, and only an insignificant amount is harvested by above-ground organisms. Even in woodlands which are harvested commercially, at least two thirds of the productivity is returned to the soil by way of leaf fall, self-pruning of limbs, etc. (see Table 9-5).

Macfadyen (1961) has analyzed energy flow in a pasture and concludes that less than one quarter of the energy is consumed by cattle and other herbivores, the rest being respired by the plants or returned to the soil either in dead plant parts or as fecal material. It should be noted also that in the above-ground food chain in a pasture the energy flow is grasses → rumen microorganisms → cattle → man; the microbes play a crucial but often neglected role. We thus see that the bulk of the primary productivity of terrestrial systems is returned to the soil, so that it is to the soil that we must also look if we are to understand the complete workings of the ecosystem. The dynamic or steady state nature of the soil has been discussed by Burges (1958), Auerbach (1958), Macfadyen (1963) and others. It is a common observation (Ovington, 1962) that the amount of litter in a forest does not increase from year to year, so that decomposition balances leaf fall (see page 147).

The FOOD CHAIN in the soil is extremely complex (Macfadyen, 1963), since there are thousands of species of microorganisms and animals and millions of numbers of them. An attempt to assess the numbers and activities of the various components was made by Macfadyen (1963) and is presented in Table 9-4. Even the simplified schemes are complex, especially at the later stages in the chain, but even in the initial stages we have only a general idea of the organisms involved. Since most of the organic material returned to the soil is in the form of complex plant structural substances (e.g., cellulose, hemicellulose, lignin), attention naturally is directed first to the organisms which attack these materials. It is generally agreed that in aerobic soils, and especially woodlands, the fungi are the primary decomposers. When a leaf falls, the small amounts of sugars present are quickly utilized by sugar fungi (Garrett, 1951), mainly Phycomycetes, which sporulate and become quiescent again. Hemicellulose-utilizing fungi develop next, followed by cellulose utilizers and finally by lignin utilizers. Because cellulose and especially lignin are degraded only with difficulty, the decomposition of these two materials proceeds slowly and more or less continuously in the litter, whereas the utilization of the other materials is sporadic. According to Burges (1958), the hyphae of

TABLE 9-4. Figures from a Hypothetical Grasslands Soil Community Showing Order of Magnitude of Numbers, Biomass, and Metabolism for the Main Biological Groups[a]

Group of organisms	Weight of organism, (mg)	Results of metabolism experiments — O₂ uptake (Cu mm per hour per individual)	Temperature (°C)	Calories per day per g at 16°C[c]	Approximate estimates grassland per sq m — Numbers	Mass (g)	Calories (per year[e])
Bacteria[b]	10^{-9}	7×10^{-9}	20	575	10^{15}	1000	113
Fungi[b]			20	161		400	355
Protozoa[b]	0.05	10^{-2}	22.5	14	5×10^{8}	38	180
Nematoda	0.001	1.2×10^{-3}	16	144	10^{7}	12	160
Lumbricidae	5000	300	16	7	10^{3}	120	62
Enchytracidae	0.14	0.117	16	100	10^{6}	12	96
Mollusca[d]	1500	1000	28	29	50	10	38
Myriapoda	25	10	19	36	500	12.5	5
Isopoda	22.7	9	19	36	500	5	
Opiliones	18	10.5	19	53	40	0.4	
Acari—							
Parasitids	0.2	0.5	16	280	5×10^{3}	1.0	64
Oribatei	0.25	0.12	14	72	2×10^{5}	2.0	30
Araneae	10	3.0	19	27	600	6.0	34
Coleoptera	250	60	13	39	100	1.0	8
Diptera	610	105	13	29	200	1.0	6
Collembola	0.46	0.55	16	144	5×10^{4}	5.0	153

[a] From Macfadyen (1963). Numbers and biomass are typical for areas in which the respective groups are abundant, i.e., most groups would be uncommon in some grasslands and none of them would be as common as this in one place together. Also the balance of groups would be quite different in, say, moorland or woodland. Figures in the same horizontal row do not necessarily correspond where independent estimates are available.

[b] Figures for microorganisms are only available per g of soil; these have been multiplied by 10^4 to give an extremely approximate estimate on a square metre basis.

[c] Metabolism figures are corrected to 16°C. Values are in small (g) calories.

[d] Molluscan figures based on snails, weight of soft parts only.

[e] Daily metabolism figures for 16°C are multiplied by 212 to correct for annual temperature cycle in N. Europe. Values in large Calories.

Owing to effects of microbial antagonism rates for natural conditions are far lower than in the laboratory, but no valid estimates are possible. Note that the total from field experiments on undisturbed soil is around 5000 Cal./year.

filamentous fungi are active for only the first few hundred microns back from the tip; behind this zone the hyphae are vacuolate or empty, the protoplasm having moved towards the tip.

The cellophane burial studies of Tribe (1957) revealed that the fungi which developed on this modified cellulose eventually became moribund and the dead hyphae then became colonized with bacteria; upon exhaustion of the substrate the fungi sporulated. Following the bacteria, nematodes, protozoa, mites, and other animals developed, presumably eating the bacteria. A simplified food chain might thus be leaf litter → fungi → bacteria → animals, although there are many complexities which can modify this chain. There are, for instance, some bacteria which can utilize cellulose and may play a significant role in its initial decomposition under some conditions. In water-logged soils or bogs, the anaerobic conditions which develop prevent the growth of fungi, and cellulose decomposition may not occur, thus leading to the eventual accumulation of peat. In these anaerobic conditions the animal fauna is poorly developed or absent.

Although the soil animals are small in both biomass and numbers compared to the fungi and bacteria, they play an important and possibly critical role in keeping the decomposition processes in operation. Macfadyen (1961) has called this the catalytic action of animals on soil metabolism. Earthworms, for instance, cause the fragmentation of leaf litter and pull the pieces down into the soil where microbial action can proceed. Animals bring about the mechanical fragmentation of soil crumbs, thus increasing the surface area available for adsorption of nutrients, water, and microbial cells. By their movements, many animals bring about the distribution of microbial inoculum. Fecal matter, corpses, and exuviae of animals provide localized sites of high organic matter where microbes can develop and from which they can spread into surrounding soil. After the plant substrate in a localized area is exhausted, the microbial cells which have formed contain energy which is locked up and which can be liberated when the cells are eaten by animals. Earthworms show distinct leaf preferences and may play a considerably greater role in decomposition of some litters than of others (Gilbert and Bocock, 1960).

The ENERGY FLOW within forest soils can be measured by determining the rate at which litter falls on a representative area. (The fall of tree branches, cones, and fruits should also be measured since they may form a significant part of the total productivity [Ovington, 1962].) Since the forest floor ecosystem is in a steady state, and because usually no significant transport of material out of the system occurs, the rate of fall is equal to the rate of decomposition when averaged over the whole year. Note that the weight of litter does not reveal anything about the turnover rate. Coniferous forests may have a litter weight three to five times the annual litter fall, showing that the annual litter fall takes three to five years to decompose, whereas in deciduous woodlands there is little litter carry-over from year to year, showing that decomposition is completed within one year. However, the annual litter fall from conifers is often much greater than that in deciduous forests, so that the annual turnover in the coniferous forest may be greater than in the deciduous one (Ovington, 1962). The rate of decomposition of litter under specific conditions can be determined by measuring the rate of weight loss of leaves which are confined within nylon mesh bags (Shanks and Olson, 1961; Gilbert and Bocock, 1960) or are identified by strings (Witkamp and Olson, 1963). The rate of breakdown is influenced not only by tree species but also by temperature and moisture (Shanks and Olson, 1961). In addition, the humus which develops under one kind of tree may not be well suited for the decomposition of litter from another tree species (Gilbert and Bocock, 1960). The relative contributions of various processes to energy flow in a forest are shown in Table 9-5.

TABLE 9-5. ENERGY FLOW FOLLOWING PHOTOSYNTHESIS OF SCOTS PINE PLANTATIONS FOR THE 18-YEAR PERIOD FROM 17 TO 35 YEARS AFTER PLANTING

	Energy content (10^{10} cal/hectare)	Percentage utilization of total incident solar radiation
In gross primary plant production	340	2.46
Released by respiration of producer plants	160	1.16
In net primary plant production	180	1.30
Accumulation in living trees	61	0.44
Accumulation in ground flora	< 1	< 0.01
Accumulation in litter layers	6	0.04
Removed in timber of harvested trees	31	0.23
Left in roots of harvested trees	13	0.09
Released by litter decomposition	68	0.49

From Ovington (1962). This table shows that more energy is consumed by microbial decomposition in the litter than is either removed in the harvest of timber or is accumulated in living trees.

BIOGEOCHEMICAL CYCLES

WATER is a highly variable quality of terrestrial systems and plays a dominant role in determining the structure and function of the system. Water is held in the soil in two ways, either by adsorption onto surfaces, or as free water between the interstices of the particles. In this latter environment water exists in thin sheets or films of very irregular shape, and different soils vary greatly in their capacity to absorb and retain water (Russell and Russell, 1950). The pore space is usually 30–50% of the total volume of a soil, and in a well-drained soil the volumes of the respective components are 50 (soil particles): 10 (air): 40 (water) (Burges, 1958). Water and air compete for the space between the soil particles, and the former can drive out the latter, so that a water-logged soil may completely lack free air, the only oxygen being that which is dissolved in the water. Since the dissolved oxygen is quickly consumed by plant roots and soil organisms and because diffusion of oxygen from the air is very slow, water-logged soils become rapidly anaerobic, with profound influences on their biogeochemical activities. Pearsall (1938) has presented redox potential measurements of various soils under various conditions of water saturation and packing. He found that if a soil was saturated with water, the redox potential gradually fell, but the change in redox potential did not occur if the soil was sterilized first by heating or by toluene treatment. Pearsall found that most woodland soils were oxidizing in summer and reducing in winter. Pearsall (1938) and Pearsall and Mortimer (1939) showed that a lowering in redox potential is associated with an increase in pH, an increase in the amount of replaceable iron, an increase in sulfide concentration, and other changes. Some of the interactions between redox potential and carbon, nitrogen, and sulfur transformations have been discussed earlier in this chapter in relation to aquatic environments and sediments, and the concepts advanced there are also directly applicable to water-logged soils, although the organic matter which provides the energy source for the various transformations is present in much higher amounts in water-logged soils than in lake sediments. In rice paddies, flooding leads to the creation of water-logged soils and indirectly to increases in the availability of iron and other minerals as a result of the reactions attendant on the anaerobic conditions (Grist, 1959). The rice plant roots remain aerobic because oxygen is provided via extensive air spaces within the roots. Parenthetically, a rice paddy has some aspects of an aquatic ecosystem; nitrogen-fixing blue-green algae, for instance, grow extensively in paddies, and nitrogen fixation is of considerable significance (Grist, 1959).

Air penetrates well-drained soils readily, and OXYGEN is never deficient even in the deepest portions, although the CO_2 concentration is often much higher in the soil than in the air (Russell and Russell, 1950). Since growth of some fungi is inhibited by increased CO_2 (Burges, 1958), drastic increases may affect their distribution. However, to a first approximation a well-drained soil can be considered a basically aerobic environment, with anaerobic conditions occurring only in restricted microenvironments where metabolic activities of facultative organisms are sufficient to reduce the oxygen content.

As Vallentyne (1962) has discussed, the insolubility of most organic carbon materials insures that in aquatic habitats they will settle into anaerobic environments and be preserved but that in terrestrial habitats they will remain at the surface of the soil and be subjected to rapid destruction. For this reason one would expect the CARBON cycle to proceed to completion more rapidly in terrestrial environments than in aquatic situations. Also, as opposed to aquatic environments, there is very little if any transport of organic matter into or out of a terrestrial ecosystem, so that the carbon cycle is essentially self-contained; CO_2 from the atmosphere is fixed by the plants which eventually die and topple to earth where their organic remains are oxidized by the soil microflora and fauna, and the CO_2 is returned to the atmosphere again. Although most of the CO_2 is released, some of it may be carried deeply into the ground by percolating water and can cause the dissolution of limestone rocks, thus leading to the formation of caves. Because of the spatial separation between the processes of photosynthesis and decay, it is possible to measure the rate of decay by measuring the rate of CO_2 formation or oxygen consumption in the soil. Such studies on soil respiration, when coupled with measurements of temperature and moisture content and with knowledge of the nature of the organic residues, can provide much information about the processes occurring in the soil. As noted earlier, transport of substances downward from the surface results in the formation of a soil profile, and at different depths in a profile decomposition reactions are proceeding at different rates. An analysis of soil metabolism in a podzol soil developing under *Pinus sylvestris* has been made by Burges and his colleagues (Burges, 1963; Williams, 1963; Parkinson and Coups, 1963) with the results shown in Table 9-6. Fungal infection of the needles occurs at least five to six months before the needles fall, but these needle parasites gradually or rapidly decrease after the needles reach the ground and are replaced by true soil fungi, mainly ascomycetes. The needles remain in the L layer for about six months until they have become covered with other needles, then pass into the F_1 layer. As needle fall continues, the older needles become compressed and the mass becomes moister. Sporulation of the fungi then occurs, but the conidiophores and spores are gradually removed by the grazing of mites and other soil fauna. After about two years, the needles enter the F_2 layer and become colonized with basidiomycetes. Through the activity of the fungi and microfauna, the needles are gradually reduced. Some carbon is lost as CO_2 and the rest as soluble materials which are leached away and eventually accumulate as residues at the surface of the mineral soil in the H layer. Fungi active in chitin digestion can be found in this layer which is formed primarily by the accumulation of fecal pellets and exoskeletons of the fauna (Gray and Bell, 1963). In this acid soil (pH 3.5–4.5) bacteria and actinomycetes would not be expected to play much of a role and were in fact found only in small numbers ($<10^5/$ gram).

TABLE 9-6. Microbial Activity in a Podzol Soil Profile

Horizon or layer	Length of time in layer	Fungal dilution (plate count)	Hyphae (meters/ ml soil section)	O_2 uptake (μ liters/ 5 hr/g)	Organic matter (%)	O_2 uptake/g organic matter
L (pine needles)	6 months			2366	98.5	2400
F_1 (needles entire but black and decaying)	2 years			1400	98	1400
F_2 (needles fragmented)	7–8 years			245	89	270
H (raw humus, black)		281,900	5.56	81	55	150
A_1 (siliceous		199,800	3.96	13	17	78
A_2 gray layer)		27,250	3.78	4.5	1.9	240
B_1 (precipitated humus, dark brown to black)		11,370	1.09	9.8	10.6	92
B_2 (precipitated iron oxides)		1970	0.37	2.9	5.2	57
C (parent material)		225	0.03	1.4	1.4	96

Data of Burges (1963) and Parkinson and Coups (1963).

In general the biochemical changes which take place during decomposition are complex. The initial litter is composed mainly of organic materials of varying degrees of susceptibility to decay; those most easily digested (e.g., water-soluble materials, hemicellulose) are eliminated first, cellulose disappears later, and lignin remains the longest. As Burges (1958) has pointed out, litter in its initial form is not a highly favorable medium for microbial growth, as it is low in vitamins and other growth factors and its physical structure makes it resistant to attack. During the initial phase of decomposition, those organisms which can grow and synthesize vitamins and other factors alter the structure so that the litter becomes more compact and better insulated from environmental fluctuations. Alexander (1961) has pointed out that three separate processes can be distinguished during decomposition: breakdown of litter, synthesis of new biological tissue in the form of microbial cells, and excretion of metabolic end products. Litter usually has a C:N ratio of 40 or 50:1, whereas microbial protoplasm has a C:N ratio of around 10:1. Thus by following changes in the C:N ratio of the litter, one can determine the rate of conversion of plant material into microbial protoplasm. Because of the relatively low nitrogen content of litter, microbial development may be limited by a deficiency of this element for protoplasmic synthesis, and decomposition may be accelerated by the addition of nitrogen fertilizers (Russell and

Russell, 1950). The formation of bacterial protoplasm could probably be followed by measuring the appearance of α, ϵ-diaminopimelic acid, an amino acid found in bacterial cell walls but not in plant materials, and this amino acid is detected in significant amounts in agricultural soils (Abelson, 1963). Other biochemicals, such as nucleic acids, might also serve as markers for the newly synthesized microbial protoplasm.

The term HUMUS is used to encompass the organic fraction of the soil itself, as distinguished from the organic matter of the litter, and as such humus is a product of the activities of the microbial flora (Swain, 1963; Alexander, 1961). Humus is not an entity but a complex mixture of materials; the reader is referred to Swain (1963) for a detailed discussion of its chemical nature. Humus is not a fixed portion of the soil but is in a dynamic state, being continuously synthesized and destroyed. This is most readily seen in the tropics where high temperatures promote rapid microbial action, and the organic matter in forest soil is rapidly depleted after the cover is removed, being essentially gone in one year (Cunningham, 1963). Even in temperate climates, the organic fraction of a soil decreases gradually upon cultivation (Russell and Russell, 1950), and accumulation of organic matter is dependent on high rainfall (which promotes plant growth and reduces aeration of the soil) and low temperature (which retards microbial action). According to Richards (1952), in well-aerated soils, between 0° and 20°C there is greater organic production than breakdown, at 25°C breakdown and production are equal, and above 25°C breakdown exceeds production and no humus accumulates. The organic fraction of every soil is in delicate equilibrium with its plant cover. By using the radiocarbon dating technique Tamm and Östlund (1960) have shown that the age of a humus sample from the A horizon of a Swedish forest soil was approximately contemporary, and that of the B horizon was 370 ± 100 years old. Since the site sampled had been covered with forest for about 9000 years, the relatively young age of material even from the lower B horizon suggested that the organic material of this fraction is being continually broken down and replenished from above. The forest in question occurs in a cool, moist climate where decomposition is slow, and in warmer and drier areas where decomposition is faster the age of soil organic matter would probably be even lower. The residence times of decaying litter in a podzolic soil are given in Table 9-6.

The annual uptake of CO_2 by all plants is about $1/35$ of the total CO_2 of the atmosphere of the world, and if decomposition did not occur, it might be supposed that the atmospheric CO_2 would be rapidly depleted, but since the oceans and limestone rocks contain the bulk of the CO_2 (see Figure 2-1), the CO_2 lost from the atmosphere would soon be replaced. Eventually though, in the absence of decomposition, all of the carbon of the earth would end up in litter. The significance of decomposition in the losses of productivity even in a forest in which the wood is harvested is shown in Table 9-5 where it is seen that more energy is released by decomposition than is removed in timber.

The amount of NITROGEN present in rocks is quite low, and because most nitrogen compounds are either soluble or volatile, in contrast to carbon and sulfur, there is little tendency for nitrogen to accumulate in vast deposits. Nitrogen enters a terrestrial ecosystem as ammonia and nitrate from rain water or as biologically fixed nitrogen. Most emphasis on this latter process has been understandably placed on agricultural soils, so that we have little data for natural ecosystems. Russell and Russell (1950) have described experiments showing that the nitrogen content of an agricultural soil increases when it is allowed to return to grassland, so that the nitrogen content may double within 50 years or so. Ovington (1962) has suggested that much of the increase in nitrogen which occurs in woodlands is probably due to biological fixation. It is unlikely that symbiotic nitrogen fixation by legumes is of much significance in NATURAL habitats, although certain leguminous and nonleguminous plants which fix nitrogen symbiotically may function as pioneer plants in the colonization of new areas. Rather, it is likely that nitrogen fixation in established grasslands and forests is brought about predominantly by free-living bacteria of the genera *Azotobacter* and *Clostridium*. Alexander (1961) has reviewed the activities of these organisms and has demonstrated that when the organic matter content is high and the pH and redox potential are appropriate, these organisms probably fix significant amounts of nitrogen. Olsen (1932) and Gilbert and Bocock (1960) have shown that the nitrogen content of decomposing leaf litter increases under certain conditions.

Recently, Chang and Knowles (1965) have provided direct evidence that nitrogen fixation does occur in soil and litter. They incubated samples at 30°C for 29 days in either aerobic or anaerobic atmospheres enriched with N_2^{15}. Some of their results are presented in Table 9-7 and show that nitrogen fixation was more frequent under anaerobic than under aerobic conditions in all the soil types studied in their unamended state. The addition of glucose stimulated nitrogen fixation. They also found that during anaerobic incubation nitrogen fixation was significantly correlated with an increase in the number of clostridia and that these organisms were present in greater numbers than *Azotobacter* in the original soils. Thus there now seems no doubt that in temperate forest soils, increase in nitrogen is due to nonsymbiotic nitrogen-fixing bacteria, and that the anaerobic clostridia make the most significant contribution. Little is known about the nitrogen economy of tropical soils, but because of the great number of naturally occurring legumes and other symbiotic nitrogen fixers in the tropics, it might be expected that symbiotic nitrogen fixation would be more significant here than in temperate regions. Loss of nitro-

TABLE 9-7. Nitrogen Fixation in Soils and Litter as Measured with $N_2{}^{15}$ [a]

	1% glucose added	Aerobic samples (0.1 atm. $N_2{}^{15}$, 0.2 atm. O_2, 0.7 atm. He)		Anaerobic samples (0.1 atm. $N_2{}^{15}$, 0.9 atm. He)	
		N^{15} atoms (% excess[b])	Rate of nitrogen fixation[c]	N^{15} atoms (% excess[b])	Rate of nitrogen fixation[c]
St. Bernard	−	0.001		0.128[++]	1.63
sandy loam	+	0.156[++]	1.78	0.221[++]	3.76
Muck	−	0.013[+]	1.48	0.023[++]	4.14
	+	0.018[+]	1.96	0.045[++]	8.17
Mull Litter + F horizon	−	−0.005		0.030[++]	4.17
Mull A_1	−	0.007		0.088[++]	4.34
	+	0.016[+]	0.49	0.103[++]	5.45
Mor Litter	−	0.000		0.333[++]	29.2
Mor F horizon	−	0.004		0.016[+]	1.95

[a] Reproduced from Chang and Knowles (1965).
[b] All are excesses over the corresponding sterile control. Incubation 29 days at 30°C.
[c] Rate of nitrogen fixation expressed as mg $\times$ 10^{-4} nitrogen fixed per day per gram dry soil.
NOTE: + and ++ indicate gains of at least 0.01 and 0.02 N^{15} atoms % over control and denote significant nitrogen fixation.

gen is extensive in tropical rain forests because of leaching and rapid decomposition (Richards, 1952), and it would seem reasonable that these great forests would have evolved mechanisms for replenishing lost nitrogen.

When plant remains are returned to the soil, the nitrogen of plant proteins is converted by deamination to ammonia. This product can then be assimilated directly by microbes or plant roots, or it can be converted to nitrate by nitrifying bacteria (Alexander, 1961). Nitrification occurs readily in neutral well-drained soils, but it is inhibited in anaerobic or highly acidic soils. If materials high in protein such as manure are added to soils, the rate of nitrification is increased; nitrification occurs rapidly in manure piles and aerobic sewage treatment plants. Indeed, nitrification was first discovered by Schloesing and Muntz when they attempted to purify sewage by passing it through a sand column, an early forerunner of the soil perfusion technique (Lees, 1955) which has been used extensively to study the nitrification process in the laboratory. Because nitrate is readily assimilated by plants and because nitrification is accompanied by other changes in the soil of benefit to plants (Alexander, 1961), it is considered a valuable process. It is likely that the nitrate deposits in caves and in the Chilean desert also have a biological origin, probably being derived from nitrification in guano deposits and accumulating because of the lack of leaching in these arid environments (Hutchinson, 1950).

If a soil becomes water logged, the resultant anaerobic conditions will lead to denitrification and the loss of nitrogen from the soil as the gases N_2 and N_2O. Denitrification is brought about by a variety of facultative organisms which can utilize nitrate as an electron acceptor under anaerobic conditions in place of oxygen, but since organic compounds are required as an energy source for denitrification, the process will not occur in the absence of organic matter. Even well-drained soils may experience some denitrification if large amounts of organic residues are applied, since this will result in localized regions of partial anaerobiosis. In rice paddies, fertilizer must be added as ammonia, since nitrate is quickly eliminated by denitrification in these anaerobic flooded soils; the rice plant utilizes ammonia effectively (Grist, 1959).

In many aerobic habitats it is likely that nitrogen moves in a cycle within the habitat from plant to soil and back to plant again without ever leaving the system. The relative amount of nitrogen used by the ecosystem from within as compared with that used from without has apparently not been assessed directly, but it could be done with the use of N^{15} tracers.

Only rarely does SULFUR become a limiting element for plant growth (Russell and Russell, 1950). In contrast to the complex interactions of the sulfur cycle in aquatic environments, the sulfur cycle on land is relatively simple. Sulfur is derived in significant quantities from sulfate in many rocks, and sulfate is also present in fairly large amounts in rain water. Plants and most microorganisms can assimilate sulfate directly. The organic sulfur in plant proteins is returned to the soil in the litter, where it is decomposed by a large variety of microorganisms with the release of H_2S. Some microorganisms can also convert organic sulfur to sulfate directly without the intermediate production of H_2S (Alexander, 1961). Under aerobic conditions, H_2S is readily oxidized by chemosynthetic sulfur bacteria (mainly *Thiobacillus*) with the formation of sulfate. One species, *Thiobacillus denitrificans,* is able to oxidize H_2S anaerobically with the use of nitrate as an electron acceptor. Except in water-logged soils, it is unlikely that any significant amounts of H_2S will accumulate. If elemental sulfur is added to soils, it is oxidized to sulfuric acid, with a concomitant lowering of the pH and a mobilization of mineral nutrients; elemental sulfur is sometimes added for agricultural reasons (Alexander, 1961). Sulfate reduction occurs in water-logged soils, brought about by bacteria which utilize sulfate as an electron acceptor for the oxidation of organic materials, with the formation of H_2S. The reader is referred to the earlier section on aquatic environments for a more detailed consideration of some aspects of sulfur transformations.

Microorganisms as Control
Agents in Macroecosystems

It seems likely that the control agents of macroecosystems are microorganisms. An important aspect of a control device is that a small change in the device can result in a large change in the system. Even though microorganisms are small, they exert large effects on macroecosystems through their activities. The turnover of chemical elements in the biogeochemical cycles are examples of such controls. The production of vitamins is another example, a small amount of a vitamin leading to the appearance of a vastly larger amount of protoplasmic mass in an organism requiring it. Indeed, growth factor requirements, which frequently seem to be ecologically detrimental, may be actually beneficial to the ecosystem and thus to the organism, if they lead to a better control of growth and productivity of the system. Pathogenic and symbiotic microorganisms also exert marked controls on systems. It is an old saying in medicine that an individual rarely dies a natural death; even a person suffering from a presumably nonmicrobial disease such as cancer usually succumbs as a result of a microbial infection which was able to become established in the weakened body. When population density becomes excessive, malnutrition often occurs, followed by weakened resistance to infection, disease, and death. Thus pathogenic organisms play important and possibly crucial roles in the control of population levels, whether in forest, grassland, or ocean. Without microorganisms ecosystems might consist of large numbers of weakened individuals, and the ecosystem would function poorly if at all. With these creatures eliminated by infection, the remaining organisms of the ecosystem might function better.

The role of symbionts as control agents is also evident. The strategic location of the mycorrhizal fungus at the periphery of a root perhaps best illustrates the point; the fungus controls the gate through which the vital nutrients flow. The symbiotic nitrogen-fixing bacteria also serve as unique control agents, affecting the whole nitrogen economy of the community of which they are a part, since the initial colonization of a bare site by a nitrogen-fixing plant could lead to an increased production of organic matter and a stimulation of nonsymbiotic nitrogen fixers and the eventual establishment of a balanced ecosystem with a smoothly functioning nitrogen cycle. For example, Crocker and Major (1955) studied the changes in organic nitrogen content of ground in Alaska which had been laid bare by a receding glacier. The pioneer vegetation on these sites is dominated by alder, a species of nonlegume symbiotic nitrogen fixing trees. Initially, the organic nitrogen content of the soil was very low, but as the alder developed and matured the organic nitrogen level rose to a peak. Once the alder had been replaced in the climax forest by spruce, no further increase in soil nitrogen occurred, and in fact there were noticeable decreases.

With germ-free ecosystems (perhaps a *Daphnia-Chlorella* food chain) the role of microorganisms as control agents might be directly demonstrated. Demonstration might also be achieved in nature by the use of antibiotics to eliminate microorganisms in natural systems. Some of the more dramatic microbial control agents have been discovered by more or less random means or through the study of a process which later turned out to be microbial. Perhaps a systematic approach towards this problem would reveal many new things.

Applied Microbiology and Microbial Ecology

Pasteur said that there were no applied sciences, only science and the applications of science. The tremendous fundamental discoveries of Pasteur and his eminently successful attempts to apply these discoveries are ample justification for Pasteur's attitude. Of the specialties within microbiology (e.g., physiology, genetics), probably none has more opportunity for direct application for the benefit of mankind than microbial ecology. This is both a strength and a weakness. It is a strength in that it provides a satisfactory justification for the field of microbial ecology. It is a weakness in that the applications have tended to get ahead of the science; we attempt to harvest the sea without adequately knowing the extent of or the controls on primary productivity; we attempt to reforest without understanding the nature or extent of the mycorrhizal symbioses; we attempt to look for new antibiotics without understanding the role of antibiotics in nature. When we suddenly discover a human fungal pathogen which grows naturally in the soil (e.g., *Histoplasma capsulatum*), we attempt to get rid of it without understanding the ecology of the organism. This impatience to get into action is understandable. But can we justify a narrow view of our chosen field? Why, for instance, do we know so much about agricultural soils and so little about grassland, forest, and tropical soils? Even though they may not be as economically important, might not the concepts we would learn there stand us in good stead behind the plow?

I believe that the concepts advanced in this book are applicable in numerous ways throughout most of the specialties which call themselves applied microbiological sciences. Further, I believe that the fragmentation of the so-called applied sciences has prevented them from realizing how much they could learn from each other. Soil microbiology and marine microbiology, for instance, are not such distant cousins, when they are viewed as applications of certain basic principles of microbial ecology. Thus, what I am suggesting is that because microbial ecology encompasses the language and concepts common to many applied disciplines, all applied microbiologists will be immeasurably stronger and more effective if they are microbial ecologists first.

Global Ecology

The earth as a whole is a macrocosm in steady state with insignificant amounts of import or export of matter (meteorites and moon rockets notwithstanding) but with considerable amounts of energy import from the sun. The role of microorganisms (mainly algae) in capturing some of this light energy and converting it into biologically useful energy has been discussed earlier in this chapter. On a global basis, perhaps one half of the gross primary productivity derives from microorganisms, mainly in the sea (Ryther, 1959), although much of this productivity is inaccessible to man and is thus currently of less significance than the productivity of terrestrial environments. In terms of the biogeochemical cycles, the role of microorganisms in all environments is large, as is evident from the discussions of this chapter. Without microorganisms as decomposers of organic remains, the living world would eventually run out of CO_2. Without the participation of microorganisms in the nitrogen cycle, the number of species in the biosphere would be vastly diminished. And in most other transformations of ecological significance, microorganisms play an important or exclusive role.

To the GEOLOGIST, microorganisms are also of considerable interest. Manganese nodules on the ocean floor, sulfur deposits in Louisiana, acid mine waters in the Midwest, and bog iron deposits in many locations all probably have their origin in microbial activities (Kuznetsov et al., 1963). But the role of microorganisms in weathering is probably of even greater global significance, although our knowledge here is quite meager. It is not even clear how one would devise relevant experiments to assess the quantitative significance of microbial action in weathering, but the potential importance makes it urgent that work be started in this direction. The geologist may also find a whole new field opening up with respect to fossil microorganisms (Barghoorn and Tyler, 1965).

The EXOBIOLOGIST, who is part astronomer, part geologist, and part biologist also has a considerable interest in microorganisms, and the ecological concepts presented in this book may be of some value in helping him to assess the possible distribution and role of microorganisms on other

planets. Because of the diversity, ubiquity, and versatility of microorganisms, they are obvious candidates for the colonization of new habitats.
The pioneer flora of Krakatoa consisted almost exclusively of blue-green
algae (Richards, 1952), as does the flora of the Yellowstone hot springs
(Copeland, 1936).

We thus see that microorganisms pervade our world at every level,
from the smallest crevice of a soil crumb to the globe as a whole and may
possibly exist in the universe of which that globe is a part. And the future
of microbial ecology holds nothing but promise.

References

Abelson, P. H. 1963. Geochemistry of amino acids, p. 431-455. *In* I. A. Breger, ed., Organic geochemistry. Pergamon Press, Oxford.

Adams, M. H. 1959. Bacteriophages. Interscience, N. Y. 592p.

Ahmadjian, V. 1962. Lichens, p. 817-822. *In* R.A. Lewin, ed., Physiology and biochemistry of algae. Academic Press, N. Y.

Ahmadjian, V. 1965. Lichens. Ann. Rev. Microbiol. 19:1-20.

Akai, S. 1959. Histology of defense in plants, p. 392-434. *In* J. G. Horsfall and A. E. Dimond, eds., Plant Pathology, Vol. 1. Academic Press, N. Y.

Alexander, M. 1961. Introduction to soil microbiology. John Wiley & Sons, N. Y. 472p.

Alexander, M. 1964. Biochemical ecology of soil microorganisms. Ann. Rev. Microbiol. 18:217-252.

Allee, W. C., A. E. Emerson, O. Park, T. Park, and K. Schmidt. 1949. Principles of animal ecology. Saunders, Philadelphia. 837p.

Allen, E. K., and O. N. Allen. 1958. Biological aspects of symbiotic nitrogen fixation, p. 48-118. *In* W. Ruhland, ed., Handbuch der Pflanzenphysiologie, Vol. VIII. Springer, Berlin.

Allen, M. B. 1956. Excretion of organic compounds by Chlamydomonas. Arch. Mikrobiol. 24:163-168.

Allen, O. N. 1957. Experiments in soil bacteriology, 3d ed. Burgess Publ. Co., Minneapolis. 117p.

Allen, P. J. 1959. Physiology and biochemistry of defense, p. 435-467. *In* J. G. Horsfall and A. E. Dimond, eds., Plant Pathology, Vol. 1. Academic Press, N. Y.

American Public Health Association. 1953. Standard methods for the examination of dairy products, microbiological and chemical, 10th ed. Amer. Publ. Health Assoc., New York. 345p.

American Public Health Association. 1961. Standard methods for the examination of water and wastewater, including bottom sediments and sludges, 11th ed. Amer. Publ. Health Assoc., New York. 626p.

Anderson, E. S. 1957. The relations of bacteriophages to bacterial ecology, p. 189-217. *In* Microbial ecology, Seventh Symp. Soc. Gen. Microbiol. Cambridge Univ. Press.

Andrewartha, H. G. 1961. Introduction to the study of animal populations. Univ. of Chicago Press, Chicago. 281p.

Annison, E. F., and D. Lewis. 1959. Metabolism in the rumen. Methuen & Co., London. 184p.

Atwood, K. C., L. K. Schneider, and F. J. Ryan. 1951. Selective mechanisms in bacteria. Cold Spring Harbor Symp. Quant. Biol. XVI:345-355.

Auerbach, S. I. 1958. The soil ecosystem and radioactive waste disposal to the ground. Ecology 39:522-529.

Baas-Becking, L. G. M. 1959. Geology and microbiology. Contribution to marine microbiology. N. Z. Oceanograph. Inst. Mem., No. 3:48-64.

Baker, J. M. 1963. Ambrosia beetles and their fungi, with particular reference to *Platypus cylindrus* Fab., p. 232-265. *In* Symbiotic associations, Thirteenth Symp. Soc. Gen. Microbiol. Cambridge U. Press.

Bamforth, S. S. 1960. Daily changes in natural ciliate populations. J. Protozool. 7 (Supplement):17 (Abstract no. 60).

Bamforth, S. S. 1963. Microhabitat and community structure as ecological factors for protozoa, p. 301-302. *In* J. Ludvík, J. Lom and J. Vávra, eds., Progress in protozoology. Academic Press, N. Y.

Barghoorn, E. S., and S. A. Tyler. 1965. Microorganisms from the Gunflint chert. Science 147:563-577.

Barker, H. A. 1961. Fermentations of nitrogenous organic compounds, p. 151-201. *In* I. C. Gunsalus and R. Y. Stanier, eds., The bacteria, Vol. II. Academic Press, N. Y.

Barnett, A. J. G., and R. L. Reid. 1961. Reactions in the rumen. Edward Arnold, London. 252p.

Barshad, I. 1964. Chemistry of soil development, p. 1-70. *In* F. E. Bear, ed., Chemistry of the Soil, 2nd ed. Reinhold Pub. Corp., N. Y.

Bartlett, M. S. 1960. Stochastic population models in ecology and epidemiology. Methuen & Co., London. 90p.

Barton, A. A. 1950. Some aspects of cell division in *Saccharomyces cerevisiae*. J. gen. Microbiol. 4:84-86.

Bates, J. L., and P. V. Liu. 1963. Complementation of lecithinase activities by closely related pseudomonads: its taxonomic implication. J. Bacteriol. 86:585-592.

Bawden, F. C. 1964. Plant viruses and virus diseases, 4th ed., p. 272-273. Ronald Press, N. Y. 361p.

Becker, G. 1959. Biological investigations on marine borers in Berlin-Dahlem, p. 62-76. *In* D. L. Ray, ed., Marine boring and fouling organisms. Univ. of Wash. Press, Seattle.

Beerstecher, E. 1954. Petroleum microbiology. Elsevier Press, Houston. 375p.

Benz, G. 1963. Physiopathology and histochemistry, p. 299-338. *In* E. A. Steinhaus, ed., Insect pathology, Vol. 1. Academic Press, N. Y.

Bessey, E. A. 1950. Morphology and taxonomy of fungi. Blakiston Co., Philadelphia. 791p.

Beyers, R. J. 1963. The metabolism of twelve aquatic laboratory microecosystems. Ecol. Monographs 33:281-306.

Bigger, J. W., and J. H. Nelson. 1941. The growth of coliform bacilli in distilled water. J. Pathol. Bacteriol. 53:189-206.

Bisset, K. A. 1955. The cytology and life-history of bacteria, 2nd ed. Williams & Wilkins, Baltimore. 164p.

Björkman, E. 1949. The ecological significance of the ectotrophic mycorrhizal association in forest trees. Svensk Botanisk Tidskrift 43:223-262.

Blaxter, K. L. 1962. The energy metabolism of ruminants. C. C. Thomas, Springfield, Ill. 829p.

Bloch, H. 1964. Bakterielle Adaptation in der Chemotherapie. Bibliotheca Microbiol., Fasc. 4:95-105.

Bond, G. 1958. Symbiotic nitrogen fixation by non-legumes, p. 216-231. *In* E. G. Hallsworth, ed., Nutrition of the legumes. Academic Press, N. Y.

Bond, G. 1963. The root nodules of non-leguminous angiosperms, p. 72-91. *In* Symbiotic associations, Thirteenth Symp. Soc. Gen. Microbiol. Cambridge U. Press.

Bonner, J. T. 1959. The cellular slime molds. Princeton U. Press, Princeton. 149p.

Bonventre, P. F., and L. L. Kempe. 1960. Physiology of toxin production by *Clostridium botulinum* types A and B I. Growth, autolysis, and toxin production. J. Bacteriol. 79:18-23.

Bowen, J. F., and F. W. Beech. 1964. The distribution of yeasts on cider apples. J. Appl. Bacteriol. 27:333-341.

Bradfield, J. R. G., and D. B. Cater. 1952. Electron-microscopic evidence on the structure of spirochaetes. Nature 169:944-946.

Braun, W. 1953. Bacterial genetics. Saunders, Philadelphia. 238p.

Breger, I. A., ed., 1963. Organic geochemistry. Pergamon Press, Oxford. 658p.

Brian, P. W. 1957. The ecological significance of antibiotic production, p. 168-188. *In* Microbial ecology, Seventh Symp. Soc. Gen. Microbiol. Cambridge U. Press.

Brinton, C. C., Jr., P. Gemski, Jr., and J. Carnahan. 1964. A new type of bacterial pilus genetically controlled by the fertility factor of *E. coli* K 12 and its role in chromosome transfer. Proc. Nat. Acad. Sci. 52:776-783.

Brock, T. D. 1956. A method for studying antibiotic diffusion in agar. Antib. & Chemo. 7:243-246.

Brock, T. D. 1961. Milestones in microbiology. Prentice-Hall, Englewood Cliffs, N. J. 275p.

Brock, T. D. 1966. The habitat of *Leucothrix mucor*, a widespread marine microorganism. Limnol. and Oceanogr. 11:303-307.

Brock, T. D., and M. L. Brock. 1961. Reversal of azaserine by phenylalanine. J. Bacteriol. 81:212-217.

Brock, T. D., and M. L. Brock. 1966a. Autoradiography as a tool in microbial ecology. Nature 209:734-736.

Brock, T. D., and M. L. Brock. 1966b. Temperature optima for algal development in Yellowstone and Iceland hot springs. Nature 209:733-734.

Brock, T. D., and G. Moo-Penn. 1962. An amino acid transport system in *Streptococcus faecium*. Arch. Biochem. Biophys. 98:183-190.

Brockwell, J. 1963. Accuracy of a plant-infection technique for counting populations of *Rhizobium trifolii*. Appl. Microbiol. 11:377-383.

Brooks, M. A. 1963a. The microorganisms of healthy insects, p. 215-250. *In* E. A. Steinhaus, ed., Insect Pathology, Vol. 1. Academic Press, N. Y.

Brooks, M. A. 1963b. Symbiosis and aposymbiosis in arthropods, p. 200-231. *In* Symbiotic associations, Thirteenth Symp. Soc. Gen. Microbiol. Cambridge U. Press.

Brown, A. D. 1964. Aspects of bacterial response to the ionic environment. Bacteriol. Rev. 28:296-329.

Brown, R. M., Jr., D. A. Larson, and H. C. Bold. 1964. Airborne algae: their abundance and heterogeneity. Science 143:583-585.

Buchanan, R. E., and E. I. Fulmer. 1930. Physiology and biochemistry of bacteria, Vol. III. Williams & Wilkins, Baltimore. 575p.

Buchner, P. 1953. Endosymbiose der Tiere mit pflanzlichen Mikroorganismen. Birkhäuser, Basel. 771p.

Buller, A. H. R. 1934. Researches on *fungi*, Vol. VI. Longmans, Green & Co. Ltd., London. 513p.

Bünning, E. 1964. The physiological clock; endogenous diurnal rhythms and biological chronometry. Academic Press, N. Y. 145p.

Burgeff, H. 1961. Mikrobiologie des Hochmoores. Fischer, Stuttgart. 197p.

Burges, A. 1958. Micro-organisms in the soil. Hutchinson Univ. Library, London. 188p.

Burges, A. 1963. The microbiology of a podzol profile, p. 151-157. *In* J. Doeksen and J. Van der Drift, eds., Soil organisms. North-Holland Publ. Co., Amsterdam.

Burkhardt, H. J., J. V. Maizel, and H. K. Mitchell. 1964. Avenacin, an antimicrobial substance isolated from *Avena sativa*. II. Structure. Biochemistry 3:426-431.

Caldwell, P. C. 1954. An investigation of the intracellular pH of crab muscle fibres by means of micro-glass and micro-tungsten electrodes. J. Physiol. 126:169-180.

Challinor, S. W., and A. H. Rose. 1954. Interrelationships between a yeast and a bacterium when growing together in defined medium. Nature 174:877-878.

Chang, P.-C., and R. Knowles. 1965. Non-symbiotic nitrogen fixation in some Quebec soils. Can. J. Microbiol. 11:29-38.

Chase, A. M. 1964. Bioluminescence—production of light by organisms, p. 389-421. In A. C. Giese, ed., Photophysiology, Vol. II. Academic Press, N. Y.

Clarke, F. W. 1924. The data of geochemistry, 5th ed. U. S. Geological Survey Bull. 770. Govt. Printing Office, Wash., D. C.

Clayton, R. K. 1964. Phototaxis in microorganisms, p. 51-77. In A. C. Giese, ed., Photophysiology, Vol. II. Academic Press, N. Y.

Clements, F. E., and V. E. Shelford. 1939. Bio-ecology. John Wiley & Sons, N. Y. 425p.

Cochrane, V. W. 1958. Physiology of fungi. John Wiley & Sons, N. Y. 524p.

Coleman, G. S. 1963. The growth and metabolism of rumen ciliate protozoa, p. 298-324. In Symbiotic associations, Thirteenth Symp. Soc. Gen. Microbiol. Cambridge U. Press.

Collins, E. B. 1955. Action of bacteriophage on mixed strain cultures III. Strain dominance due to the action of bacteriophage and variations in the acid production of secondary growth bacteria. Appl. Microbiol. 3:137-140.

Collins, V. G. 1963. The distribution and ecology of bacteria in freshwater. Proc. Soc. Water Treatment and Examination 12:40-73.

Collins, V. G., and C. Kipling. 1957. The enumeration of waterborne bacteria by a new direct count method. J. Appl. Bacteriol. 20:257-264.

Conover, J. T., and J. McN. Sieburth. 1964. Effect of Sargassum distribution on its epibiota and antibacterial activity. Botanica Marina VI:147-157.

Copeland, J. J. 1936. Yellowstone thermal Myxophyceae. Ann. N. Y. Acad. Sci. 36:1-229.

Cornforth, J. W., and A. T. James. 1956. Structure of a naturally occurring antagonist of dihydrostreptomycin. Biochem. J. 63:124-130.

Crocker, R. L., and J. Major. 1955. Soil development in relation to vegetation and surface age at Glacier Bay, Alaska. J. Ecol. 43:427-448.

Cronkite, E. P., V. P. Bond, T. M. Fliedner, and J. R. Rubini. 1959. The use of tritiated thymidine in the study of DNA synthesis and cell turnover in hemopoietic tissues. Lab. Inv. 8:263-277.

Crossett, R. N., E. A. Drew, and A. W. D. Larkum. 1965. Chromatic adaptation in benthic marine algae. Nature 207:547-548.

Cunningham, R. K. 1963. The effect of clearing a tropical forest soil. J. Soil Sci. 14:334-345.

Curtis, J. T. 1959. The vegetation of Wisconsin. Univ. of Wisc. Press, Madison. 657p.

Cushing, D. H. 1955. Production and a pelagic fishery. Fishery Investigations, Series II, Vol. XVIII, no. 7. H. M. Stationery Office, London.

Damian, R. T. 1964. Molecular mimicry: antigen sharing by parasite and host and its consequences. Amer. Nat. XCVIII:129-149.

Dart, P. J., and F. V. Mercer. 1964a. The legume rhizosphere. Arch. f. Mikrobiol. 47:344-378.

Dart, P. J., and F. V. Mercer. 1964b. Fine structure changes in the development of the nodules of *Trifolium subterraneum* L. and *Medicago tribuloides* Desr. Arch. f. Mikrobiol. 49:209-235.

Darwin, C. R. 1859. *In* M. Bates and P. S. Humphrey, eds., 1956. The Darwin Reader, p. 141. Charles Scribner's Sons, N. Y. 470p.

Davis, C. C. 1958. An approach to some problems of secondary production in the western Lake Erie region. Limnol. and Oceanogr. 3:15-28.

Davis, R. J., V. L. Sheldon, and S. I. Auerbach. 1956. Lethal effects of gamma radiation upon segments of a natural microbial population. J. Bacteriol. 72:505-510.

Day, F. H. 1963. The chemical elements in nature. Harrap & Co., London. 372p.

Deevey, E. S., Jr., and M. Stuiver. 1964. Distribution of natural isotopes of carbon in Linsley Pond and other New England lakes. Limnol. and Oceanogr. 9:1-11.

Deevey, E. S., Jr., M. Stuiver, and N. Nakai. 1963. Use of light nuclides in limnology, p. 471-475. *In* V. Schultz and A. W. Klement, Jr., eds., Radioecology. Reinhold Pub. Co., N. Y.

Des Abbayes, H. 1951. Traité de lichénologie. Paul Lechevalier, Paris. 217p.

DeVay, J. E. 1956. Mutual relationships in fungi. Ann. Rev. Microbiol. 10:115-140.

Dietrich, G. 1963. General oceanography. Interscience, N. Y. 588p.

Dobbs, C. G., W. H. Hinson, and J. Bywater. 1960. Inhibition of fungal growth in soils, p. 130-147. *In* D. Parkinson and J. S. Waid, eds., The ecology of soil fungi. Liverpool U. Press.

Dondero, N. C. 1961. *Sphaerotilus,* its nature and economic significance. Advances in Appl. Microbiol. 3:77-107.

Droop, M. R. 1963. Algae and invertebrates in symbiosis, p. 171-199. *In* Symbiotic associations, Thirteenth Symp. Soc. Gen. Microbiol. Cambridge U. Press.

Drost-Hansen, W. 1956. Temperature anomalies and biological temperature optima in the process of evolution. Naturwissenschaften 43:512.

Dubos, R., and A. Kessler. 1963. Integrative and disintegrative factors in symbiotic associations, p. 1-11. *In* Symbiotic associations, Thirteenth Symp. Soc. Gen. Microbiol. Cambridge U. Press.

Dubos, R. J., and R. W. Schaedler. 1962. The effect of diet on the fecal bacterial flora of mice and on their resistance to infection. J. Exptl. Med. 115:1161-1172.

Duclaux, É. 1920. Pasteur, the history of a mind. [Transl. by E. F. Smith and F. Hedges.] p. 132-133. Saunders, Philadelphia. 363p.

Dugdale, V. A., and R. C. Dugdale. 1962. Nitrogen metabolism in lakes II. Role of nitrogen fixation in Sanctuary Lake, Pennsylvania. Limnol. and Oceanogr. 7:170-177.

Dugdale, V. A., and R. C. Dugdale. 1965. Nitrogen metabolism in lakes III. Tracer studies of the assimilation of inorganic nitrogen sources. Limnol. and Oceanogr. 10:53-57.

Dugdale, R. C., V. A. Dugdale, J. C. Neess, and J. J. Goering. 1959. Nitrogen fixation in lakes. Science 130:859-860.

Dugdale, R. C., D. W. Menzel, and J. H. Ryther. 1961. Nitrogen fixation in the Sargasso Sea. Deep-Sea Research 7:297-300.

Dyer, D. L., and R. D. Gafford. 1961. Some characteristics of a thermophilic blue-green alga. Science 134:616-617.

Eagle, H., and K. A. Piez. 1962. Amino acid pools, protein synthesis and protein turnover in human cell cultures, p. 694-707. In J. T. Holden, ed., Amino acid pools. Elsevier, Amsterdam.

Eckenfelder, W. W., Jr., and D. J. O'Connor. 1961. Biological waste treatment. Pergamon Press, N. Y. 299p.

El-Badry, H. M. 1963. Micromanipulators and micromanipulation. Academic Press, N. Y. 333p.

Elliker, P. R. 1949. Practical dairy bacteriology, 1st ed. McGraw-Hill, N. Y. 391p.

Ellison, W. 1958. The role of legumes in farm ecology, p. 308-321. In E. G. Hallsworth, ed., Nutrition of the legumes. Academic Press, N. Y.

Elsasser, W. M. 1958. The physical foundation of biology; an analytical study. Pergamon Press, London. 219p.

El-Shazly, K., and R. E. Hungate. 1965. Fermentation capacity as a measure of net growth of rumen microorganisms. Appl. Microbiol. 13:62-69.

Ely, R. E., E. A. Kane, W. C. Jacobsen, and L. A. Moore. 1953. A study of the crude fiber and nitrogen-free extract fractions of orchard grass hay and the digestibility of some of the constituents by milking cows. J. Dairy Sci. 36:334-345.

Emerson, S. 1950. The growth phase in Neurospora corresponding to the logarithmic phase in unicellular organisms. J. Bacteriol. 60:221-223.

Enebo, L. 1949. Symbiosis in thermophilic cellulose fermentation. Nature 163:805.

Engelmann, T. W. 1894. Die Erscheinungsweise der Sauerstoffausscheidung chromophyllhaltiger Zellen im Licht bei Anwendung der Bacterienmethode. Arch. f. d. ges. Physiol. 57:375-386.

Ericson, L.-E., and L. Lewis. 1954. On the occurrence of vitamin B_{12}-factors in marine algae. Arkiv f. Kemi 6:427-442.

Ettinger, M. B., R. J. Lishka, and R. C. Kroner. 1954. Persistence of pyridine bases in polluted water. Ind. Eng. Chem. 46:791-793.

Evans, E. 1954. Soil recolonization tube for studying recolonization of sterilized soil by micro-organisms. Nature 173:1196.

Eyring, H., R. P. Boyce, and J. D. Spikes. 1960. Thermodynamics of living systems, p. 15-73. In M. Florkin, ed., Comparative biochemistry; a comprehensive treatise, Vol. 1. Academic Press, N. Y.

Fauré-Fremiet, E., P. Favard, and N. Carasso. 1963. Images électroniques d'une microbiocénose marine. Cahiers de Biologie Marine IV:61-64.

Fincham, J. R. S., and P. R. Day. 1963. Fungal genetics. Blackwell Scientific Publications, Oxford. 300p.

Finland, M., R. Murray, H. W. Harris, L. Kilham, and M. Meads. 1946. Development of streptomycin resistance during treatment. J. Amer. Med. Assoc. 132:16-21.

Fish, G. R. 1955. Chemical factors limiting growth of phytoplankton in Lake Victoria. J. East Afr. Agr. 21:152-158.

Fjerdingstad, E. 1964. Pollution of streams estimated by benthal phytomicro-organisms I. A saprobic system based on communities of organisms and ecological factors. Int. Revue ges. Hydrobiol. 49:63-131.

Flanders, S. E., and M. E. Badgley. 1963. Prey-predator interactions in self-balanced laboratory populations. Hilgardia 35:145-183.

Fogg, G. E. 1962. Extracellular products, p. 475-489. In R. A. Lewin, ed., Physiology and biochemistry of algae. Academic Press, N. Y.

Fogg, G. E. 1963. The role of algae in organic production in aquatic environments. Br. phycol. Bull. 2:195-205.

Fogg, G. E. 1965. Algal cultures and phytoplankton ecology. Univ. of Wisconsin Press, Madison. 126p.

Fogg, G. E., and C. Nalewajko. 1961. Extracellular products of phytoplankton. 1st Progr. Rept. to the Develop. Comm. 13p; 2nd. 13. (Also XV Intern. Congr. Limnol. Madison, 1962).

Fogg, G. E., and D. F. Westlake. 1955. The importance of extracellular products of algae in freshwater. Intern. Assoc. Theor. & Appl. Limnol. Proceedings, XII:219-232.

Forbes, S. A. 1887. The lake as a microcosm. Bull. Sci. Assoc. Peoria 1887:77-87. [Reprinted 1925. Illinois State Nat. Hist. Survey 15:537-550.]

Ford, E. B. 1964. Ecological genetics. Methuen & Co., London. 335p.

Forrest, W. W., D. J. Walker, and M. F. Hopgood. 1961. Enthalpy changes associated with the lactic fermentation of glucose. J. Bacteriol. 82:685-690.

Francis, W. 1954. Coal; its formation and composition. Edward Arnold, London. 567p.

Frank, H., M. L. Zarnitz, and W. Weidel. 1963. Über die Rezeptorsubstanz für den Phagen T5 VII. Mitt.: Elektronenoptische Darstellung und Längenbestimmung der aus T5/R5-Komplexen freigesetzten DNS. Zeitsch. f. Naturforsch. 18b:281-284.

Frazier, W. C. 1958. Food microbiology. McGraw-Hill, N. Y. 472p.

Fred, E. B., I. L. Baldwin, and E. McCoy. 1932. Root nodule bacteria and leguminous plants. Univ. of Wisconsin studies in science, no. 5. 343p.

Freter, R., and A. Ozawa. 1963. Explanation for limitation of populations of Escherichia coli in broth cultures. J. Bacteriol. 86:904-910.

Gainey, P. L., and T. H. Lord. 1952. Microbiology of water and sewage. Prentice-Hall, New York. 430p.

Gale, E. F. 1940. The production of amines by bacteria. 3. The production of putrescine from arginine by Bacterium coli in symbiosis with Streptococcus faecalis. Biochem. J. 34:853-857.

Garrett, S. D. 1951. Ecological groups of soil fungi: a survey of substrate relationships. New Phytologist 50:149-166.

Garric, R. K. 1965. The cryoflora of the Pacific Northwest. Amer. J. Botany 52:1-8.

Gause, G. F. 1934. The struggle for existence. Williams & Wilkins, Baltimore. 163p.

Gause, G. F. 1936. The principles of biocoenology. Quart. Rev. Biol. 11:320-336.

Gessner, F. 1955. Discussion in Fogg, G. E., and D. F. Westlake. The importance of extracellular products of algae in freshwater, p. 232. Intern. Assoc. Theor. & Appl. Limnol. Proc. XII:219-232.

Giese, A. C. 1962. Cell physiology, 2nd ed. Saunders, Philadelphia. 592p.

Gilbert, O., and K. L. Bocock. 1960. Changes in leaf litter when placed on the surface of soils with contrasting humus types II. Changes in the nitrogen content of oak and ash leaf litter. J. Soil Sci. 11:10-19.

Glick, D. 1961. Quantitative chemical techniques of histo- and cytochemistry, Vol. I. Interscience Publ., N. Y. 470p.

Glick, D. 1963. Quantitative chemical techniques of histo- and cytochemistry, Vol. II. Interscience Publ., N. Y. 513p.

Goldfine, H., and K. Bloch. 1963. Oxygen and biosynthetic reactions, p. 81-103. In B. Wright, ed., Control mechanisms in respiration and fermentation. Ronald Press, N. Y.

Goldschmidt, V. M. 1954. Geochemistry, A. Muir, ed., Clarendon Press, Oxford. 730p.

Golueke, C. G., and Oswald, W. J. 1964. Role of plants in closed systems. Ann. Rev. Plant Physiol. 15:387-408.

Goreau, T. 1961. Problems of growth and calcium deposition in reef corals. Endeavour 20:32-39.

Gortner, R. A. 1949. Outlines of biochemistry, 3d ed., R. A. Gortner, Jr., and W. A. Gortner, eds., John Wiley & Sons, N. Y. 1078p.

Gray, F. V., G. B. Jones, and A. F. Pilgrim. 1960. The rates of production of volatile fatty acids in the rumen. Austral. J. Agr. Res. 11:383-388.

Gray, F. V., R. A. Weller, A. F. Pilgrim, and G. B. Jones. 1962. A stringent test for the artificial rumen. Austral. J. Agr. Res. 13:343-349.

Gray, F. V., R. A. Weller, and G. B. Jones. 1965. The rates of production of volatile fatty acids in the rumen II. Measurement of production in an artificial rumen and application of the isotope dilution technique to the rumen of a sheep. Austral. J. Agr. Res. 16:145-157.

Gray, T. R. G., and T. F. Bell. 1963. The decomposition of chitin in an acid soil, p. 222-230. In J. Doeksen and J. Van der Drift, eds., Soil organisms. North-Holland Publ. Co., Amsterdam.

Gregory, P. H. 1961. The microbiology of the atmosphere. Leonard Hill, London. 251p.

Grist, D. H. 1959. Rice, 3d ed. Longmans, London. 466p.

Gucluer, S. M., and M. G. Gross. 1964. Recent marine sediments in Saanich Inlet, a stagnant marine basin. Limnol. and Oceanogr. 9:359-376.

Guirard, B. M., and E. E. Snell. 1962. Nutritional requirements of microorganisms, p. 33-93. *In* I. C. Gunsalus and R. Y. Stanier, eds., The bacteria, Vol. IV. Academic Press, N. Y.

Gunsalus, I. C., and C. W. Shuster. 1961. Energy-yielding metabolism in bacteria, p. 1-58. *In* I. C. Gunsalus and R. Y. Stanier, eds., The bacteria, Vol. II. Academic Press, N. Y.

Hale, M. E., Jr. 1961. Lichen handbook; a guide to the lichens of eastern North America. Smithsonian Institution, Washington, D. C. 178p.

Halldal, P. 1962. Taxes, p. 583-593. *In* R. A. Lewin, ed., Physiology and bio-chemistry of algae. Academic Press, N. Y.

Halvorson, H. 1962. Physiology of sporulation, p. 223-264. *In* I. C. Gunsalus and R. Y. Stanier, eds., The bacteria, Vol. IV. Academic Press, N. Y.

Halvorson, H. O., ed., 1961. Spores II. Burgess, Minneapolis. 296p.

Hamon, Y., and Y. Péron. 1963. Étude du pouvoir bactériocinogène dans le genre Listeria. II. Individualité et classification des bactériocines en cause. Ann. Inst. Pasteur 104:55-65.

Harley, J. L. 1959. The biology of mycorrhiza. Leonard Hill, London. 233p.

Harley, J. L. 1963. Mycorrhiza, p. 79-103. *In* W. B. Turrill, ed., Vistas in botany, Vol. III. Pergamon Press, Oxford.

Harold, R., and R. Y. Stanier. 1955. The genera Leucothrix and Thiothrix. Bacteriol. Rev. 19:49-58.

Hartman, R. T. 1960. Algae and metabolites of natural waters, p. 38-55. *In* C. A. Tryon, Jr., and R. T. Hartman, eds., The ecology of algae. Special publication no. 2, Pymatuning Laboratory of Field Biology, Univ. of Pittsburgh, Penn.

Harvey, H. W. 1957. The chemistry and fertility of sea waters, 2nd ed. Cambridge U. Press. 234p.

Hassouna, M. G., and P. F. Wareing. 1964. Possible role of rhizosphere bacteria in the nitrogen nutrition of *Ammophila arenaria*. Nature 202:467-469.

Hatch, A. B. 1936. The role of mycorrhizae in afforestation. J. Forestry 34:22-29.

Hatch, A. B., and K. D. Doak. 1933. Mycorrhizal and other features of the root systems of Pinus. J. Arnold Arboretum 14:85-99.

Hayes, F. R. 1964. The mud-water interface. Oceanogr. Mar. Biol. Ann. Rev. 2:121-145.

Hayes, W. 1964. The genetics of bacteria and their viruses. John Wiley & Sons, N. Y. 740p.

Hedgepeth, J. W., ed., 1957. Treatise on marine ecology and paleoecology, Vol. I. Geol. Soc. America Memoir 67. 1296p.

Hely, F. W., and J. Brockwell. 1962. An exploratory survey of the ecology of *Rhizobium meliloti* in inland New South Wales and Queensland. Australian J. Agr. Res. 13:864-879.

Henderson, M. E. K., and R. B. Duff. 1963. The release of metallic and silicate ions from minerals, rocks, and soils by fungal activity. J. Soil Sci. 14:236-246.

Henrici, A. T. 1928. Morphologic variation and the rate of growth of bacteria. C. C. Thomas, Springfield, Illinois. 194p.

Henrici, A. T., and D. E. Johnson. 1935. Studies of freshwater bacteria II. Stalked bacteria, a new order of Schizomycetes. J. Bacteriol. 30:61-93.

Heukelekian, H., and A. Heller. 1940. Relation between food concentration and surface for bacterial growth. J. Bacteriol. 40:547-558.

Heumann, W., and R. Marx. 1964. Feinstruktur und Funktion der Fimbrien bei dem sternbildenden Bakterium *Pseudomonas echinoides.* Arch. f. Mikrobiol. 47:325-337.

Hill, M. N., ed., 1963. The sea, Vol. 2. Interscience Publ., N. Y. 554p.

Hinshelwood, C. N. 1946. The chemical kinetics of the bacterial cell. The Clarendon Press, Oxford. 284p.

Hoffman, H. 1964. Morphogenesis of bacterial aggregations. Ann. Rev. Microbiol. 18:111-130.

Hofsten, B. v. 1962. The effect of copper on the growth of *Escherichia coli.* Exptl. Cell Res. 26:606-607.

Hollings, M. 1962. Viruses associated with a die-back disease of cultivated mushroom. Nature 196:962-965.

Hollings, M., D. G. Gandy, and F. T. Last. 1963. A virus disease of a fungus: dieback of cultivated mushroom. Endeavour 22:112-117.

Holman, W. L., and D. M. Meekison. 1926. Gas production by bacterial synergism. J. Infect. Dis. 39:145-172.

Holzman, H. E. 1959. Some consequences of introducing a genetically defined population of a European syngen of *Paramecium aurelia* into an American pond. Science 130:1418.

Hoogenhout, H., and J. Amesz. 1965. Growth rates of photosynthetic microorganisms in laboratory cultures. Arch. f. Mikrobiol. 50:10-24.

Horsfall, J. G., and A. E. Dimond, eds., 1959. Plant pathology, Vol. 1. Academic Press, N. Y. 674p.

Hungate, R. E. 1960. Symposium: selected topics in microbial ecology I. Microbial ecology of the rumen. Bacteriol. Rev. 24:353-364.

Hungate, R. E. 1962. Ecology of bacteria, p. 95-119. *In* I. C. Gunsalus and R. Y. Stanier, eds., The bacteria, Vol. IV. Academic Press, N. Y.

Hungate, R. E. 1963. Symbiotic associations: the rumen bacteria, p. 266-297. *In* Symbiotic associations, Thirteenth Symp. Soc. Gen. Microbiol., Cambridge U. Press.

Hungate, R. E., G. D. Phillips, A. McGregor, D. P. Hungate, and H. K. Buechner. 1959. Microbial fermentation in certain mammals. Science 130:1192-1194.

Hunter, G. J. E. 1947. Phage-resistant and phage-carrying strains of lactic streptococci. J. Hyg. 45:307-312.

Hutchinson, G. E. 1950. Survey of contemporary knowledge of biogeochemistry. 3. The biogeochemistry of vertebrate excretion. Bull. Amer. Mus. Natural Hist. 96:1-554.

Hutchinson, C. E. 1952. The biogeochemistry of phosphorus, p. 1-35. *In* L. F. Wolterink, ed., The biology of phosphorus. Mich. State Coll. Press, East Lansing, Mich.

Hutchinson, G. E. 1957. A treatise on limnology, Vol. I. John Wiley & Sons, N. Y. 1015p.

Hutner, S. H., and L. Provasoli. 1964. Nutrition of algae. Ann. Rev. Plant Physiol. 15:37-56.

Hutner, S. H., L. Provasoli, and H. Baker. 1961. Development of microbiological assays for biochemical, oceanographic, and clinical use, p. 95-113. Microchemical Journal, Symposium Series, Vol. 1. Interscience, N. Y.

Hutner, S. H., L. Provasoli, J. J. A. McLaughlin, and I. J. Pintner. 1956. Biochemical geography: some aspects of recent vitamin research. The Geographical Review 46:404-407.

Hynes, H. B. N. 1960. The biology of polluted waters. Liverpool U. Press. 202p.

Hynes, H. B. N. 1963. Imported organic matter and secondary productivity in streams. Proc. XVI Intern. Congr. Zool. 3:324-329.

Ingraham, J. L. 1962. Temperature relationships, p. 265-296. *In* I. C. Gunsalus and R. Y. Stanier, eds., The bacteria, Vol. IV. Academic Press, N. Y.

Ingram, M. 1957. Micro-organisms resisting high concentrations of sugars or salts, p. 90-133. *In* Microbial ecology, Seventh Symp. Soc. Gen. Microbiol. Cambridge U. Press.

Ingold, C. T. 1953. Dispersal in fungi. Clarendon Press, Oxford. 197p.

Ivànovics, G. 1962. Bacteriocins and bacteriocin-like substances. Bacteriol. Rev. 26: 108-118.

Jacob, F., and É. L. Wollman. 1961. Sexuality and the genetics of bacteria. Academic Press, N. Y. 374p.

Jahn, T. L., and E. C. Bovee. 1965. Movement and locomotion of microorganisms. Ann. Rev. Microbiol. 19:21-58.

Jannasch, H. W. 1960. Denitrification as influenced by photosynthetic oxygen production. J. gen. Microbiol. 23:55-63.

Jennings, H. S. 1906. Behavior of the lower organisms. Columbia U. Press, N. Y. [Reprinted 1962 by Indiana U. Press, Bloomington, Ind.]

Jensen, H. L. 1958. The classification of the rhizobia, p. 75-86. *In* E. G. Hallsworth, ed., Nutrition of legumes. Academic Press, N. Y.

Jones, D., and E. Griffiths. 1964. The use of thin soil sections for the study of soil micro-organisms. Plant and Soil 20:232-240.

Kadavy, J. L., and G. M. Dack. 1951. The effect of experimentally inoculating canned bread with spores of *Clostridium botulinum* and *Bacillus mesentericus*. Food Res. 16:328-337.

Kaplan, I. R., and T. A. Rafter. 1958. Fractionation of stable isotopes of sulfur by thiobacilli. Science 127:517-518.

Kempner, E. S. 1963. Upper temperature limit of life. Science 142:1318-1319.

Kihara, H., and E. E. Snell. 1960. Peptides and bacterial growth IX. Release of double inhibitions with single peptides. J. Biol. Chem. 235:1415-1418.

Knaysi, G. A. 1951. Elements of bacterial cytology, 2nd ed. Comstock, Ithaca, N. Y. 375p.

Koch, A. 1963. On the role of symbionts in wood-destroying insects, p. 151-161. *In* Recent progress in microbiology, Vol. III. Univ. of Toronto Press.

Kodicek, E. 1949. The effect of unsaturated fatty acids on gram-positive bacteria, p. 217-232. *In* Selective toxicity and antibiotics, Symp. Soc. Exptl. Biol., Vol. III. Cambridge U. Press.

Kohn, A., and M. Lion. 1961. Anhydrobiosis—a model of a cryptobiotic stage, p. 15-31. *In* N. Grossowicz, S. Hestrin, and A. Keynan, eds., Cryptobiotic stages in biological systems. Elsevier, Amsterdam.

Kol, E. 1957. Über die Verbreitung der schnee- und eisbewohnenden Mikroorganismen in Europa I. Arch. Hydrobiol. 53:574-582.

Kolkwitz, R., and M. Marsson. 1908. Ökologie der pflanzlichen Saprobien. Ber. Deut. Bot. Ges. 26a: 505-519.

Kriss, A. E. 1963. Marine microbiology, deep sea. [Transl. by J. M. Shewan and Z. Kabata.] Oliver & Boyd, Edinburgh. 536p.

Krumbein, W. E., and J. Pochon. 1964. Écologie bactérienne des pierres altérées des monuments. Ann. Inst. Pasteur 107:724-732.

Kubiëna, W. L. 1938. Micropedology. Collegiate Press, Ames, Iowa. 243p.

Kuznetsov, S. I. 1959. Die Rolle der Mikroorganismen im Stoffkreislauf der Seen. VEB Deutscher Verlag der Wissenschaften, Berlin. 301p.

Kuznetsov, S. I., M. V. Ivanov, and N. N. Lyalikova. 1963. Introduction to geological microbiology. English edition edited by C. H. Oppenheimer. McGraw-Hill, N. Y. 1963.

Lackey, J. B., and E. W. Lackey. 1961. The habitat and description of a new genus of sulphus bacterium. J. gen. Microbiol. 26:29-39.

Lackey, J. B., and D. B. Smith. 1956. Factors influencing development of biological flocs, p. 108-115. *In* Brother J. McCabe and W. W. Eckenfelder, Jr., eds., Biological treatment of sewage and industrial wastes, Vol. I. Reinhold, N. Y.

Lamanna, C. 1959. The most poisonous poison. Science 130:763-772.

Lamanna, C., and M. F. Mallette. 1959. Basic bacteriology, 2nd ed. Williams & Wilkins, Baltimore. 853p.

Lammers, W. T. 1962. Density gradient separation of plankton and clay from river water. Limnol. and Oceanogr. 7:224-229.

Lammers, W. T. 1963. Density-gradient separation of organic and inorganic particles by centrifugation. Science 139:1298-1299.

Lange, N. A., ed., 1956. Handbook of chemistry, 9th ed. McGraw-Hill, N. Y. 1969p.

La Rivière, J. W. M. 1963. Cultivation and properties of *Thiovulum majus* Hinze, p. 61-72. *In* C. H. Oppenheimer, ed., Marine microbiology. C. C. Thomas, Springfield, Ill.

Larsen, H. 1962. Halophilism, p. 297-342. *In* I. C. Gunsalus and R. Y. Stanier, eds., The bacteria, Vol. IV. Academic Press, N. Y.

Last, F. T., and F. C. Deighton. 1965. The non-parasitic microflora on the surfaces of living leaves. Trans. Brit. mycol. Soc. 48:83-99.

Lebeau, J. B., and J. G. Dickson. 1955. Physiology and nature of disease development in winter crown rot of alfalfa. Phytopathology 45:667-673.

Lederberg, J. 1952. Cell genetics and hereditary symbiosis. Physiol. Rev. 32:403-430.

Lees, H. 1955. Biochemistry of autotrophic bacteria. Butterworths Sci. Publ., London. 112p.

Legroux, R., and J. Magrou. 1920. État organisé des colonies bactériennes. Ann. Inst. Pasteur 34:417-431.

Lengemann, F. W., and N. N. Allen. 1955. The development of rumen function in the dairy calf I. Some characteristics of the rumen contents of cattle of various ages. J. Dairy Sci. 38:651-656.

Lev, M. 1963. Studies on bacterial associations in germ-free animals and animals with defined floras, p. 325-334. In Symbiotic associations, Thirteenth Symp. Soc. Gen. Microbiol. Cambridge U. Press.

Lewin, R. A. 1956. Extracellular polysaccharides of green algae. Can. J. Microbiol. 2:665-672.

Lewin, R. A. 1959. Leucothrix mucor. Biol. Bull. 117:418.

Lightbown, J. W., and F. L. Jackson. 1956. Inhibition of cytochrome systems of heart muscle and certain bacteria by the antagonists of dihydrostreptomycin: 2-alkyl-4-hydroxyquinoline N-oxides. Biochem. J. 63:130-137.

Lilly, V. G., and H. L. Barnett. 1951. Physiology of the fungi. McGraw-Hill, N. Y. 464p.

Linford, M. B. 1942. Methods of observing soil flora and fauna associated with roots. Soil Sci. 53:93-103.

Lochhead, A. G. 1958. Soil bacteria and growth-promoting substances. Bacteriol. Rev. 22:145-153.

Lochhead, A. G., and F. E. Chase. 1943. Qualitative studies of soil microorganisms: V. Nutritional requirements of the predominant bacterial flora. Soil Sci. 55:185-195.

Lotka, A. J. 1956. Elements of mathematical biology. Dover, N. Y. 465p.

Luckey, T. D. 1963. Germfree life and gnotobiology. Academic Press, N. Y. 512p.

Lund, J. W. G. 1950. Studies on Asterionella formosa Hass. II. Nutrient depletion and the spring maximum. J. Ecol. 38:1-35.

McCabe, Brother J., and W. W. Eckenfelder, Jr., eds., 1958. Biological treatment of sewage and industrial wastes, Vol. II. Reinhold, N. Y. 330p.

McDonough, E. S., R. Van Prooien, and A. L. Lewis. 1965. Lysis of Blastomyces dermatitidis yeast-phase cells in natural soil. Amer. J. Epidemiol. 81:86-94.

McElroy, W. D. 1961. Bacterial luminescence, p. 479-508. In I. C. Gunsalus and R. Y. Stanier, eds., The bacteria, Vol. II. Academic Press, N. Y.

Macfadyen, A. 1961. Metabolism of soil invertebrates in relation to soil fertility. Ann. appl. Biol. 49:215-218.

Macfadyen, A. 1963. Animal ecology; aims and methods, 2nd ed. Pitman, London & N. Y. 344p.

McKee, H. S. 1962. Nitrogen metabolism in plants. Clarendon Press, Oxford. 728p.

McLaren, A. D. 1963. Biochemistry and soil science. Science 141:1141-1147.

MacLeod, R. A. 1965. The question of the existence of specific marine bacteria. Bacteriol. Rev. 29:9-23.

McMahon, J. W., and F. H. Rigler. 1965. Feeding rate of *Daphnia magna* Straus in different foods labeled with radioactive phosphorus. Limnol. and Oceanogr. 10:105-113.

Maizel, J. V., J. J. Burkhardt, and H. K. Mitchell. 1964. Avenacin, an antimicrobial substance isolated from *Avena sativa*. I. Isolation and antimicrobial activity. Biochemistry 3:424-426.

Manil, P. 1958. The legume-rhizobia symbiosis, p. 124-133. *In* E. G. Hallsworth, ed., Nutrition of the legumes. Academic Press, N. Y.

Manten, A. 1948. Phototaxis, phototropism, and photosynthesis in purple bacteria and blue-green algae. Schotanus & Jens, Utrecht. 87p.

Marples, M. J. 1965. The ecology of the human skin. Charles C. Thomas Publ., Springfield, Ill. 970p.

Marston, H. R. 1948. The fermentation of cellulose *in vitro* by organisms from the rumen of sheep. Biochem. J. 42:564-574.

Mason, B. 1958. Principles of geochemistry, 2nd ed. John Wiley & Sons, N. Y. 310p.

Mathews, M. M., and W. R. Sistrom. 1959. Function of carotenoid pigments in non-photosynthetic bacteria. Nature 184:1892–1893.

Mathews, M. M., and W. R. Sistrom. 1960. The function of the carotenoid pigments of *Sarcina lutea*. Arch. f. Mikrobiol. 35:139-146.

Means, C. W., G. M. Savage, F. Reusser, and H. J. Koepsell. 1962. Design and operation of a pilot-plant fermentor for the continuous propagation of filamentous microorganisms. Biotechnol. and Bioengineering IV:5-16.

Melin, E. 1959. Mycorrhiza, p. 605-638. *In* W. Ruhland, ed., Handbuch der Pflan-zenphysiologie, Vol. XI. Springer, Berlin.

Melin, E. 1963. Some effects of forest tree roots on mycorrhizal Basidiomycetes, p. 125-145. *In* Symbiotic associations, Thirteenth Symp. Soc. Gen. Microbiol. Cambridge U. Press.

Menzel, D. W. 1964. The distribution of dissolved organic carbon in the Western Indian Ocean. Deep-Sea Res. 11:757-765.

Menzies, J. D. 1963. The direct assay of plant pathogen populations in soil. Ann. Rev. Phytopathol. 1:127-142.

Mergenhagen, S. E., J. C. Thonard, and H. W. Scherp. 1958. Studies on synergistic infections I. Experimental infections with anaerobic streptococci. J. Inf. Dis. 103:33-44.

Meyer, G. H., M. B. Morrow, O. Wyss, T. E. Berg, and J. L. Littlepage. 1962. Antarctica: the microbiology of an unfrozen saline pond. Science 138:1103-1104.

Meynell, G. G., and T. V. Subbaiah. 1963. Antibacterial mechanisms of the mouse gut I: Kinetics of infection by *Salmonella typhi-murium* in normal and strepto-mycin-treated mice studied with abortive transductants. Brit. J. Exptl. Pathol. 44:197-208.

Miller, M. W. 1961. The Pfizer handbook of microbial metabolites. Blakiston Division, McGraw-Hill, N. Y. 772p.

Minshall, G. W. 1965. Community dynamics and economics of a woodland springbrook: Morgan's Creek, Meade County, Kentucky. Dissertation (Ph.D.), Univ. of Louisville, Kentucky. 261p.

Mitchison, J. M. 1961. The growth of single cells III. *Streptococcus faecalis.* Exptl. Cell Res. 22:208-225.

Mortlock, R. P., D. D. Fossitt, and W. A. Wood. 1965. A basis for utilization of unnatural pentoses and pentitols by *Aerobacter aerogenes.* Proc. Nat. Acad. Sci. 54:572-579.

Mosse, B. 1963. Vesicular-arbuscular mycorrhiza: an extreme form of fungal adaptation, p. 146-170. *In* Symbiotic associations, Thirteenth Symp. Soc. Gen. Microbiol. Cambridge U. Press.

Mossel, D. A. A., and M. Ingram. 1956. The physiology of the microbial spoilage of foods. J. appl. Bacteriol. 18:232-268.

Moulder, J. W. 1964. The psittacosis group as bacteria. John Wiley & Sons, N. Y. 95p.

Mueller, J. A., and T. M. Sonneborn. 1959. Killer action on cells other than *Paramecium.* Anat. Rec. 134:613.

Mundt, J. O., J. H. Coggin, Jr., and L. F. Johnson. 1962. Growth of *Streptococcus faecalis* var. *liquefaciens* on plants. Appl. Microbiol. 10:552-555.

Muscatine, L., and H. M. Lenhoff. 1963. Symbiosis: on the role of algae symbiotic with hydra. Science 142, 15 November:956-958.

Nelson, R. R., R. D. Wilcoxson, and J. J. Christensen. 1955. Heterocaryosis as a basis for variation in *Puccinia graminis* var. *tritici.* Phytopathology 45:639-643.

Newell, R. C. 1963. Studies on the behaviour, ecology and physiology of *Peringia* (=*Hydrobia*) *ulvae* (Pennant). Thesis, Dept. of Zoology, Westfield College, London.

Noguchi, H. 1921. Cristispira in North American shellfish. A note on a spirillum found in oysters. J. Exptl. Med. 34:295-315.

Norén, B. 1960. Notes on the bacteriolytic activity of *Myxococcus virescens.* Svensk Bot. Tidskrift 54:550-560.

Norris, D. O. 1958. Lime in relation to the nodulation of tropical legumes, p. 164-182. *In* E. G. Hallsworth, ed., Nutrition of the legumes. Academic Press, N. Y.

Nossal, G. J. V., and O. Mäkelä. 1962. Autoradiographic studies on the immune response I. The kinetics of plasma cell proliferation. J. Exptl. Med. 115:209-230.

Novick, A. 1955. Growth of bacteria. Ann. Rev. Microbiol. 9:97-110.

Novick, A., and L. Szilard. 1951. Genetic mechanisms in bacteria and bacterial viruses I. Experiments on spontaneous and chemically induced mutations of bacteria growing in the chemostat. Cold Spring Harbor Symp. Quant. Biol. 16:337-343.

Nüesch, J. 1963. Defence reactions in orchid bulbs, p. 335-343. *In* Symbiotic associations, Thirteenth Symp. Soc. Gen. Microbiol. Cambridge U. Press.

Nurmikko, V. 1956. Biochemical factors affecting symbiosis among bacteria. Experientia 12:245-249.

Nutman, P. S. 1958. The physiology of nodule formation, p. 87-107. *In* E. G. Hallsworth, ed., Nutrition of the legumes. Academic Press, N. Y.

Nutman, P. S. 1963. Factors influencing the balance of mutual advantage in legume symbiosis, p. 51-71. *In* Symbiotic associations, Thirteenth Symp. Soc. Gen. Microbiol. Cambridge U. Press.

Odum, E. P. 1959. Fundamentals of ecology, 2nd ed. Saunders, Philadelphia. 546p.

Odum, E. P., and A. A. de la Cruz. 1963. Detritus as a major component of ecosystems. AIBS (Amer. Inst. Biol. Sci.) Bull. 13:39-40.

Odum, E. P., and E. J. Kuenzler. 1963. Experimental isolation of food chains in an old-field ecosystem with the use of phosphorus-32, p. 113-120. *In* V. Schultz and A. W. Klement, Jr., eds., Radioecology. Reinhold, N. Y.

Odum, H. T., and E. P. Odum. 1955. Trophic structure and productivity of a windward coral reef community on Eniwetok Atoll. Ecol. Monogr. 25:291-320.

Olsen, C. 1932. Studies on nitrogen fixation I. Nitrogen fixation in dead leaves of forest beds. Compt. Rend. Lab. Carlsberg 19(9):11-36.

Oppenheimer, C. H. 1960. Bacterial activity in sediments of shallow marine bays. Geochim. Cosmochim. Acta 19:244-260.

Oppenheimer, C. H., ed., 1963. Symposium on marine microbiology. C. C. Thomas, Springfield, Ill. 769p.

Oppenheimer, C. H., and W. Drost-Hansen. 1960. A relationship between multiple temperature optima for biological systems and the properties of water. J. Bacteriol. 80:21-24.

Ottolenghi, E., and C. M. MacLeod. 1963. Genetic transformation among living pneumococci in the mouse. Proc. Nat. Acad. Sci. 50:417-419.

Ovington, J. D. 1962. Quantitative ecology and the woodland ecosystem concept. Advances in Ecological Research 1:103-192. Academic Press 1962.

Ozawa, A., and R. Freter. 1964. Ecological mechanism controlling growth of *Escherichia coli* in continuous flow cultures and in the mouse intestine. J. Infect. Dis. 114:235-242.

Pardee, A. B. 1962. The synthesis of enzymes, p. 577-630. *In* I. C. Gunsalus and R. Y. Stanier, eds., The bacteria, Vol. III. Academic Press, N. Y.

Park, D. 1956. Effect of substrate on a microbial antagonism, with reference to soil conditions. Trans. Brit. mycol. Soc. 39:239-259.

Park, D. 1963. The ecology of soil-borne fungal disease. Ann. Rev. Phytopath. 1:241-258.

Parkinson, D., and E. Coups. 1963. Microbial activity in a podzol, p. 167-175. *In* J. Doeksen and J. Van der Drift, eds., Soil organisms. North-Holland Publ. Co., Amsterdam.

Parkinson, D., G. S. Taylor, and R. Pearson. 1963. Studies on fungi in the root region I. The development of fungi on young roots. Plant and Soil 19:332-349.

Parmeter, J. R., Jr., W. C. Snyder, and R. E. Reichle. 1963. Heterokaryosis and variability in plant-pathogenic fungi. Ann. Rev. Phytopath. 1:51-76.

Parsons, T. R. 1963. Suspended organic matter in sea water. Progress in Oceanogr. 1:205-239.

Pearsall, W. H. 1938. The soil complex in relation to plant communities I. Oxidation-reduction potentials in soils. J. Ecol. 26:180-193.

Pearsall, W. H., and C. H. Mortimer. 1939. Oxidation-reduction potentials in waterlogged soils, natural waters and muds. J. Ecol. 27:483-501.

Person, Clayton. 1966. Genetical adjustment of fungi to their environment. In G. C. Ainsworth and A. S. Sussman, eds., The fungi, Vol. 3. Academic Press, N. Y. (in press).

Phaff, H. J., and E. P. Knapp. 1956. The taxonomy of yeasts found in exudates of certain trees and other natural breeding sites of some species of Drosophila. Antonie van Leeuwenhoek 22:117-130.

Phillips, J. E. 1964. The ecological role of phosphorus in waters with special reference to microorganisms, p. 61-81. In H. Heukelekian and N. C. Dondero, eds., Principles and applications in aquatic microbiology. John Wiley & Sons, N. Y. 452p.

Pohunek, M. 1961. Streptococci antagonizing the vaginal Lactobacillus. J. Hyg. Epidemiol. Microbiol. Immunol. (Prague) 5:267-270.

Poindexter, J. S. 1964. Biological properties and classification of the Caulobacter group. Bacteriol. Rev. 28:231-295.

Pollock, M. R. 1946. Adaptation of "nitratase" in washed suspensions of bacteria. Brit. J. Exptl. Pathol. 27:419-432.

Pomeroy, L. R. 1963. Experimental studies of the turnover of phosphate in marine environments, p. 163-166. In V. Schultz and A. W. Klement, Jr., eds., Radioecology. Reinhold, N. Y., and Amer. Inst. Biol. Sci., Washington, D. C.

Pomeroy, L. R., E. E. Smith, and C. M. Grant. 1965. The exchange of phosphate between estuarine water and sediments. Limnol. and Oceanogr. 10:167-172.

Postgate, J. R., and J. R. Hunter. 1963. The survival of starved bacteria. J. appl. Bacteriol. 26:295-306.

Potter, M. C. 1908. Bacteria as agents in the oxidation of amorphous carbon. Roy. Soc. (London), Proc., B. 80:239-259.

Pramer, D. 1964. Nematode-trapping fungi. Science 144:382-388.

Precht, H., J. Christophersen, and H. Hensel. 1955. Temperatur und Leben. Springer, Berlin. 514p.

Prescott, D. M., ed., 1964. Methods in cell physiology, Vol. I. Academic Press, N. Y. 465p.

Pringsheim, E. G. 1957. Observations on Leucothrix mucor and Leucothrix cohaerens nov. sp. Bacteriol. Rev. 21:69-81.

Pringsheim, E. G. 1959. Heterotrophie bei Algen und Flagellaten, p. 303-326. In W. Ruhland, ed., Handbuch der Pflanzenphysiologie, Vol. XI. Springer, Berlin.

Proctor, V. W. 1957. Studies of algal antibiosis using Haematococcus and Chlamydomonas. Limnol. and Oceanogr. 2:125-139.

Provasoli, L. 1958a. Nutrition and ecology of protozoa and algae. Ann. Rev. Microbiol. 12:279-308.

Provasoli, L. 1958b. Effect of plant hormones on Ulva. Biol. Bull. 114:375-384.

Provasoli, L. 1963. Organic regulation of phytoplankton fertility, p. 165-219. In M. N. Hill, ed., The sea, Vol. 2. Interscience, N. Y.

Provasoli, L., J. J. A. McLaughlin, and M. R. Droop. 1957. The development of artificial media for marine algae. Archiv f. Mikrobiol. 25:392-428.

Provasoli, L., and K. Shiraishi. 1959. Axenic cultivation of the brine shrimp *Artemia salina*. Biol. Bull. 117:347-355.

Purko, M., W. O. Nelson, and W. A. Wood. 1951. The associative action between certain yeasts and *Bacterium linens*. J. Dairy Sci. 34:699-705.

Quastel, J. H. 1954. Soil metabolism. Roy. Soc. (London), Proc., B. 143:159-178.

Quastler, H., ed., 1953. Essays on the use of information theory in biology. Univ. of Illinois Press, Urbana, Ill. 273p.

Quastler, H. 1958. A primer on information theory, p. 3-49. *In* H. P. Yockey, ed., Symposium on information theory in biology. Pergamon Press, N. Y.

Quispel, A. 1959. Lichens, p. 577-604. *In* W. Ruhland, ed., Handbuch der Pflanzenphysiologie, Vol. XI. Springer, Berlin.

Rahn, O. 1945. Injury and death of bacteria by chemical agents. Biodynamica, Normandy, Missouri. 184p.

Raper, J. R., M. G. Baxter, and A. H. Ellingboe. 1960. The genetic structure of the incompatibility factors of *Schizophyllum commune:* the A-factor. Proc. Nat. Acad. Sci. 46:833-842.

Raper, J. R., G. S. Krongelb, and M. G. Baxter. 1958. The number and distribution of incompatibility factors in Schizophyllum. Amer. Nat. 92:221-232.

Ray, D. L. 1959. Nutritional physiology of Limnoria, p. 46-60. *In* D. L. Ray, ed., Marine boring and fouling organisms. Univ. of Wash. Press, Seattle.

Raymont, J. E. G. 1963. Plankton and productivity in the oceans. Pergamon Press, Oxford. 660p.

Reddish, G. F., ed., 1954. Antiseptics, disinfectants, fungicides, and chemical and physical sterilization. Lea & Febiger, Philadelphia. 841p.

Redfield, A. C., B. H. Ketchum, and F. A. Richards. 1963. The influence of organisms on the composition of sea-water, p. 26-77. *In* M. N. Hill, ed., The sea, Vol. 2. Interscience Publ., N. Y.

Reese, E. T., ed., 1963. Advances in enzymic hydrolysis of cellulose and related materials. Pergamon Press, N. Y. 290p.

Reese, E. T., and M. Mandels. 1963. Enzymatic hydrolysis of β-glucans, p. 197-234. *In* E. T. Reese, ed., Advances in enzymic hydrolysis of cellulose and related materials. Pergamon Press, N. Y.

Reusser, F. 1961. Theoretical design of continuous antibiotic fermentation units. Appl. Microbiol. 9:361-366.

Reusser, F., H. J. Koepsell, and G. M. Savage. 1961. Degeneration of *Streptomyces niveus* with repeated transfers. Appl. Microbiol. 9:342-345.

Richards, P. W. 1952. The tropical rain forest; an ecological study. Cambridge U. Press. 450p.

Riley, G. A. 1963. Organic aggregates in seawater and the dynamics of their formation and utilization. Limnol. and Oceanogr. 8:372-381.

Robbins, W. J., A. Rolnick, and F. Kavanagh. 1950. Production of hydrocyanic acid by cultures of a basidiomycete. Mycologia 42:161-166.

Rodhe, W. 1963. Discussion *in* G. A. Riley, ed., Marine Biology I, p. 25-33. Amer. Inst. Biol. Sci., Washington, D. C. 286p.

Roeser, J. 1961. The effect of cold shock on bacteria. Thesis (A.M.), Indiana University, Bloomington, Ind.

Rogers, H. J. 1961. The dissimilation of high molecular weight substances, p. 257-318. *In* I. C. Gunsalus and R. Y. Stanier, eds., The bacteria, Vol. II. Academic Press, N. Y.

Rosebury, T. 1962. Microorganisms indigenous to man. Blakiston, N. Y. 435p.

Rovira, A. D. 1965. Interactions between plant roots and soil microorganisms. Ann. Rev. Microbiol. 19:241-266.

Rowell, J. B., and J. B. DeVay. 1954. Genetics of *Ustilago zeae* in relation to basic problems of its pathogenicity. Phytopathology 44:356-362.

Ruinen, J. 1956. Occurrence of *Beijerinckia* species in the 'phyllosphere.' Nature 177:220-221.

Ruinen, J. 1961. The phyllosphere I. An ecologically neglected milieu. Plant and Soil 15:81-109.

Russell, *Sir* E. J., and E. W. Russell. 1950. Soil conditions and plant growth, 8th ed. Longmans, Green & Co., London. 635p.

Ryan, F. G., G. W. Beadle, and E. L. Tatum. 1943. The tube method of measuring the growth rate of *Neurospora*. Amer. J. Bot. 30:784-799.

Ryther, J. H. 1959. Potential productivity of the sea. Science 130:602-608.

Ryther, J. H. 1963. Geographic variations in productivity, p. 347-380. *In* M. N. Hill, ed., The sea, Vol. 2. Interscience Publ., N. Y.

Ryther, J. R., and R. R. L. Guillard. 1959. Enrichment experiments as a means of studying nutrients limiting to phytoplankton production. Deep-Sea Res. 6:65-69.

Safferman, R. S., and M.-E. Morris. 1963. Algal virus: isolation. Science 140:679-680.

Sager, R., and F. J. Ryan. 1961. Cell heredity. John Wiley & Sons, N. Y. 411p.

Salle, A. J. 1961. Fundamental principles of bacteriology, 5th ed. McGraw-Hill, N. Y. 812p.

Salton, M. R. J. 1960. Microbial cell walls. John Wiley & Sons, N. Y. 94p.

Saz, A. K., D. L. Lowery, and N. Citri. 1964. Nonpenicillin-like cyclic peptides as inducers of, and substrates for, staphylococcal and *Bacillus cereus* penicillinases. Bacteriol. Proc. 1964:99.

Saz, A. K., S. Watson, S. R. Brown, and D. L. Lowery. 1963. Antimicrobial activity of marine waters I. Macromolecular nature of antistaphylococcal factor. Limnol. and Oceanogr. 8:63-67.

Schaeffer, W. I., P. E. Holbert, and W. W. Umbreit. 1963. Attachment of *Thiobacillus thiooxidans* to sulfur crystals. J. Bacteriol. 85:137-140.

Schneider, I. R., T. O. Diener, and R. S. Safferman. 1964. Blue-green algal virus LPP-1: purification and partial characterization. Science 144:1127-1130.

Schramm, J. R. 1966. Plant colonization studies on black wastes from anthracite mining in Pennsylvania. Trans. Amer. Phil. Soc. 56: part 1, 194p.

Sedlaczek, L. 1964. Heat balance of growth of some bacterial cultures. Acta Microb. Polonica 13:101-112.

Setchell, W. A. 1903. The upper temperature limits of life. Science 17:934-937.

Shaffer, B. M. 1962. The Acrasina. Advances in Morphogenesis 2:109-182.

Shanks, R. E., and J. S. Olson. 1961. First-year breakdown of leaf litter in Southern Appalachian forests. Science 134:194-195.

Shaukat-Ahmed, and H. J. Evans. 1961. The essentiality of cobalt for soybean plants grown under symbiotic conditions. Proc. Nat. Acad. Sci. 47:24-36.

Sieburth, J. McN. 1959. Gastrointestinal microflora of Antarctic birds. J. Bacteriol. 77:521-531.

Sieburth, J. McN. 1964. Polymorphism of marine *Arthrobacter* as a function of multiple-temperature optima and nutrition. Bact. Proc. 1964:37.

Sieburth, J. McN., and J. T. Conover. 1965. Slicks associated with *Trichodesmium* blooms in the Sargasso Sea. Nature 205:830-831.

Siegel, R. W. 1960. Hereditary endosymbiosis in *Paramecium bursaria*. Exptl. Cell Res. 19:239-252.

Siegel, R. W. 1961. Direct and indirect evidence that free-living ciliates conjugate in nature. J. Protozool. 8:27-29.

Silver, W. S., Y. M. Centifanto, and D. J. D. Nicholas. 1963. Nitrogen fixation by the leaf-nodule endophyte of *Psychotria bacteriophila*. Nature 199:396-397.

Siu, R. G. H. 1951. Microbial decomposition of cellulose, with special reference to cotton textiles. Reinhold, N. Y. 531p.

Slobodkin, L. B. 1962a. Growth and regulation of animal populations. Holt, Rinehart & Winston, N. Y. 184p.

Slobodkin, L. B. 1962b. Energy in animal ecology. Advances in Ecological Research 1:69-101.

Smith, D. C. 1963. Experimental studies of lichen physiology, p. 31-50. *In* Symbiotic associations, Thirteenth Symp. Soc. Gen. Microbiol. Cambridge U. Press.

Smith, G. M. 1950. The fresh-water algae of the United States, 2nd ed. McGraw-Hill, N. Y. 719p.

Smith, J. M. B., and M. J. Marples. 1964. A natural reservoir of penicillin-resistant strains of *Staphylococcus aureus*. Nature 201:844.

Smithies, O. 1965. Antibody induction and tolerance. Science 149:151-156.

Soldo, A. T. 1963. Axenic culture of *Paramecium*—some observations on the growth behavior and nutritional requirements of a particle-bearing strain of *Paramecium aurelia* 299λ. Ann. N. Y. Acad. Sci. 108:380-388.

Sonneborn, T. M. 1959. Kappa and related particles in *Paramecium*. Advances in Virus Research VI:229-356.

Sonneborn, T. M., and M. Schneller. 1960. Measures of the rate and amount of aging on the cellular level, p. 290-291. *In* The biology of aging, Amer. Inst. Biol. Sci. Symp. No. 6. Washington, D. C.

Sorokin, J. I. 1964a. A quantitative study of the microflora in the Central Pacific Ocean. Journal du Conseil 29:25-40.

Sorokin, J. I. 1964b. On the primary production and bacterial activities in the Black Sea. Journal du Conseil 29:41-60.

Spaulding, E. H., L. Zubrzycki, and J. H. Lanphear. 1964. Continuous-flow culture studies with mixed strains of Escherichia coli: isolation of a lytic factor. Bacteriol. Proc. 1964:68.

Spector, W. S., ed., 1956. Handbook of biological data. Saunders, Philadelphia. 584p.

Spoehr, H. A., J. H. C. Smith, H. H. Strain, H. W. Milner, and G. J. Hardin. 1949. Fatty acid antibacterials from plants. Carnegie Institution Wash. Publ. No. 586. 67p.

Stanier, R. Y. 1942. The Cytophaga group: a contribution to the biology of myxobacteria. Bacteriol. Rev. 6:143-196.

Stanier, R. Y. 1953. Adaptation, evolutionary and physiological: or Darwinism among the micro-organisms, p. 1-20. In Adaptation in micro-organisms, Third Symp. Soc. Gen. Microbiol. Cambridge U. Press.

Stanier, R. Y., and G. Cohen-Bazire. 1957. The role of light in the microbial world: some facts and speculations, p. 56-89. In Microbial ecology, Seventh Symp. Soc. Gen. Microbiol. Cambridge U. Press.

Stanier, R. Y., M. Doudoroff, and E. A. Adelberg. 1963. The microbial world, 2nd ed. Prentice-Hall, Englewood Cliffs, N. J. 753p.

Stark, W. H., J. Stadler, and E. McCoy. 1938. Some factors affecting the bacterial population of freshwater lakes. J. Bacteriol. 36:653-654.

Starkey, R. L. 1958. Interrelations between microorganisms and plant roots in the rhizosphere. Bacteriol. Rev. 22:154-172.

Starr, M. P., and V. B. D. Skerman. 1965. Bacterial diversity: the natural history of selected morphologically unusual bacteria. Ann. Rev. Microbiol. 19:407-454.

Steeman Nielsen, E. 1963. Productivity, definition and measurement, p. 129-164. In M. N. Hill, ed., The sea, Vol 2. John Wiley & Sons, N. Y.

Stent, G. S. 1963. Molecular biology of bacterial viruses. Freeman, San Francisco. 474p.

Stephens, J. M. 1963. Immunity in insects, p. 273-297. In E. A. Steinhaus, ed., Insect pathology, Vol. 1. Academic Press, N. Y.

Stewart, W. D. P. 1964. Nitrogen fixation by Myxophyceae from marine environments. J. gen. Microbiol. 36:415-422.

Stocker, B. A. D. 1959. Bacterial genetics and infectious disease. J. Med. Education 34:354-365.

Stolp, H., and M. P. Starr. 1963. Bdellovibrio bacteriovorus gen. et sp. n., a predatory, ectoparasitic, and bacteriolytic microorganism. Antonie van Leeuwenhoek 29:217-248.

Stolp, H., and M. P. Starr. 1965. Bacteriolysis. Ann. Rev. Microbiol. 19:79-104.

Strasdine, G. A., and D. R. Whitaker. 1963. On the origin of the cellulase and chitinase of Helix pomatia. Can. J. Biochem. & Physiol. 41:1621-1626.

Strickland, J. D. H. 1965. Phytoplankton and marine primary production. Ann. Rev. Microbiol. 19:127-162.

Sussman, A. S. 1965. Dormancy of soil microorganisms in relation to survival, p. 99-110. *In* K. F. Baker and W. C. Snyder, eds., Ecology of soil-borne plant pathogens. Prelude to biological control. Univ. of California Press, Berkeley.

Swain, F. M. 1963. Geochemistry of humus, p. 87-147. *In* I. A. Breger, ed., Organic geochemistry. Pergamon Press, Oxford.

Sweeney, B. M., and J. W. Hastings. 1962. Rhythms, p. 687-700. *In* R. A. Lewin, ed., Physiology and biochemistry of algae. Academic Press, N. Y.

Tabor, H., C. W. Tabor, and S. M. Rosenthal. 1961. The biochemistry of the polyamines: spermidine and spermine. Ann. Rev. Biochem. 30:579-604.

Talling, J. F. 1957. The growth of two plankton diatoms in mixed cultures. Physiol. Plantarum 10:215-223.

Tamm, L. O., and H. G. Östlund. 1960. Radiocarbon dating of soil humus. Nature 185:706-707.

Tanami, J. 1959. Studies on germfree animals. J. Chiba Med. Soc. 35:1-24.

Taub, F. B., and A. M. Dollar. 1964. A *Chlorella-Daphnia* food-chain study: the design of a compatible chemically defined culture medium. Limnol. and Oceanogr. 9:61-74.

Taylor, A. C. 1962. Cell adhesiveness and the adaptation of cells to surfaces, p. 169-182. *In* M. J. Brennan and W. L. Simpson, eds., Biological interactions in normal and neoplastic growth; a contribution to the host-tumor problem. Little, Brown, Boston.

Toennies, G., B. Bakay, and G. D. Shockman. 1959. Bacterial composition and growth phase. J. Biol. Chem. 234:3269-3275.

Toennies, G., and G. D. Shockman. 1958. Growth chemistry of *Streptococcus faecalis*, p. 365-394. *In* Fourth Intern. Congr. Biochem., Vol. XIII.

Tribe, H. T. 1957. Ecology of micro-organisms in soils observed during their development upon buried cellulose film, p. 287-298. *In* Microbial ecology, Seventh Symp. Soc. Gen. Microbiol. Cambridge U. Press.

Umbreit, W. W., R. H. Burris, and J. F. Stauffer. 1957. Manometric techniques. Burgess Publ. Co., Minneapolis. 338p.

Vallentyne, J. R. 1962. Solubility and the decomposition of organic matter in nature. Arch. Hydrobiol. 58:423-434.

Vallentyne, J. R. 1963. Environmental biophysics and microbial ubiquity. Ann. N. Y. Acad. Sci. 108:342-352.

van Krevelen, D. W. 1963. Geochemistry of coal, p. 183-247. *In* I. A. Breger, ed., Organic geochemistry. Pergamon Press, Oxford.

van Niel, C. B. 1955. Natural selection in the microbial world. J. gen. Microbiol. 13:201-217.

Vincent, J. M. 1958. Survival of the root nodule bacteria, p. 108-123. *In* E. G. Hallsworth, ed., Nutrition of the legumes. Academic Press, N. Y.

Visser, S. A. 1964. Origin of nitrates in tropical rainwater. Nature 201:35-36.

Vonk, H. J. 1964. Comparative biochemistry of digestive mechanisms, p. 347-401. *In* M. Florkin and H. S. Mason, eds., Comparative biochemistry; a comprehensive treatise, Vol. VI. Academic Press, N. Y.

Waksman, S. A. 1932. Principles of soil microbiology, 2nd ed. Williams & Wilkins, Baltimore. 894p.

Waksman, S. A. 1945. Microbial antagonisms and antibiotic substances. Commonwealth Fund, N. Y. 350p.

Waksman, S. A. 1961. The role of antibiotics in nature. Perspectives in Biology and Medicine 4:271-287.

Walker, D. J., and W. W. Forrest. 1964. The application of calorimetry to the study of ruminal fermentation in vitro. Austral. J. Agr. Res. 15:299-315.

Wallhäusser, K. H. 1951. Die antibiotischen Beziehungen einer natürlichen Mikroflora. Arch. Mikrobiol. 16:201-236.

Warcup, J. H. 1960. Methods for isolation and estimation of activity of fungi in soil, p. 3-21. In D. Parkinson and J. S. Waid, eds., The ecology of soil fungi. Liverpool U. Press.

Warren, C. E., J. H. Wales, G. E. Davis, and P. Doudoroff. 1964. Trout production in an experimental stream enriched with sucrose. J. Wildlife Management 28:617-660.

Webley, D. M., M. E. K. Henderson, and I. F. Taylor. 1963. The microbiology of rocks and weathered stones. J. Soil Sci. 14:102-112.

Weibull, C. 1960. Movement, p. 153-205. In I. C. Gunsalus and R. Y. Stanier, eds., The bacteria, Vol. I. Academic Press, N. Y.

Weiss, P. A. 1962. Cells and their environment, including other cells, p. 3-20. In M. J. Brennan and W. L. Simpson, eds., Biological interactions in normal and neoplastic growth; a contribution to the host-tumor problem. Little, Brown, Boston.

Westerdijk, J. 1949. The concept "association" in mycology. Antonie v. Leeuwenhoek 15:187-189.

Whitehead, W. L., and I. A. Breger. 1963. Geochemistry of petroleum, p. 248-332. In I. A. Breger, ed., Organic geochemistry. Pergamon Press, Oxford.

Whitford, L. A. 1960a. The current effect and growth of fresh-water algae. Trans. Amer. Micros. Soc. 79:302-309.

Whitford, L. A. 1960b. Ecological distribution of fresh-water algae, p. 2-10. In C. A. Tryon, Jr., and R. T. Hartman, eds., The ecology of algae. Special Publication no. 2, Pymatuning Laboratory of Field Biology, Univ. of Pittsburgh, Penn.

Wiame, J. M. 1958. Le cycle du soufre dans la nature, p. 103-120. In W. Ruhland, ed., Handbuch der Pflanzenphysiologie, Vol. IX. Springer, Berlin.

Wiegert, R. G., and F. C. Evans. 1964. Primary production and the disappearance of dead vegetation of an old field in southeastern Michigan. Ecology 45:49-63.

Wiener, N. 1948. Cybernetics; or, control and communication in the animal and the machine. Technology Press, Cambridge, Mass. 194p.

Williams, S. T. 1963. The distribution of fungi in the horizons of a podsolised soil, p. 158-166. In J. Doeksen and J. Van der Drift, eds., Soil organisms. North-Holland Publ. Co., Amsterdam.

Wilson, G. S., and A. A. Miles. 1957. Topley and Wilson's principles of bacteriology and immunity, Vol. II, 4th ed. Williams & Wilkins, Baltimore. 1224p.

Wilson, P. W. 1958. Asymbiotic nitrogen fixation, p. 9-47. *In* W. Ruhland, ed., Handbuch der Pflanzenphysiologie, Vol. VIII. Springer, Berlin.

Winkler, E. M. 1965. Weathering rates as exemplified by Cleopatra's Needle in New York City. J. Geol. Educ. 13:50-52.

Winogradsky, S. 1949. Microbiologie du sol; problèmes et méthodes. Masson, Paris. 861p.

Witkamp, M., and J. S. Olson. 1963. Breakdown of confined and nonconfined oak litter. Oikos 14:138-147.

Wolf, F. A., and F. T. Wolf. 1947. The fungi, Vol. II. John Wiley & Sons, N. Y. 538p.

Wolfe, R. S. 1964. Iron and manganese bacteria, p. 82-97. *In* H. Heukelekian and N. C. Dondero, eds., Principles and applications in aquatic microbiology. John Wiley, N. Y.

Wood, E. J. F. 1963. Ecology of algae, protozoa, fungi and viruses, p. 28-39. *In* C. H. Oppenheimer, ed., Symposium on marine microbiology. C. C. Thomas, Springfield, Ill.

Wood, E. J. F., and C. H. Oppenheimer. 1962. Note on fluorescence microscopy in marine microbiology. Z. f. Allg. Mikrobiol. 2:164-165.

Wood, R. K. S. 1955. Pectic enzymes secreted by plant pathogens and their role in plant infection, p. 263-293. *In* Mechanisms of microbial pathogenicity, Fifth Symp. Soc. Gen. Microbiol. Cambridge U. Press.

Wood, R. K. S. 1960. Chemical ability to breach the host barriers, p. 233-272. *In* J. G. Horsfall and A. E. Dimond, eds., Plant pathology, Vol. 2. Academic Press, N. Y.

Woods, D. D., and M. A. Foster. 1964. Metabolic considerations relating to the life of bacteria *in vivo*, p. 30-43. *In* Microbial behavior *"in vivo"* and *"in vitro,"* Fourteenth Symp. Soc. Gen. Microbiol. Cambridge U. Press.

Worley, C. L. 1939. Interpretation of comparative growths of fungal colonies growing on different solid media. Plant Physiol. 14:589-593.

Wuhrmann, K. 1964a. Microbial aspects of water pollution control. Adv. Appl. Microbiol. 6:119-151.

Wuhrmann, K. 1964b. Adaptationen bei Gesellschaften von Mikroorganismen in Wasser. Bibliotheca Microbiol., Fasc. 4:52-64.

Yockey, H. P., ed., 1958. Symposium on information theory in biology. Pergamon Press, N. Y. 418p.

Yonge, C. M. 1963. The biology of coral reefs. Advances in Marine Biology 1:209-260.

Zillioux, E. J., and D. F. Wilson. 1964. On the survival and propagation of *Acartia tonsa* in laboratory culture. Paper presented at 27th Annual Meeting, Amer. Soc. Limnol. Ocean., Miami Beach, June, 1964.

ZoBell, C. E. 1943. The effect of solid surfaces upon bacterial activity. J. Bacteriol. 46:39-56.

ZoBell, C. E. 1946. Marine microbiology, a monograph on hydrobacteriology. Chronica Botanica, Waltham, Mass. 240p.

ZoBell, C. E. 1958. Ecology of sulfate reducing bacteria. Producers Monthly 22(7): 12-29.

Zvyagintsev, D. G. 1962. Some regularities of adsorption of microorganisms on ion exchange resins. Microbiology (USSR) 31:275-277.

Index

Lichen (Cont.)
  growth, 92
    in laboratory, 124-125
    rate, 125
  as a microbial colony, 92
  as a mutualistic association, 116
  physiology, 125
  pigments, 125
  role in weathering, 245
Liebig's Law, 40
Light:
  energy in microbial ecosystems, 168-169
  gradients, 41
  as limiting factor in aquatic environments, 224
  as primary energy source, 54-56
  red, amount of energy available from, 54
Lignin:
  decomposition of, in soil, 247-249
  microbial decomposition of, 77
  preservation of, in sediments, 232
Limestone:
  dissolution of, by CO_2, 11
  microbial colonization of, 245
Limiting factor, law of, 40
Limnoria, 196, 204
Long Island Sound, productivity in, 223
Lumbricidae, 248
Luminescence in bacteria, 196
Lycogala flavofuscum, longevity of, 69
Lysis:
  of bacteria by *Bdellovibrio*, 136-138
  of cellulose-utilizing fungi, 158
  as factor in cryptic growth, 102
  role of cell wall in preventing, 59
Lysogeny, ecological aspects of, 134-135
Lysozyme, 189
Lytic enzymes:
  as antagonistic agents, 133-134
  produced by:
    myxobacteria, 136
    parasitic fungi, 139

M

Macoma balthica, 226
Macroformations, 91
Magnesium, 12
Man, dispersal of microorganisms by, 87
Manganese, 12
  dioxide hydrate, 20
  nodules, 260
Marine:
  environment:
    counting microorganisms in, 167
    microbial dispersal in, 85
    nitrogen fixation in, 237
    oxygen relations of, 231
    production of antibiotics in, 133
  microorganisms, 47
  organisms, absence of resting structures in, 70
Medicago tribuloides, 207, 209
Medium, culture, in counting microorganisms, 167

Membranes:
  affecting diffusion, 9
  inorganic, at mud water interface, 9
Mesophile, 38, 45
Metabolism:
  rate of, relation to cell size, 164-165
  of soil organisms, 248
Metals:
  insoluble sulfides, 14
  ions, as factor limiting diatom growth, 98
Methane:
  bacteria, 119
  formation in lake sediments, 234
  production in rumen, 199
Methanobacterium, 204
Methanobacterium ruminantium, 200
Microbial:
  colony, formation of, 91
  ecology, 1
    autecology and synecology in, 24
    microscopic aspects of, 23-24
    population aspects of, 90
    relation to microbial physiology, 90
  ecosystems, contrast to macroecosystems, 159
  populations, formation of, 90
  spoilage, 8
  variation, 29
Microbiology, origin of in microscopic studies, 24
Micrococcus, 43
Microcosm, 168
Microenvironment, 31
  chemical analysis of, 17
  contrast with macroenvironment, 16-17
  study by radioautography, 50
Micromanipulation techniques, use in microenvironmental analysis, 17
Microorganisms (*See also* specific groups)
  in air, 81-82
  associated with humus, 21
  association with organic particles in sea water, 21
  dispersal by animals, 86-87
  existence in extreme environments, 2
  influence on higher organisms, 2
  living at extreme environments, 43
  marine, 47
  in rain water, 84-85
  in rhizosphere, 186
  in terrestrial food chains, 247
Microscope:
  as amplifier, 24
  low sensitivity of, in studying pure cultures, 25
  use in:
    counting microorganisms, 166
    microenvironmental analyses, 17
Microscopic analysis, 23-24
Milk:
  counting microorganisms in, 167
  microbial succession in, 158-159
Mimicry, 183
  molecular, 191
Mine:
  wastes, reforestation of, role of mycorrhizal fungi in, 217